A PATH
through TEILHARD'S
PHENOMENON

THEMES FOR TODAY
James O'Gara, General Editor

W. HENRY
KENNEY, S.J.

A PATH
through TEILHARD'S
PHENOMENON

PFLAUM PRESS, DAYTON, OHIO

1970

Library of Congress Catalog Card Number: 69-20172
Pflaum Press
38 West Fifth Street
Dayton, Ohio 45402
© 1970 by W. Henry Kenney, S.J. All rights reserved
Printed in the United States of America

CONTENTS

FOREWORD

Despite appearances, *The Phenomenon of Man* is a difficult book. Its author wanted to make it accessible not only to specialists but to every educated reader. Like Bergson, he wrote in a style which has almost nothing technical about it, except a number of neologisms. But in it he condensed the results of prolonged scientific research and profound reflection on the problems of anthropology. This is what has escaped general notice: his method is far more rigorous and his concepts are far more precise than many a reader suspects. Therefore, we should be grateful when someone offers to guide us step by step through this reading. It is to such a task that Father W. Henry Kenney, S.J., has applied himself. He has done so with his multiple competence as a scientist, a philosopher, and a theologian. We can follow him confidently along the path which he marks out for us. After the publication of *The Phenomenon of Man*, there was a period of infatuation and denigration, both of which were often ill-formed. Now that that has passed, Father Kenney's book will greatly help those who wish to devote themselves seriously and dispassionately to the study of Teilhardian thought.

Henri de Lubac, S.J.,
Member, Institute of France

PREFACE

The need of a companion study of Teilhard de Chardin's *The Phenomenon of Man* has been apparent right from this writer's first—and perplexed—reading of it in 1959. Continuing contacts with students and various audiences have reinforced the perception of that need.

Teilhard, while he was writing *The Phenomenon of Man* in 1940, confessed: "I hope that the Lord will help me [in the writing], since it is entirely as an attempt to make His countenance seen and loved that I am taking such pains, which sometimes I could well be spared."[1]

"Such pains!" There are multiple ways of using one's times and talents. This author has been frequently tempted to let the *Path* "go its own way," but his encounters with readers who found great light and hope in Teilhard's works encouraged him to see the *Path* to completion.

As with most books of this nature, there are many hidden persons to whom the author owes debts of gratitude. The administration of Xavier University is responsible for the freedom of a sabbatical summer (1966), Shell Oil Company for a grant which financed the quiet and amenities of life at the Bellarmine School of Theology (North Aurora, Illinois), questioning students and audiences for showing the need and the dimensions of this study. Special gratitude goes to those who served as "guinea pigs" by reading and criticizing the first draft; they helped very much to improve the *Path's* usefulness. Like

Teilhard, this author has been helped most of all by his Jesuit confreres—in numbers and ways too countless to tell.

ACKNOWLEDGMENTS

Grateful acknowledgment is made for permission to include excerpts from the following copyrighted publications:

THE APPEARANCE OF MAN by Pierre Teilhard de Chardin. Copyright 1956 by Editions du Seuil. Copyright © 1965 in the English translation by Wm. Collins Sons & Co., Ltd., London, and Harper & Row, Publishers, Inc., New York.

THE DIVINE MILIEU by Pierre Teilhard de Chardin. Copyright 1957 Editions du Seuil, Paris. English translation—Copyright © 1960 by Wm. Collins Sons & Co., Ltd., London, and Harper & Row, Publishers, Inc., New York.

THE FUTURE OF MAN by Pierre Teilhard de Chardin. Translated from the French by Norman Denny. Copyright 1959 by Editions du Seuil. Copyright © 1964 in the English translation by Wm. Collins Sons & Co., Ltd., London, and Harper & Row, Publishers, Inc., New York.

HYMN OF THE UNIVERSE by Pierre Teilhard de Chardin. Copyright 1961 by Editions du Seuil. Copyright © 1965 in the Engish translation by Wm. Collins Sons & Co., Ltd., London, and Harper & Row, Publishers, Inc., New York.

LETTERS FROM A TRAVELLER by Pierre Teilhard de Chardin. Copyright © 1962 in the English translation by Wm. Collins Sons & Co., Ltd., London, and Harper & Row, Publishers, Inc. Copyright © 1956, 1957 by Bernard Grasset.

THE MAKING OF A MIND by Pierre Teilhard de Chardin. Copyright © by Editions Bernard Grasset. Copyright © 1965 in the English translation by Wm. Collins Sons & Co., Ltd., London, and Harper & Row, Publishers, Inc., New York.

MAN'S PLACE IN NATURE by Pierre Teilhard de Chardin. Copyright © 1956 by Editions Albin Michel. Copyright © 1966 in the English translation by Wm. Collins Sons & Co., Ltd., London, and Harper & Row, Publishers, Inc., New York.

THE PHENOMENON OF MAN by Pierre Teilhard de Chardin. Copyright by Editions du Seuil. Copyright © 1959 in the English translation by Wm. Collins & Co., Ltd., London, and Harper & Row, Publishers, Inc., New York. (Quotations are from 1965 Torchbook edition.)

THE VISION OF THE PAST by Pierre Teilhard de Chardin. Copyright © 1966 in the English translation by Wm. Collins Sons & Co., Ltd., London, and Harper & Row, Publishers, Inc., New York. Copyright © 1957 by Editions du Seuil.

WRITINGS IN TIME OF WAR by Pierre Teilhard de Chardin. Copyright © 1965 by Editions Bernard Grasset. Copyright © 1968 in the English translation by Wm. Collins Sons & Co., Ltd., London, and and Harper & Row, Publishers, Inc., New York.

TEILHARD DE CHARDIN AND THE MYSTERY OF CHRIST by Christopher F. Mooney. Copyright © 1964, 1965, 1966 by Christopher F. Mooney.

THE THOUGHT OF TEILHARD DE CHARDIN by Emile Rideau. Original French edition © 1965 Editions du Seuil. English translation © 1967 Wm. Collins Sons & Co., Ltd., London.

AN INTRODUCTION TO TEILHARD DE CHARDIN by N. M. Wildiers. English translation copyright © 1968 by Wm. Collins Sons & Co., Ltd., London, and Harper & Row, Inc., New York.

THE LIFE OF TEILHARD DE CHARDIN by Robert Speaight. Copyright © 1967 by Robert Speaight.

THE RELIGION OF TEILHARD DE CHARDIN by Henri de Lubac, S.J. Copyright © 1962 by Editions Montaigne, Paris. English translation copyright © 1967 by Wm. Collins Sons & Co., Ltd., London, and Desclee Co., Inc., New York.

TEILHARD DE CHARDIN: THE MAN AND HIS MEANING by Henri de Lubac, S.J. Copyright © 1965 by Burns and Oates Ltd. Published by Hawthorn Books, Inc., 70 Fifth Avenue, New York, N.Y.

THE THOUGHT OF TEILHARD DE CHARDIN by Michael H. Murray. Copyright © 1966 by The Seabury Press, Inc.

TEILHARD DE CHARDIN: A BIOGRAPHICAL STUDY by Claude Cuénot. French text copyright © by Librairie Plon. English translation copyright © 1965 by Helicon Press, Inc.

THE SCREWTAPE LETTERS & SCREWTAPE PROPOSES A TOAST by C. S. Lewis. Copyright © 1961 by C. S. Lewis.

THE COMPLETE BIBLE: AN AMERICAN TRANSLATION. Copyright © 1939 by the University of Chicago.

EVOLUTION AFTER DARWIN, edited by Sol Tax. Copyright © 1960 by the University of Chicago.

1

WHY (AND WHAT IS) THE *PATH?*

This book is for "general readers"—those who have been attracted to the thought of Teilhard de Chardin. It is specifically for those who have begun to read his *The Phenomenon of Man* and stopped—with admissions of defeat—in the face of its multiple difficulties.

Why the PATH?

Because this writer has encountered scores of such frustrated readers, it was easy enough to see a need for a companion study which would supply them with the help necessary for a persevering, meaningful and fruitful reading of the *Phenomenon*. Other difficult books and authors, such as the Book of Genesis, *Alice in Wonderland,* James Joyce, have called forth their "Skeleton Keys," "Paths" and "Reader's Guides." Few readers of the *Phenomenon* have the heroic determination of a mother of several preschoolers, who with an unabridged dictionary blazed her way through the *Phenomenon*. With "general readers" and scholars she shared the conviction that this work is the principal work of Teilhard. Hence, if one is to have more than a passing grasp of Teilhard's thought, *The Phenomenon of Man* must be read with results far more than those of penance and persistence.

The difficulties of reading Teilhard's magnum opus are real

1

and many. First, it was *not* written for the "general reader" but for fellow scientists, who rightly can be presumed to have a working knowledge of biology, geology, paleontology and anthropology. Second, the *Phenomenon* is an extremely structured book. This makes it very dense for the "general reader," who is more used to works which do not attempt so much and which consequently have less structure and complexity. Sometimes the *Phenomenon's* structure is not immediately clear, so it is easy to lose one's way. A third difficulty is that Teilhard's book was written for *agnostic* scientists; hence, it is almost impossible for it to have the same meaning and value for a Christian or a theistic reader.[1] More than that, the tight literary limits imposed by reason of its chosen audience cause the *Phenomenon* to raise for the Christian reader scores of thorny questions, which cannot be pursued there. These questions *are* explored in other Teilhardian writings; the Christian reader has a "right" to know Teilhard's thought on these.

(Let the author humbly and forthrightly admit here that initially he tried to write for *all* readers—believers and unbelievers, Christians and non-Christians—but as the writing progressed it became clearer and clearer that an attempt at an adequate explanation of the *Phenomenon* necessarily involved an ever-expanding exposition of the Christian dimensions of Teilhard's thought. This is not found in the *Phenomenon*. Is the projected audience of this *Path* only a Christian one? This was never the author's intention, and it is still his hope that the *Path* will be equally useful to Christian and non-Christian readers. On particular points, for example, "Teilhard and the Future of Science," the author has been able to be as "neutral" as Teilhard apparently is in the bulk of *The Phenomenon of Man*. But the attempt to explain in depth his magnum opus has made neutrality pragmatically impossible, however desirable and desired it may be.)

There are, in addition, the linguistic difficulties: first, neologisms—words coined by Teilhard for both radically new concepts and for old established ones; second, his highly analogical use of words, that is, using the same word for slightly related but largely different meanings, for example, consciousness, Omega, freedom; and third, Teilhard's almost constant use of very technical, scientific terminology.

There is, finally, the substantive hurdle: Teilhard is trying to enlarge our intellectual horizons with a new and creative vision and synthesis. Fundamental knowledge and new insight, as Aristotle observed, "make a bloody entrance." None of us easily changes his or her *Lebenswelt*—our lived outlook on the world—we do not easily "put on the eyes" of another and see what he sees.

The PATH's *"Trails"*

Hopefully this study will provide the "general reader" with the means necessary to find his way around or through these several difficulties. Specifically this companion study provides:

1. Orientation essays for the separate books and sections of the *Phenomenon*; these are aimed at making explicit the book's structure, thus helping the reader to remain oriented.

2. Auxiliary essays which will fill out the lines of Teilhard's synthesis. These are especially necessary for the theological dimensions of his thought. Some of his key theoretical constructs—complexity/consciousness, convergence—demand a co-ordinated discussion, since in the text they are frequently treated partially and in many different sections.

3. A glossary which explains the meaning of scientific terms, key concepts and Teilhard's coined words. The glossary is ampler than other English glossaries because it seeks to provide the needed linguistic help for the "general reader" of the *Phenomenon*.

4. At the end of each chapter are indicated the relevant passages of the *Phenomenon* to be read. Key words are noted so that they may be investigated in the glossary prior to reading the suggested passages. Especially difficult passages are noted.

For instance, quite frequently readers do not recognize, because of Teilhard's style, what is being put forth as an objection or as a position to be critically evaluated. Also noted are parallel readings, both from other works of Teilhard and from Teilhardian studies.

5. Finally, since this study serves something of the purpose of a teacher, questions are frequently posed and guesses hazarded so that the reader will be spurred to a deeper personal penetration of Teilhard's vision.

The essays which make up most of our *Path* are designed to aid the "general reader" to make his own path through *The Phenomenon of Man*. Nevertheless, these essays stand on their own feet; they can be profitably read *without* a concomitant reading of the *Phenomenon*, much like other studies of Teilhard's thought.

Readers will soon discover that a radical reordering of the *Phenomenon* is audaciously suggested by the *Path*. Its author would be hard pressed to justify such tampering if he had not discovered through repeated semesters and seminars that the *Phenomenon's* order is simply not consonant with the interests and tastes of the "general reader" or the average college class. Quite recently, though, the author discovered that the rearranged order suggested in the *Path* enabled most of his students to further their comprehension of Teilhard when their reading of a rearranged *Phenomenon* was preceded by lectures quite similar to the essays in the *Path*. Not only were far more students meaningfully engaged by a reading of the *Phenomenon*, but also the level of comprehension was altogether greater than when a straight beginning-to-end reading was attempted. Encouraged by this empirical success, the author is sanguine enough to believe that many "general readers" will experience from their use of the *Path* a similar fruitfulness.

One consequence of the *Path's* reordering is that the study of the highly scientific and technical midsection of the *Phenomenon* (roughly, pages 67-212) is quite skimpy. In a later recasting of

The Phenomenon of Man, entitled *Man's Place in Nature,* Teilhard covered the same ground in about seventy-five pages far less technically. In the *Path,* we will seek from this section only those ideas which are very important for Teilhard's life-and-world-view.

Let it be clearly understood that this companion study is *not* for those readers who have an adequate background in the several sciences presupposed by the *Phenomenon.* Such readers are more likely to be able to make their own way. Nor is this study for scholars who have available the research instruments necessary for analyzing the *Phenomenon.* Finally, this writer's debt to many scholars is large and is acknowledged by the references found in the text and in the bibliography.

Some Practicalities

1. *Quotations.* In the body of the *Path* quotations from *The Phenomenon of Man* will be indicated simply by a number in parenthesis. The few exceptions will be cases when an alternate rendering of the French is used. These and all other references will be footnoted.

References to *The Phenomenon of Man* are to be the second, revised edition of 1965. Herein is a difficulty for holders of a first edition.

2. *Beloved Copy of the* PHENOMENON. So you have (as does the author) a beloved copy of the first edition (1959) of *The Phenomenon of Man.* You must be told that the revisions in the second edition *are* significant and that there is an increasing discrepancy in the paginations of the two editions after about page 175. An increase in Harper and Row sales of the second edition will obviously not solve the problem of a reader who wishes to continue using a beloved first edition. But there is a way. Using any second edition, marginally note in your first edition the pagination of the second edition. Within a short time, you are using your beloved first edition and have the ready ability to find second edition references.

3. *A Promise.* In the very near future the author will make available *A Running Commentary and Glossary for The Phenomenon of Man* (at least for the Preface; Foreword; Book I, Chapters I and II; Book II, Chapter III; Book IV; Epilogue; Postscript; and Appendix). Since many of the difficulties in the reading of the *Phenomenon* are linguistic, an alternate translation is frequently suggested in order to make luminous what was obscure; a ready definition of a doubtful word speeds comprehension; an early warning on Teilhard's shift in the usage of a word helps to avoid misunderstanding. Not all readers desire such detail, but for those who do, it will be given in *A Running Commentary and Glossary.*

4. *Let us begin!*

2

BEHIND THE *PHENOMENON*–A PROBLEM

The Phenomenon of Man is a difficult book. The root of the difficulty lies, of course, in the complex person that Teilhard was: simultaneously a committed Jesuit priest and a dedicated scientist. There is good reason for saying that such a hybrid combination is impossible. Teilhard's life, however, serves as living proof of the viability of his double dedication and vocation. Not only was he able to unify his scientific and religious vocations, but he succeeded in living both of them fully.

No biography of Teilhard will be attempted here. Our annotated bibliography directs the reader to the many biographies available in English. But we must look at the man behind *The Phenomenon of Man* in order to get a comprehensive view of the fundamental problem he tackles and the overall view he proposes as a solution.

The problem behind *The Phenomenon of Man* is basically a problem of love. Therefore, it is not primarily a problem of philosophy—understood in the sense of a coherent and rational world view. It is first and foremost a problem of living rather than a problem of knowing. Love is located more at the center of our lives than is knowledge. But we need not fabricate illusory problems. Love *is* rooted in knowledge. But when there is a

7

problem in loving, there is a corresponding problem in knowing. Inasmuch as the *Phenomenon* tries to suggest an answer to a problem of love, it is necessarily an attempt to enlarge man's knowledge, to innovate in man's way of looking at himself and his world.

Perhaps the copywriter for the jacket of N. M. Wildiers' *An Introduction to Teilhard de Chardin* exaggerates: "Teilhard moves into a position beside Freud and Marx as one of the great prophetic and formative voices in the development of the modern consciousness." Nonetheless, some explanation must be given for the great and continuing appeal of Teilhard's writings. He himself thought that he was given the talent not of inventing anything but of " 'resounding' in tune with a certain vibration, a certain human and religious note which at the moment is all around us, and in which people have recognized and redis-covered one another."[1] Because he experienced the problem of love quite acutely, large numbers of contemporary men and women listen to Teilhard so readily, for in him they hear the resonances of the sounds of their own souls.

Teilhard's Love of "This Ridiculous World"

All the biographies agree on Teilhard's strikingly deep love of matter, of this world, of the cosmos. Very early in life his love of matter was symbolized by rocks, with their apparent solidity and indestructibility. His love of Auvergne, his birth-place, is intimately tied in with his love of matter. "To Auvergne I owe my delight in nature. Auvergne it was that gave me my most precious possessions: a collection of pebbles and rocks still to be found there, where I lived."[2] An early Jesuit teacher, Père Henri Bremond, reminisced about the "dis-concertingly sophisticated" young Teilhard: "it was only long afterwards that I learned the secret of his seeming indifference. Transporting his mind far away from us was another, a jealous and absorbing passion—rocks."[3] There is no question that this childhood love of the earth, focalized in rocks, underwent many transformations, the greatest of which would come from learning about cosmic evolution.

Not surprisingly, Teilhard's love of the earth was infected with the sting of an existentialist *angst*—a painful awareness of the fragility of material being, the dread experience of being propelled towards death, the nausea generated by the threatened and meaningless moments of human life. Very early he discovered that the earth and things earthly are contingent, ephemeral, fragile.

> A memory? My very first! I was five or six. My mother had snipped off a few of my curls. I picked one up and held it close to the fire. The hair was burnt up in a fraction of a second. A terrible grief assailed me; I had learnt that I was perishable. . . . What used to grieve me when I was a child? This insecurity of things. And what used I to love? My genie of iron! With a plow-hitch I believed myself, at seven years, rich with a treasure incorruptible, everlasting. And then it turned out that what I possessed was just a bit of iron that rusted. At this discovery I threw myself on the lawn and shed the bitterest tears of my existence![4]

How could one love *completely* what one had discovered to be so fragile, so corruptible? The mature Teilhard saw reasons enough for "the deliberate acceptance and delight in disgust with life, contempt for the works of man, fear of the human effort."[5] Still, "nature is never spent; there lives the dearest freshness deep down things."[6]

Imbedded in Teilhard's early love of this earth was a deeper love, a more basic thrust. He confesses:

> I had at that time [childhood] an irresistible need (both life-giving and consoling) to come to rest forever in something tangible and definite. And I searched everywhere for this beatifying Object. The story of my inner life is summed up in this search, ever dwelling on realities more and more universal and perfect. Fundamentally this deep natural tendency has remained absolutely unchanged ever since I began to know myself[7]

This passage shows Teilhard engaged in the perennial human quest for an at-one-ness or at-home-ness with the world. Perhaps forever, contemporary man has lost the at-one-ness peculiar to the Medieval man whose world is so obviously "home" in the pictures of Fra Angelico or Giotto or in Book of Hours' miniatures. Contemporary Western man lives far from nature and from the bonds that might tie him to the seasons' cycles. This is part cause of contemporary man's alienation from his world.

Another part—"the curse of entropy"—comes from his science. By the second law of thermodynamics, he sees that this earth, and ultimately this cosmos, is doomed to a "heat death," ending up as burned out ash—energyless, actionless. If science's "curse of entropy" seems too remote, we have now at every moment science's "nuclear curse." Hans J. Morgenthau puts it bluntly: "A secular age which has lost faith in individual immortality in another world, and is aware of the impending doom of the world through which it tries to perpetuate itself here and now, is left without a remedy. Once it becomes aware of its condition, it must despair."[8]

And yet, we love this world. We are attracted by its obvious beauties—"cloud-puffballs," "veined violets," "trouts' rosemoles." Ambivalent though our love is, we seek "substance," permanence, immutability for our love of this world. We seek "treasure incorruptible, everlasting." Though nature surrounds us with her impermanence, change and ephemeralness, we find ourselves with Teilhard desiring and loving the permanent, the solid, the substantial. Mircea Eliade points out the same drive in primitive man with "his thirst for the real and his terror of 'losing' himself by letting himself be overwhelmed by the meaninglessness of profane existence."[9] We may not have immediate sympathy for the primitive "solution," reminiscent in a way of Teilhard.

Objects or acts acquire a value, and in so doing become real, because they participate, after one fashion or another, in a reality that transcends them. Among countless stones, one stone becomes sacred. . . . A rock reveals itself to be sacred because its very existence is a hierophany: incompressible, invulnerable, it is that which man is not. It resists time; its reality is coupled with perenniality.[10]

This desire for permanence and perenniality is transposed by Teilhard from rocks to a larger frame of reference, one which speaks to the contemporary ear.

Matter, throwing off its veil of restless movement and multiplicity, had revealed to him its glorious unity. . . . Because it had forever withdrawn his heart from all that is merely local or individual, all that is fragmentary, henceforth for him it alone in its totality would be his father and mother, his family, his race, his unique, consuming passion.[11]

The novelist, Sherwood Anderson, testifies to the same need: to be one with the material universe.

I had suddenly an odd, and to my own seeming, a ridiculous desire to abase myself before something not human and so stepping into the moonlit road, I knelt in the dust. . . . There was no God in the sky, no God in myself, no conviction in myself that I had the power to believe in a God, and so I merely knelt in the dust in silence and no words came to my lips.
Did I worship merely the dust under my knees?[12]

"Did I worship merely the dust under my knees?" Teilhard's aim in The Phenomenon of Man is, starting from the cosmos' initial "dust," to construct a scientific view which validates man's instinctive love of his world and his search for ultimacy. Science thus far has tended to breed anxiety, turmoil and despair in man. Teilhard feels that this comes from a shortsighted science, a science that does not extend its own dimensions to their religious limits. He aims, therefore, in the Phenomenon to discern a love of this world and a hope for ourselves and mankind, a love free from neurosis and a hope free from despair.

With such love of and hope for a world no longer "ridiculous," Teilhard is confident that man will not be paralyzed but will possess "courage and the joy of action."[13]

The Exclusive Love of Jesus Christ

In Teilhard there existed a whole other side to his love, the Christian side. His love of this world was countered by a love of Jesus Christ. As the earth is symbolized for Teilhard by a rock, the person of Jesus Christ is symbolized by the image of his Sacred Heart, supporting a cross, encircled by a crown of thorns, and surrounded by an aureola of fire and light.[14]

To try to explain Teilhard—and therefore the *Phenomenon*—without his love of Jesus Christ would be like trying to explain Dante without Beatrice or David without Jonathan. The love of Jesus Christ was present at the alpha of Teilhard's life and at its omega.

> [His mother] had a plaque raised over the main entrance of the manor house, consecrating it to "the Sacred Heart of Jesus." In order to be on hand when her children awoke, she normally attended the earliest Mass at the village church, which was celebrated before dawn, walking the two miles, rain or shine, even during her pregnancies. . . . To his "dear and sainted mother," Pierre attested, "I owe the best in my soul. . . . It gives me great strength to know that the whole effort of evolution is reducible to the justification and development of love of God. That is what my mother used to tell me long ago."[15]

On the Holy Thursday before his death on Easter Sunday, 1955, Teilhard noted in his journal, as the first point of a summary of his "credo," these three Pauline verses:

> The last enemy to be overthrown will be death, for everything is to be reduced to subjection and put under Christ's feet. . . . And when everything is reduced to subjection to him, then the Son himself will also become subject to him who has reduced everything to subjection to him, so that God may be everything to everyone.[16]

The absolute centrality of Jesus Christ for Teilhard, both personally and cosmically, is the great "given" in his life. This all-encompassing love scarcely shows itself in *The Phenomenon of Man*, but blazes forth in many other writings, notably in *Writings in Time of War, Hymn of the Universe,* and *The Divine Milieu.*

Perhaps the reality, intensity and centrality of his love of Jesus Christ is only appreciated with difficulty by marginal Christians or by "Gentiles"—Teilhard's favorite name for non-believers. The problem is the same in understanding how St. Paul was completely captivated by the love of Jesus Christ.

> For, as I see it, living means Christ . . . it is now no longer I that live, but Christ that lives in me. . . . Not that I have secured it [resurrection] yet, or already reached perfection, but I am pressing on to see if I can capture it, because I have been captured by Jesus Christ.[17]

In Teilhard's case too, "the blessed reality of Christ" had captured his entire love and dedication.

> To this faith, Jesus, I hold, and this I would proclaim from the house-tops and in all places where men meet together: that You do more than simply stand apart from things as their Master, you are more than the incommunicable splendour of the universe; you are, too, the dominating influence that penetrates us, holds us, and draws us, through the inmost core of our most imperative and most deep-rooted desires; you are the cosmic Being who envelopes us and fulfils us in the perfection of his Unity. It is, in all truth, in this way, and for this that I love you above all things.[18]

In the love of Jesus Christ, there is a jealousy, an exclusiveness that tends to cause conflict and, sometimes, simplistic solutions. Christ commands: "You must love the Lord your God with your whole heart, your whole soul, and your whole mind." The follower of Jesus is well warned: "Do not think that I have come to bring peace to the earth. I have not come to bring peace but a sword. . . . No one who loves father or mother more than he loves me is worthy of me, and no one who loves son or daughter more than he loves me is worthy of me. . . ." Further, there is the segregation of the Christian from this world: "My kingdom is not a kingdom of this world. . . . If the world hates you, remember that it hated me first. . . . But it is because you do not belong to the world, but I have selected you from the world that the world hates you. . . . I make no request for the world."[19] It would seem that the lover and follower of Jesus Christ must hate the world and leave it behind. And this is one form that love of Christ has historically taken: flight to the desert or to the enclosed monastery. (It does not solve all scriptural problems but it helps considerably to note the two quite different usages of "world," especially in Saints John and Paul. "The Pauline and Johannine idea of the world as the epitome of evil does not cancel out the usual notion of the world—verified throughout the New Testament— as the embodiment of God's creation."[20] The same dual usage can be seen in the Second Vatican Council's *Pastoral Constitution on the Church in the Modern World.*[21])

The apparent exclusiveness of Christ's love posed a sharp problem for Teilhard as a young Jesuit. In order to love Christ wholeheartedly, should he not give up his "worldly" vocation of geology so that the love of Christ would be without rival?

> At that moment I would have gone off the rails if it had not been for the solid common sense of Père T. . . . What he did, in fact, was simply to assure me that my crucified God looked for a "natural" development of my being [as a scientist], as well as for its sanctification [as a Jesuit, growing in love of Christ].[22]

But the problem continued: Is Christ such a jealous lover that no other lover can coexist or be subordinated to that love?

There are certainly many Christian and non-Christian factors which support an exclusive, jealous love of Christ, one which excludes a love of this world. The recurring theme of many authentic mystics is "Deus solus"—God alone. Christ himself spoke of the "one thing necessary," so that all other loves would seem to be not only unnecessary but to be actual hindrances to possessing "the better part." *The Imitation of Christ*, the Christian classic of asceticism certainly used by Teilhard, is forthright: "Study, therefore, to wean thy heart from love of visible things, and to betake thee to things unseen. . . . Use temporal goods, but desire eternal. . . . And whatsoever is not God is nothing, and ought to be accounted as nothing."[23] Frequently the Church teaches the people of God to ask for the grace of "despising earthly things and of loving heavenly things," and this even on the feast of that great lover of this world, St. Francis of Assisi![24] Teilhard himself felt that Christianity carried something of an intrinsic inducement to be false with this world. "There is a danger that belief in God may (by a distortion, of course, but the danger is still there, in fact) make us lazy, preoccupied with our own 'petty salvation', charitable only as a matter of form. . . ."[25]

This echoes a charge to which Teilhard was very sensitive: if you love Christ, you cannot love this world and you must be a deserter. He frames the nonbeliever's charge thus:

> Christianity . . . is bad or inferior because it does not lead its followers to levels of attainment beyond the ordinary human powers; rather it withdraws them from the ordinary ways of humankind and sets them on other paths. It isolates them instead of merging them with the mass. . . . He [the Christian] appears to be interested, but in fact, because of his religion, he simply does not believe in the human effort as such. His heart is not really with us. Christianity nourishes deserters and false friends; that is what we cannot forgive.[26]

The French phenomenologist, Merleau-Ponty, makes just this charge.

> Because the subject is contingent, undetermined and free, success is never guaranteed to the search for truth and the establishment of values. According to Merleau-Ponty, Christians cannot admit this; and therefore, they cannot earnestly collaborate in this

search. They are worthless for this world and it is impossible, or at least very difficult, to hold a dialogue with them.[27]

Despite such dangers and accusations, Teilhard was not pre- pared to give up or diminish his love of Jesus Christ. The only substantive charge that could be brought against him, he felt, was that he attempted "to exalt Christ above all things."[28] More than anything, the very quality of his lifelong, mortifying obedience, undertaken and continued for Christ, proves that his talk about Christ was more than talk. But speaking of Christ is a life-necessity for an ardent lover. When as a young Jesuit his superior counseled him, "Work for Jesus Christ, but don't speak of him," Teilhard replied, "If I have become a Jesuit, or rather if I have received the unmerited favor of serving as a Jesuit in the Church militant, it is precisely to speak of Jesus Christ."[29]

Two Loves—Tension and Conflict

The evidence is abundant; the conclusion is forced on us: Teilhard had an uncommon love of this world, a depth of feeling for the *whole* of material reality. *And* he had an even greater love of Jesus Christ, the center of his life and thought.

What we would expect from the intense existence of these two loves did exist: conflict, tension, strife. The Gospel teach- ing on the impossibility of loving and serving two masters leads us to this expectation. "No slave can belong to two masters, for he will either hate the one and love the other, or stand by one and make light of the other."[30] Still, since both of Teilhard's loves were *good*, the simple rejection of one of the loves seems out of the question. Nor is this what he did.

Before Teilhard was able to "resolve" the problem of his two loves, he first had to experience the full force of the conflict.

Does it mean, then, that to be a Christian he must renounce being a man, a man in the full extent and depth of the word, avidly and passionately a man? If we are to follow Christ and share in his heavenly body, must we abandon the hope that every time our efforts succeed in mastering a little more determinism, every time a little more truth is won and a little more progress achieved, we make contact with and begin to make available some small portion of the absolute? If we are to be united with Christ, must we dissociate ourselves from *the forward drive inseparable from this* intoxicating, pitiless *cosmos* that carries us along and asserts itself in the mind of each one of us?[31]

The love of rocks and the love of the Sacred Heart—can they be composed or is the rift irreparable? The reconciliation of Christianity and the "spirit of the earth," he writes in 1916, "has always been for me the real problem of my interior life—rather as the question of Rome for Newman or the sense of the demands of the soul for Psichari—I mean the problem of reconciling progress and Christian detachment—of reconciling a passionate and legitimate love of all that is greatest in Earth, and the unique quest for the Kingdom of Heaven."[32]

One could think that Teilhard felt himself to be fighting a purely personal battle when trying to reconcile his two loves. This is exactly how he did not see it. The conflict of loves which he experienced clamored for a personal solution, but at the same time he was convinced that this conflict was microcosmic, or a small-scale reflection of the same conflict existing in mankind itself. In the very personal *How I Believe*, Teilhard states, "Have we not here in an individual experience, the particular solution, or at least one sketched out, of the great Spiritual problem at which the advancing front of Humanity is at present hurling itself?"[33] Again and again he asserts that the conflict of the two loves, involving obviously two faiths and two hopes, is the root contemporary problem.

On the one side, in the form of modern humanism, we have a sort of neo-paganism, bursting with life but still lacking a head; on the other side, in the form of Christianity, a head in which the circulation of the blood has slowed down. . . . Can we possibly fail to see that these two halves are designed to be combined into one whole?[34]

Teilhard felt himself to be called to be an apostle of reconciliation between these two halves or loves. "And once again,
I was conscious within myself of the inspiration that calls me
to the great work of reconciling the supreme and absolute love
of God with the lower (but still legitimate and necessary) love
of life embraced under its natural forms."[35] For this apostolate
he felt that, being both priest and scientist, he had the special
opportunity of experiencing both loves to the fullest. "The
originality of my belief is that it has its roots in two domains
of life usually considered antagonistic. By education and by
intellectual formation, I belong to the 'Children of Heaven.'
But by temperament and by professional studies I am a 'Child
of Earth.' "[36]

In order to reconcile the two loves, it was also necessary to
understand and to criticize *both*. Teilhard shrewdly observed
that "when people love what they criticize, they can criticize
without danger."[37] In his criticism of the Church of the 1920's
and 1930's, Teilhard frequently sounds like one deputed to
list all the Church's sins and deficiencies prior to a reforming
ecumenical council. Rideau has collected Teilhard's criticisms
of the Church—supposedly the bearer of Christ's spirit and
love: a lack of openness to modern humanism and the aspirations of the new consciousness; a defective concept of charity
("resigned and static"); an incomplete, if not obsolete, notion
of God; an almost exclusive use of judicial and moralistic
rhetoric; individualistic concept of salvation; an unrealistic attitude towards the world and lack of any real contact with it.[38]
On the other hand, as much as he loved the world, Teilhard
was critical of its "tumultuous surge of cosmic and humanitarian aspirations [which] are dangerously imprecise and still
more dangerously 'impersonal' in their expression: the new
faith in the world. . . . Worldly faith is not enough in itself
to move the earth forward."[39]

Teilhard's criticism of the world is not merely a specification of Christ's warning to beware of the world—"the world that is cultivated for its own sake, the world closed in on itself, the world of pleasure, the damned portion of the world that falls back and worships itself."[40] Teilhard's criticism was centered more upon the new and "rival star" that the world has become in the consciousness of modern man "something greater than himself, something that can, in a way, be 'adored.' . . . [To that world] we may certainly attribute the irresistible rise of the great myths (communism, nationalism) whose emergence and impact are rocking the foundations of our ancient civilization."[41]

Teilhard's own critical summary of the conflict (and we can justifiably substitute "love" for "faith") states: "Worldly faith, in short, is not enough in itself to move the earth forward: but can we be sure that the Christian faith in its ancient interpretation is still sufficient of itself to carry the world upward?"[42]

Evolution—Reconciliation of Conflicting Loves

The simplest solution for the problem of the conflicting loves of world and of Christ would be the rejection of one or the other of the loves. We could opt for the "secular city" with Harvey Cox and dispense with a transcendent God.[43] Or we could forsake the "secular city" and seek "God alone" in the desert. Either solution was clearly unthinkable for Teilhard.

In a most general way evolution *is* his resolution for the conflicting loves of God and world. He was convinced that a Christian could not be "double-hearted" in his loves; somehow his loves must be unified in such a way as to do justice to both loves. Evolution is the key to such unification, but not evolution understood merely as the origin of higher species from lower ones. Rather, the two loves are seen as grounded in two evolutions (cosmic and Christic), which interpenetrate and reinforce one another. More particularly, there are not two more or less equal loves or evolutions, but there is the relationship of subordination of the part to the whole. The difficulty in conceiving and expressing this relationship accounts for some of the misunderstanding and criticism of Teilhard.

He frequently says that that there is only one evolution and therefore only one love. This love is for "the Body of Christ whose charity animates and recreates all things."[44] But the reality is more complex, and so we find frequent expression of *two* evolutions, *two* loves. Teilhard's reconciliation includes not only the rejection of a static world and a static Christ, but the positive vision of the evolving world as an integral part of the whole, growing body of Christ.

An example may help. When somebody steps on my foot, a *part* of me, I can and do say, "Why did you step on *me* [the *whole*]?" In the case of the human person, the part is so integrally a part *of* the whole that the whole is touched when the part is touched. Yet, I can and do say that the part *is not* the whole; I am *not* my foot. Here is expressed the real distinction which exists between the integral part and the whole.

In somewhat the same way, there is one whole, Christ; there is one growth, Christ's. But an integral part of this whole is the world which truly evolves. Just as there is no conflict between my foot and me, so there is no conflict but rather the closest possible unification between Christ and the world, between Christ's love and the world's growth. These are not "separate and equal" realities and loves which ought to conflict. On the contrary, they are interpenetrating and reinforcing realities and loves.[45]

The reconciliation of these two loves would not have been achieved if Teilhard had not enlarged the very meaning of evolution, his key to the reconciliation. He had to enlarge the perspectives of biological evolution to cosmic proportions— proportions that would include past *and* future, the subhuman *and* the human, the individual *and* the social. This is the work of *The Phenomenon of Man*. If the theory of evolution itself does not evolve into a truly cosmic vision, there is, according to Teilhard, no possibility of reconciling our loves.

Corresponding to this effort to expand the theory of evolution is a parallel effort, in other writings, to enlarge and evolve the concept of Christ to cosmic proportions. Only thus, following the lead of St. Paul and many early Christian writers, could Teilhard discover a reconciliation between God and world, between a love of the secular and the eternal cities.

> Everywhere on earth, at this moment, the two essential components of the ultra-human, love of God and faith in the world, each in a state of extreme sensitivity to the other, pervade the new spiritual atmosphere created by the emergence of the idea of evolution. These two components are everywhere in the air, but they are not generally strong enough, *both at the same time*, to combine with one another in *one and the same subject*. In me, by pure chance . . . their relative proportions happen to be correct, and the fusion has been effected spontaneously—not powerful enough, yet, to propagate itself explosively—but nevertheless sufficiently so as to establish that the process is possible and that, *sooner or later, there will be a chain-reaction.*[46]

Teilhard discovers, then, not the mere reconciliation of these two loves but their harmonious reinforcement, capable of causing a creative chain-reaction.

He frequently can speak of the unification of the two loves as bringing "peace and limitless scope for his being to expand."[47] This testimony, however, has to be coupled with his experience of continuing risks and challenges. Five years before his death Teilhard revealed:

> Today I encounter still the risks to which he is exposed who finds himself compelled by inner constraint to leave the well beaten track . . . in order to search out [another] way to heaven. . . . To synthesize the "Upward" [God alone] and the "Forward" [world's evolution]. . . . To reach heaven by bringing earth to perfection. To Christify matter. There is the whole adventure of my life, a great and magnificent adventure, during which I am still often afraid, but to which it was impossible not to have committed myself.[48]

Evolution and GENESIS

In 1959 at the University of Chicago, fifty outstanding international scholars assembled for a Darwin Centennial Celebration. They drafted the following definition of evolution:

> *Evolution* is definable in general terms as a one-way irreversible process in time, which during its course generates novelty, diversity, and higher levels of organization. It operates in all sectors of the phenomenal universe but has been most fully described and analyzed in the biological sector.[49]

This very concise definition implies that all the higher forms of nonliving and living matter have proceeded from the simplest particles of matter by a successive organizational process. Though these experts hold for a universal or cosmic evolution, they indicate that the evidence is most abundant and the analysis has been most cogent in the realm of biological evolution.

The nonscientist can and does appreciate to a degree the force of the evidence for evolution. The most important evidence is paleontological, the fossil record which, in the earth's timed layers, shows successively higher forms of living things appearing after lower forms. Perhaps evolutionists would not have to interpret the evidence as indicating that the lower somehow caused the higher. But the other evidences for evolution, from comparative anatomy, genetics, physiology, biochemistry, biogeography, taxonomy, embryology, together with the paleontological evidence, constitute an evidential convergence such that any other explanation is almost unthinkable.[50] John Henry Newman was so impressed by the evidence that he said, "I will either go whole hog with Darwin, or, dispensing with time and history altogether, hold, not only the theory of distinct species but that also of the creation of fossil-bearing rocks."[51] Now, a hundred years after *The Origin of the Species,* it is almost impossible to find a scientist, non-Christian or Christian, working in the life sciences who is an antievolutionist.

When the theory of evolution was introduced to human thought, it is true that Christians in general greeted it as a grave threat to the biblical account of creation. For fifty years there was open conflict between evolutionists and most Christians. Even now fundamentalist Christians still appeal to a literal interpretation of the Book of Genesis as certain proof against evolution. In the Catholic Church the most important document relating to evolution is Pius XII's encyclical letter, *Humani Generis*, which appeared in 1950. The Pope made it clear that "the teaching authority of the Church does not forbid that . . . research and discussions . . . take place with regard to the origin of the human body . . . from pre-existent matter."[52] Pius XII insists on the divine creation of the human soul, leaving clearly open the question of how man's body came to be. He acknowledges the existence of facts which seem to indicate some form of evolution.[53]

The chief source of difficulty has been the biblical account of the origin of man in the first two chapters of Genesis. It should be sufficient to note that the present writer knows of no significant biblical scholar who now expresses difficulty on this score. Going beyond the task of showing that there is no conflict between the Bible and science are several theologians who seek to insert evolutionary insights into a biblical framework.[54]

Briefly, Genesis and evolution are not in conflict because Genesis says nothing pro or con evolution. Before one can be in conflict with a position, one must know it. The author of Genesis was, along with the rest of the human race until the middle of the nineteenth century, in complete ignorance of biological evolution. Hence, the human author of Genesis could neither affirm nor deny evolution.

Still, the Genesis account *appears* to teach God's immediate creation of individual animal species and of man. The Bible also *appears* to teach that the sun goes around the earth. But as Galileo justly observes, "The Bible was not written to teach us astronomy," and he goes on to cite the aphorism: "The intention of the Holy Ghost is to teach us how to go to heaven, not how the heavens go."[55]

We could restate the aphorism: The Bible teaches us how the human species is to rise to God, not how the human species arose. According to John L. McKenzie, S.J., the Genesis account of the seven days is a backdrop for the essential biblical teaching.

> It [Genesis 1 and 2] is less a story of how man came to be than of what man is. It is important to see that man is like God, but is not God; it is important also to see that man is like the lower forms of life, but is not one of them. This the Hebrew story tells us. . . ."[56]

The Bible is, therefore, not an astronomy, geography or biology textbook; it is primarily theology: what man is in relation to God and creation, and what God has done and is doing to reconcile man with himself.

Accordingly it is an equally misguided apologetics that would try to establish by Genesis either the evolutionistic or creationistic origin of animal species, including man. One could—with unlimited peril—argue that Genesis actually teaches evolution. God "molded man out of the dust of the ground," and this could as well have been done directly as indirectly, by way of many intermediate and lower animal species. Such reasoning is quite as farfetched as that which seeks to establish Genesis as the proponent of antievolutionism.

Teilhard's forthright espousal of evolution (for *scientific reasons*) and his attempts to rethink central dogmatic positions (especially original sin) were the causes of the beginning of his practical difficulties, in 1925, with his Jesuit superiors and Roman authorities. He first encountered the theory of evolution in 1910; it was an intellect-shaking experience: "I was thirty when I abandoned the antiquated static dualism and emerged into a universe in process of guided evolution. What an intellectual revolution!"[57] This encounter generated in him a "consciousness . . . [of] the deep, all-embracing, ontological drift of the universe."[58] What can escape our notice is that Teilhard, apparently from the beginning of his "intellectual revolution," saw that the present scene of evolution is not in biology but in the realm of man's spirit.

> This is the *general "drift" of matter* towards spirit. This move-ment must have its term: one day the whole divinisable sub-stance of matter will have passed into the souls of men; all the chosen dynamisms will have been recovered: and then our world will be ready for the Parousia [Christ's appearance at the end of time].[59]

A further step in Teilhard's thought has been introduced here. The fulfillment of human evolution coincides with the Parousia or term of Christ's evolution.

Evolution and Christ's Body

One of the mysterious chapters in the history of Teilhard's intellectual life is how he came to such a dynamic grasp of the Mystical Body of Christ and His evolution. During his theo-logical studies at Hastings, the tone of theology was legalistic and rationalistic. Certainly, Teilhard's Christological insight was somehow the result of contact with the prime scriptural evi-dence, especially that of Saints John and Paul.

For St. Paul the principle confirmation of the reality of Christ's Body in this world was when on his way to Damascus he experienced Jesus in an unmistakable—and *communal*—way.

> Now Saul, still breathing murderous threats against the Lord's disciples, went to the high priest, and asked him for letters to the synagogues in Damascus, so that if he found any men or women there who belonged to the Way, he might bring them in chains to Jerusalem. But on his journey, as he was approach-ing Damascus, a sudden light flashed around him from heaven, and he fell to the ground. Then he heard a voice saying to him, "Saul, Saul! Why do you persecute me?"

"Who are you, sir?" he asked.

"I am Jesus, whom you are persecuting," said the voice.[60]

What is disconcerting here is that the voice does *not* ask, "Why do you persecute my friends?" or "Why do you persecute my Christians?" Nothing of the sort. The voice says, "Why do you persecute *me*?" Since the speaker has already identified himself as Jesus, whom Saul knows died of crucifixion several years before, Saul (and every Christian) has the perplexing problem of grasping how it is that when he persecutes plebeian Christians in Damascus (or Harlem, or Calcutta), he persecutes Christ personally. What sort of identity exists between Christ and the Christians?

After presenting to a college class a similar sketch of Paul's encounter with Christ, this writer received the shocked question of a student: "Why, isn't that pantheism?" At the time, perhaps shocked by the shock of the questioner, this writer feebly offered some subtle distinction; never again! This is the mystery that Paul had to live with, the mystery that every Christian has to live with; it is the mystery which Teilhard probed throughout his adult life.[61]

Together with the organic unity of Christ and members of his Body is the equally essential property of his Body: growth. Perhaps the best Pauline expression of the growth of Christ's Body is: "And 'he gave' some men as apostles, and some as prophets . . . for *building up* the body of Christ until we all become one in faith and in the knowledge of the Son of God, and form that perfect man who is Christ *come to full stature*."[62] Paul indicates that Christ as he exists now in his risen Body is in a state of growth or evolution to "full stature."

For the final state of Christ, St. Paul uses the term *pleroma*, the fullness or completeness which Christ will possess at the end of his growth, which is the end of time. Within history, then, there is a Christogenesis going on. At the same time there is anthropogenesis, mankind proceeding to higher forms of psychosocial existence. As a consequence, this question occurred to Teilhard (and occurs to every Christian possessed of the same data): What is the relation between the two apparently separate processes of evolution, human and Christic?

> If men could only see that in each one of them there is an element of the Pleroma, would not that, Lord, effect the reconciliation between God and our age? If only they could understand that, with all its natural richness and its massive reality, the universe can find fulfilment only in Christ; and that Christ, in turn, can be attained only through a universe that has been carried to the very limit of its capabilities.

> For God, willing his Christ (= the Pleroma), willed Man [and willing man,] he initiated the immense movement of material and organic evolution. Only one thing is willed, and only one thing made, in all the turmoil of the Universe.[63]

There is precedent enough for Teilhard's quest to adapt Christianity to contemporary evolutionary thought. He himself adverted to the early Christian adaptation. "During the first century of the Church, Christianity made its decisive entry into human thought, boldly assimilating the Jesus of the Gospels to the Logos of Alexandria."[64] In subsequent ages "devotion to the Savior has varied its expression. . . . Homage to Christ the universal King, so dear to the Middle Ages, changed into the loving memory of the Jesus as he lived and died in the Holy Land."[65] John XXIII, when he opened the Ecumenical Council, sharply distinguished between "the substance of the ancient doctrine" and "the way it is presented." The Council, he exhorted, should seek to present the authentic doctrine "through the methods of research and through the literary forms of modern thought."[66]

With evolution as the controlling new idea of the twentieth century, it is not surprising that a Christian thinker would try, as Teilhard did, to appropriate evolution's insights for the proclamation of the "good news."

And since Christ was born, and ceased to grow, and died, *every-*

*thing has continued in motion because he has not yet attained
the fullness of his form.* He has not gathered about Him the last
folds of the garment of flesh and love woven for him by his
faithful. *The mystical Christ has not reached the peak of his
growth—nor, therefore, has the cosmic Christ.* Of both we may
say that *they are* and at the same time *are becoming*: and it is in
the continuation of this engendering that there lies the ultimate
driving force behind all created activity. By the Incarnation,
which redeemed man, the very Becoming of the Universe, too,
has been transformed. Christ is the term *of even the natural*
evolution of living beings; evolution is holy.[67]

The Aim of the PHENOMENON

It is deceptive to speak of the aim of the *Phenomenon.*
Teilhard was as full of aims and motives as are we. Certainly
he was trying to resolve for himself his problem of two loves:
"the discontinuity he experienced between love of God and love
of the world, between human achievement and the kingdom of
Christ, between Christian detachment and personal self-develop-
ment, between the data of revelation and scientific research."[68]
His quest for a reconciliation and unification of these parts of
his life was rewarded in the writing of the *Phenomenon* by an
increased seeing and feeling of the *whole.*

Intricately bound up with this aim is the very love of Jesus
Christ. While he was writing *The Phenomenon of Man* he
confessed:

> I feel that I have seldom worked so entirely for God alone. I am
> sure He will give me the light and the strength to complete as
> it should be completed what I wish to say *only for Him.* . . . I
> hope that the Lord will help me [to complete the book], since
> it is entirely as an attempt to make His countenance seen and
> loved that I am taking such pains, which sometimes I could well
> be spared.[69]

One could question how strictly he meant that the aim of work
was *"only for Him."* Surely he worked for his prospective
readers, both non-Christian and Christian. What were his aims
for them?

Here, Teilhard's aims coincide with the legitimate expectations of his readers. What can the "Gentile," the nonbeliever, expect from *The Phenomenon of Man*? He can rightly expect *to see*: to see the "huge past" and the "fantastic future" joined in one meaningful vision. To see the world moving in a directed way, and so to grasp the abiding meaning of the cosmos. To overcome, therefore, the experience of absurdity bred by partial and disconnected viewpoints. To hope, cosmically, for the ultimate success of terrestrial evolution, and personally for the permanent value of himself and his achievements. And to love: to love more cosmically and confidently, so to overcome fear and anxiety. Finally, the "Gentile" can legitimately expect that the *Phenomenon* would help him to be "open" to the "good news" of Christianity as as integral complement of his cosmic view and love.

What can the Christian reader of the *Phenomenon* expect? He can expect an increase of both his loves, of this world and of Christ, and a more intimate union of these loves. He can expect to see the world as part and parcel of the evolving Christ, to feel the "sense of the earth," whereby the cosmic genesis is experienced as good. He can expect growth in reinforcing loves: Christ loved in the world and the world loved in Christ.

For both non-Christian and Christian readers, Teilhard wanted what he wanted for himself. His lifelong aim was for the *whole*, for a unified and coherent seeing and loving of all that was, is, and is coming to be. Or, we could say, he strove to unify for himself and others the two loves: the love of this world in its progress and the love of Jesus Christ coming "to full stature."

At the beginning of this chapter, we employed synecdoches—rocks and Sacred Heart—to characterize Teilhard's loves. Now, we can say that *The Phenomenon of Man* is aimed at helping others to unite the love of rocks with the love of the Sacred Heart, the love of this world with the world's God, and from these united loves to find the earth suffused with fire.

> *Throughout* my life, *by means of* my life, the world has little
> by little caught fire in my sight until, aflame all around me, it
> has become almost completely luminous from within. . . . Such
> has been my experience in contact with the earth—the diaphany
> [showing forth] of the Divine at the heart of the universe on
> fire . . . Christ; his heart; a fire: capable of penetrating every-
> where and, gradually, spreading everywhere.[70]

In more restrained rhetoric Teilhard gives another expression
of the aim of *The Phenomenon of Man*:

> This work may be summed up as an attempt *to see* and *to make
> others see.* . . . Fuller being is closer union . . . Union increases
> only through an increase in consciousness, that is to say in
> vision. (31)†

> I repeat that my only aim . . . is to try *to see;* that is to say, to
> try to develop a *homogeneous* and *coherent* perspective of our
> general extended experience of man. A *whole* which unfolds.
> (35)

> Man finds himself capable of experiencing and discovering his
> God in the whole length, breadth and depth of the world in
> movement. (297)

READING SUGGESTIONS

NOTE: 1. The abbreviations for Teilhard's writings (e.g., *DM, MM,
SC*, etc.) are given before the Footnotes, on page 208, where also
abbreviations for the works of many other authors are noted. Abbreviations not there noted are sufficiently specific that the full publishing data may be found in the Bibliography.

2. Starred (*) items indicate especially important works and
vocabulary.

1. *Biographies of Teilhard*:
Julian Huxley's "Introduction" (*PM*, 11-28) gives some helpful in-

---

†All page references given within the text are to *The Phenomenon of
Man*, revised English edition (New York: Harper & Row, 1965).

sight into T.'s person and thought, but more penetrating is the short life by Pierre Leroy, S.J., in *DM*, 13-42 and *LT*, 15-47 and the one by his cousin in *LT*, 49-62. Even more illuminating are T.'s letters: *LT, MM* and *LTF*. The best full-length biography is Robert Speaight, *A Life of Teilhard de Chardin*, but the earlier Claude Cuénot, *Teilhard de Chardin* is especially helpful in its extensive quotations as is George Barbour, *In the Field with Teilhard de Chardin* in its intimate detail.

2. *Parallel Readings*:
   angst: *AM*, 208-210; *MM*, 163-164; de Lubac, *Religion*, 36-46; *Rideau, 110-118.
   two loves: *DM*, 43-53, 95-105; *MM*, 93, 98-99, 223-4; *WTW*, 14-18; de Lubac, *Religion*, 92-107; *Faricy, 13-31.
   reconciliation by evolution: *DM*, 112-121; *SC*, 212-213; *VP*, 151-160; *WTW*, 75-91.
   one evolution: *DM*, 56-62; de Lubac, *Religion*, 92-107.
   man as part of a whole: *DM*, 74-80.

3. *Critiques*: evolutionism: Mooney, 199-202 (211-14); one evolution: de Lubac, *Religion*, 195-205.

HYPERPHYSICS–THE SUPER-SCIENCE?

While writing *The Phenomenon of Man* in 1940, Teilhard "prophesied" to friends, "I shall have the pure scientists against me as well as the experts in pure metaphysics."[1] He was right; a very frequent criticism of the *Phenomenon* is: the scientists say it is not science, the philosophers say it is not philosophy, and the theologians say it is not theology. The usually unexpressed conclusion is that the *Phenomenon* is worthless since it will fit into no literary pigeonhole. We could balance criticism with criticism: Nobel prize zoologist Medawar's "tipsy, euphoric prose-poetry . . . excused of dishonesty only on the grounds that before deceiving others he has taken great pains to deceive himself" with prestigious biologist Huxley's "a notable and I think a seminal work."[2] The general response of philosophers, theologians and scientists has been far more positive than negative. But the literary worth of *The Phenomenon of Man* will not be solved by a nose-counting of critics, nor can we wait a hundred years for the judgment of history.

As a beginning we might well entertain the hypothesis that *The Phenomenon of Man* is a genuinely new genre of literature, as were Augustine's *Confessions* and Joyce's *Finnegan's Wake*. In which case the command which Augustine heard in the garden, *"tolle, lege"*—take and read—is very much to the point. It implies that primarily our concern will be with "Is it true?" rather than with "Is it science or philosophy or theology?" Only by experiencing at firsthand *The Phenomenon of Man* are we in a position to form our own judgment about its literary genre and worth.

Teilhard himself complicates the problem. In the *Phenomenon's* preface, he says that his book must be read "purely and simply as a scientific treatise."(29) He is most insistent that it is *not* a work of philosophy or theology, though he wants to leave the door very much open for what these fields of study can add to his own restricted study of man, which he called a "hyperphysics."[3]

Hyperphysics—Animal, Mineral or Vegetable?

It almost seems that Teilhard "doth protest too much" that the *Phenomenon* is a work of pure science, a "hyperphysics," which is a natural and necessary extension of traditional science. As it is ordinarily understood and as Teilhard understands it, science is concerned, in the first place, with *phenomena*, whatever appears and is observable. Science does not seek to know the ultimate nature or metaphysical constitution of things, but aims at making relations between appearances. Secondly, all science seeks to establish "laws of recurrence," laws which express patterns of the relationships between appearances. For example, Newton's second law of motion expresses the experimental law of recurrence of the relationship between the phenomenon of acceleration and the phenomenon of force: if the force (the antecedent) applied to a constant mass is doubled, the acceleration (the consequent) is doubled. If the force is tripled, the acceleration is tripled, and so on. What science seeks, then, is "an experimental law of recurrence which would express their successive appearance in time"(29) of various phenomena, a "coherent order between antecedents and consequents."(29) Thus far, traditional science and hyperphysics agree.

There are, however, two original elements in Teilhard's

hyperphysics which seem to take it out of the realm of science: hyperphysics must include *all* phenomena and must consider as central the phenomenon of *man*. Traditional science has generally restricted its investigations to the *material* aspects of reality. (Only the total materialist would deny that some phenomena, for example, love and beauty, are nonmaterial or have some nonmaterial aspects.) Further, science has tended not to be a general all-inclusive study of material reality, but a collection of individual and quite particular sciences, for example, organic chemistry, zoology, atomic physics. The conception of a science which would study *all* phenomena, whether material or not, whether nonhuman or human, seems to be an extension of science that may well be illegitimate. Science's power traditionally has come from its limited methods and goals. On the other hand, there is within science itself a drive towards ever more comprehensive theories and laws. The theories of Newton and Einstein are prized precisely because they unify and universalize what before was disconnected and particularized.

Perhaps even more radical is hyperphysics' attempt to deal with man "*solely* as a phenomenon" and yet "with the *whole* phenomenon."(29) What is at stake here may not be quite evident. Consider this contemporary example of a common conception of the intrinsic limits of science:

> The rational approach [of science] is based on two characteristic assumptions. The first is that nature is comprehensible; that experience may be ordered; that the world is not bewitched. The second is called the assumption of 'objectivability', i.e., that the knowing subject plays the role of a detached observer and may be left out of the world picture.[4]

However, if hyperphysics is to study *all* phenomena, certainly it must study man, who is just as observable as a growing cabbage or as the docking of a spaceship.

Teilhard entitled his work *The Phenomenon of Man,* rather than, say, *The Phenomenon of the Cosmos,* because in his view the phenomenon of man explains all other phenomena in an evolving cosmos which culminates in man. Man, truly a world —a very small but intricate world, a microcosm—recapitulates and mirrors the macrocosm, the ordered whole of created reality. Man, this distinctive part, stands for the whole and gives meaning to the whole.

What is so distinctive about man is readily observable and is therefore in the realm of phenomena: man is the self-reflective being. As a matter of fact, this is precisely what Teilhard understands by "the human phenomenon," which is the literal translation of his book's title. "By the expression 'The Phenomenon of Man,' we mean here the empirical fact of the appearance in our universe of the power of reflexion and thought."[5] But man's thinking seems to be the precise feature which most scientists say must be excluded from science. By what right, asks Teilhard?

> Man, in his special and most revealing characteristics, that is to say in what are called 'spiritual' properties is still left out of our general [scientific] pictures of the world. Hence this paradoxical fact: there is a science of the universe without man. There is also a science of man as marginal to the universe; but there is not yet a science of the universe that embraces man as such. Present-day physics (taking this word in the broad Greek sense of a 'systematic understanding of all nature') does not yet give a place to thought; which means that it still exists in complete independence of the most remarkable phenomenon exposed by nature to our observation.[6]

Teilhard is equally as insistent on man's thought as a phenomenon. "For a very long time there was no thought on earth. Now there is, and to such a degree, that the face of things is entirely changed. Now we are really viewing a purely scientific fact, a phenomenon."[7]

With its emphasis on objective and verifiable observation, traditional science would seem to rule out a consideration of something so subjective, private and unrepeatable as human thought and feeling. But it is just these that Teilhard wants to make the center of his science of hyperphysics. This explains the vigor with which he pushes the necessity for science to consider the *within*, as well as the without, of matter. Put another way, he felt that science was radically incomplete and partial if it considered only the without of matter and its manifestations. We, as men, have a without and are observable from that aspect, but we also have a within: the whole world of our knowledge and love, our theoretical constructions and aesthetic responses, our creative inspirations and appetitive reactions. These are real appearances which are observed by each of us. These are phenomena truly empirical or experienceable by intimate subjective observation, though not by objective means.

How legitimate is Teilhard's attempt to introduce the whole physical realm into science? Our answer to this question depends very much upon our conception of science. If science must be restricted to the without, to the objective and measurable, Teilhard's attempt clearly is illegitimate. But if science can be—ought to be—broadened to include the within of man, his hyperphysics is not only meaningful but necessary.

Such a "physics," as Teilhard well knows, will tend to *look* like philosophy, because philosophy seeks to study the *whole* and places special emphasis on *man*. Science and philosophy, however, "assail the real from different angles and on different planes."(30) Philosophy is interested in (to use Kant's term) the noumenal, that which is. Philosophy seeks to move from appearances of things to their very natures, while science restricts itself to the level of appearances or phenomena. A hyperphysics such as Teilhard's, because it includes *all* phenomena and especially the phenomenon of *man*, is bound to look more like philosophy and less like science. Perhaps Teilhard is correct: "The true physics is that which will, one day, achieve the inclusion of man in his wholeness in a coherent picture of the world."(36) Dr. Jonas Salk, the developer of oral polio vaccine, expresses a similar hope "for a basic science to underlie man as a whole and man in his social organization. Biology, medicine and life itself must be tied together."[8]

At the very end of the *Phenomenon*, Teilhard details his readers' possible misgivings about hyperphysics as he has developed it:

> Among those who have attempted to read this book to the end [an admission that the *Phenomenon* is a difficult book?], many will close it, dissatisfied and thoughtful, wondering whether I have been leading them through facts, through metaphysics or through dreams. . . . If we try to bring man, body and soul, within the framework of what is experimental, man obliges us to readjust completely to his measure the layers of time and space. To make room for thought in the world, I have needed to 'interiorize' matter; to imagine an energetics of the mind; to conceive a noogenesis rising upstream against the flow of entropy; to provide evolution with a direction, a line of advance and critical points; and finally to make all things double back upon *someone*. (289-90)[9]

Teilhard is ready enough to admit in all humility that he "may have gone astray at many points," but once one accepts the basic framework of his hyperphysics, something resembling his work will necessarily result. Hence, it is primarily the framework which is to be questioned.

As a matter of tactics or strategy, however, I think Teilhard would have been "readers ahead"—both scientific and general readers—if he had not specified the genre or type of writing in the *Phenomenon*, if he had not insisted that it was a book of science or a hyperphysics. It is too easy to dismiss the *Phenomenon* because it claims to be science but turns out not to be science as this or that reader understands it.

This difficulty is compounded by some history. Shortly after Teilhard wrote *The Phenomenon of Man*, he indicated to his good friend Dr. George Barbour: "Aside from the geological and paleontological studies under way, I have been able to finish up a book on Man—half scientific, half philosophical—

into which I have put the gist of the ideas closest to my heart.[10] Is it hanky-panky on Teilhard's part to write a book which he *knows* to be "half scientific, half philosophical," and then *say* that it is *totally* scientific, perhaps in order better to reach his chosen audience, agnostic fellow scientists? There is no easy resolution of this difficulty, but certain considerations are relevant. He was convinced that the domain of science could be, ought to be, enlarged beyond its traditional limits. And the *Phenomenon* is an essay, an initial effort on Teilhard's part to supply that expanded, generalized science of man. Abstractly he knew the difference between science and philosophy, but it is doubtful that this could help him; a mind so given to unification has difficulty perceiving its movement from the domain of science into that of philosophy—*if* the domains are that clearly separate. A fellow paleontologist, however, does not hesitate to say that Teilhard has moved into the fields of philosophy when, in the latter part of the *Phenomenon*, he takes up the noosphere and the direction of socialization.[11]

On the other hand, nonscientist readers are frequently critical of the *Phenomenon* because they seem unwilling to accept its severe and self-imposed limitations. Many such readers take Teilhard to task for not presenting a theology of such things as creation, original sin, redemption. This smacks too much of reproaching an architect for not having built a cathedral when he explicitly set out to build a house.[12]

Teilhard, anticipating such criticism, is very careful to note, both in general and in specifics, that philosophy and theology are empowered to say more on several critical subjects investigated by his limited hyperphysics. (A few instances are the ultimate origin of the human soul, monogenism, and the existence of the supernatural.) But, let it be added quickly, Teilhard had in mind a philosophy and theology resulting from a radical rethinking comparable to his own hyperphysics.[13]

Hyperphysics' Two Basic Assumptions

Teilhard manifests himself as a very reflective thinker in that he lays bare at the very beginning of his work his two basic assumptions.

> The first is the primacy accorded to the psychic and to thought in the stuff of the universe, and the second is the "biological" value attributed to the social fact around us.
> The pre-eminent significance of man in nature, and the organic nature of mankind. . . . (30)

Most original thinkers are unable to explicitate their assumptions; they possess of course their controlling insights but have not reflected sufficiently to make them explicit.[14] Many writers on evolution, if they followed Teilhard's lead, would indicate *their* controlling assumptions: the primacy of the material and chemical manifestations of the cosmos and, hence, the relative insignificance or unimportance of man and of psychic phenomena.

One must not think that Teilhard's assumptions are pure assumptions, that is, devoid of any evidence for their truth. In the preface it is true that he merely states his assumptions, but in the body of the book he exhibits considerable evidence for their validity. Evidence, however, is not the whole story with assumptions; human affectivity and choice are key factors. For instance, evidence alone does not decide whether a man will be racially prejudiced or not. In one sense, the evidence is the same for all men, but it is differently evaluated and weighed by free and emotional beings. Cosmically we are not forced to assign a primacy to either material or psychic phenomena. What we think is, in part, what we *choose* to think.

Teilhard's French for "two basic assumptions" reads, *"deux options primordiales"*—"two primordial options." Because these assumptions are part of a basic philosophical outlook, they are not forced upon us by reality, but merely evoked from us in such a way that appetitive factors and choice play decisive roles. This Teilhard indicates in his summary, where he says that the second assumption is "a choice" depending on experiential evidence. (303)

Can and ought science to adopt the two basic assumptions of Teilhard's hyperphysics? Teilhard indicates accurately what science *has done* with respect to the first assumption and, by implication, to the second.

> Up to the present, whether from prejudice or fear, science has been reluctant to look man in the face but has constantly circled round the human object without daring to tackle it. Materially our bodies seem insignificant, accidental, transitory and fragile; why bother about them? Psychologically, our souls are incredibly subtle and complex: how can one fit them into a world of laws and formulas? (281)

Teilhard's first assumption is stated in two quite different ways: "the primacy accorded to the psychic and to thought in the stuff of the universe," and "the pre-eminent significance of man in nature." This constitutes a complex assumption, which may be stated thus: since the psychic, and specifically thought, is the most important phenomenon in the universe, and since man is the unique bearer of this highest form of psychism, man is of preeminent importance and explanatory value in the whole realm of nature.

The second assumption is also doubly stated: "the 'biological' value attributed to the social fact around us," and "the organic nature of mankind." Teilhard is stressing the organic unity of mankind, constituting a "biological" atom or whole; like individual organisms this human superorganism is meant to grow. How growing and toward what is only partially indicated in the preface by "the combined movement towards unity."(29) The specifics of this social growth towards unity are spelled out much later in the *Phenomenon*.[15]

The PHENOMENON'S *Soul—Apologetics*

Perhaps it is a mistake, but hopefully an unavoidable one, to raise the question of apologetics. The word "apologetics" conveys to many readers all the negative overtones of "apologetical" and "apologize," of the pejorative suggestion of "a special pleading inspired by prejudice."[16]

Even in the first definition of "apologetics" in the dictionary, "to speak in defense of," we sense the nuance of a defense of the defenseless. But let us not deny that apologetics was and can be used to describe the defense of that which ought to be defended, for example, the rights of man, the value of human freedom, democratic government.

In the realm of Christian religion, "apologetics" has the generally good connotation of methods to be employed either in preparing the ground for a favorable hearing of the "good news," or in actually presenting the saving truths of Christianity to nonbelievers. Just how these aims are best pursued is subject to many and diverse thoughts.

That *The Phenomenon of Man* is a work of apologetics is abundantly clear both from the text and from the author's stated purpose. It is limited almost completely, however, to the first phase of apologetics: preparing the ground for a future receptivity to the "good news."

Though there is an ultimate subordination of the *Phenomenon's* apologetics to a Christian goal, it ought not to be concluded that the *Phenomenon's* whole value depends on this orientation. Teilhard saw a great and intrinsic value in generating in a fellow pilgrim personal insight into the direction of evolution, the value of man's personality, the significance of his immortality, and the existence of a personal and personalizing God. A reader may never hear of Christianity's further truths, but this cannot detract value from the insights which the *Phenomenon* seeks to generate.

If there is any lingering doubt that Teilhard somehow was a devotee of the "hard sell" apologetics suggested by the word "proselytize," consider the testimony of Claude Cuénot, Teilhard's biographer: "Teilhard . . . with his unconditional respect for the individual conscience, forbade himself any proselytizing, and even refrained from saying grace at meals.

Similarly, with other scientists, whether strangers or old friends, he confined his conversation to science. . . . He was ready to talk Christianity to those who wished to hear. . . ."[17]

What constantly restrains his apologetics from any tendency to dominate or conquer others intellectually and/or emotionally is that his apologetics is rooted *first* in his own need for greater insight and faith.[18] In an early work, certainly to be classed as a work of apologetics, Teilhard writes:

> In order for me to demonstrate to myself my Christian faith, I could not have (and in fact never found) any other method but to verify in myself the legitimacy of a Psychological Evolution. First I feel it necessary to descend, degree by degree, to a faith always more elementary, just to a certain fundamental intuition below which I can discern nothing more.[19]

Hence, Teilhard's defense or justification of the faith is primarily, as with the great apologetes, *"fides quaerens intellectum"*—his own faith questing a greater understanding of its riches. Quite naturally he wishes to share the quest and the findings with others.

It is no surprise, then, that Teilhard's approach to apologetics is highly personal.[20] By his double vocation, scientist and Jesuit, Teilhard has so identified himself with the spirit of this world that he was sure that what generated further light for himself would generate further light for fellow scientists.

> As far as my strength will allow me, *because I am a priest,* I would henceforth be the first to become aware of what the world loves, pursues, suffers. I would be the first to seek, to sympathize, to toil: the first in self-fulfilment, the first in self-denial—I would be more widely human in my sympathies and more nobly terrestrial in my ambitions than any of the world's servants.[21]

From his sensitivity to the mood and thought of contemporary men, especially scientists, Teilhard's apologetics in *The Phenomenon of Man* begins from what he calls the "modern disquiet."

In the foreword he exposes briefly the gnawing source of this disquiet and how it can be cured only by a completely universal view of man:

> *To see or to perish* is the very condition laid upon everything that makes up the universe, by reason of the mysterious gift of existence. And this, in superior measure, is man's condition. (31)

> Without these qualities [a new set of "senses"] to illuminate our vision, man will remain indefinitely for us—whatever is done to make us see—what he still represents to so many minds: an erratic object in a disjointed world. (34)

> When studied narrowly in himself by anthropologists or jurists, man is a tiny, even a shrinking, creature. (35)

If one is tempted to think that Teilhard is merely recording the pessimistic reaction of *other* men to the human condition, it must be remembered that he spent four years at the front in World War I. This "baptism in reality" flooded his consciousness with the immense futility of war, especially trench warfare. In addition there was his long experience in the Far East, nakedly showing its poverty and disease, but also manifesting the immensity of the earth and the diversity of mankind.

> My strongest impression at the moment is a confused one that the human world . . . is a huge and disparate thing, just about as coherent, at the moment, as the surface of a rough sea. . . . The multiplicity of human elements and human points of view revealed by a journey in the Far East is so *'overwhelming'* that one cannot conceive of a religious life, a religious organism, assimilating such a mass without being profoundly modified and enriched by it.[22]

Experience enough to feel man as "a tiny, even a shrinking creature . . . an isolated unit lost in the cosmic solitudes."

The *Phenomenon's* apologetics is aimed, therefore, at seeing man *rightly,* which is to say completely, and not as he is ex-

perienced immediately and largely at the level of emotion. There
is more: for Teilhard a corrected vision of man is immediately
in the service of action, creation, vitality. Whereas a partial
vision generates pessimism and dries up the springs of human
creativity, a coherent and comprehensive view of man fosters
"the preservation of courage and the joy of action" so necessary
for energizing the maximum potentialities of man.

The other half of Teilhard's apologetics is his "apostolate"
to his fellow Christians. This he always considered an integral
part of his whole apologetics:

> I am slowly putting together the elements of a "divinization"
> (of the earth) *ad usum Christianorum* [for the use of Christians]
> which will continue the "hominization" written *ad usum gen-
> tilium* [for the use of Gentiles, or nonbelievers]. . . . Both to-
> gether will be my apologetic, an apologetic based on evolution
> yet whose spirit seems to me to be truly and equally Christian.[23]

Since the Christian is presumed to be in possession of his Christian faith, what else does he need? Fifty years before Pope
John and the Second Vatican Council, Teilhard felt that Christians needed—to use a contemporary word—an *aggiornamento*,
an updating and rejuvenation of religion, "not by structural
alteration but by assimilation of new elements."[24] Pope John's
desire "to open windows" corresponds, it seems, to Teilhard's
aspirations of rejuvenating the Church "by assimilation of new
elements": all that is good and valid in contemporary man's
thoughts and dreams.

Teilhard was deeply chagrined when he heard Christians or
Christianity rebuked with the taunt that Christianity promotes
a "complacent acquiescence," or, as we say now, a sense of
being out of it.[25] We examined in the previous chapter the
charge against the Christian that "he simply does not believe in
the human effort as such." That is the core of the "Gentiles' "
objection against Christians and Christianity. By promoting an
individualism which is unconcerned about the whole human

venture, and by preaching an otherworldly supernaturalism, which is oblivious of the natural order and goodness of this world, Christianity is antihuman.

Another way to see the need for an apologetics for Christians is to examine Teilhard's fears for the Church he knew and loved. Being hypersensitive to the great intellectual and cultural transformations taking place in mankind, "he feared a petrifying, sterile withdrawal [of Catholicism] into itself. The effect would be to make it cease to appear what it is in reality for every age and every man: the truth of life, 'the long despaired-of answer to the question asked by every human life.' "[26]

In 1937 Teilhard experienced "an ageing Christianity . . . that no longer informs the material world," and he met too many Christians who were "diffident, timid, undeveloped, or narrow in their religion."[27] If there were no basis in historical Christianity for these charges, his apologetics for fellow Christians could be dismissed as superfluous. The truth is that in Christian spirituality there exists a whole strain of instruction, rightly described by Teilhard.

> God obviously has no need of the products of your busy activity, since he could give himself everything without you. . . . You are on a testing-ground where God can judge whether you are capable of being translated to heaven and into his presence. . . . So that it matters very little what becomes of the fruits of the earth, or what they are worth.[28]

This theme of "heaven alone" we have seen reinforced by some liturgical and scriptural teaching on "the world." Teilhard's apologetics to fellow Christians is directed, therefore, towards a seeing the intrinsic value and lovableness of this evolving world.

His apologetics can be described in several ways. There is the specifically Ignatian approach to the integration of human and Christian aspirations. Such integration calls for a "new St. Ignatius," because of the "new awareness of the value of creatures" and of man's heightened responsibilities for a world now known to be in evolution.[29] Put in another and dramatic way, Teilhard's apologetics to Christians is an attempt to "wake and liberate Catholic thought" and show them how to "Christify evolution."[30] By all counts the greatest original idea of the past hundred years is that of evolution. What Teilhard sought to do for Christians is to show them how to view Christ and the future of man over against the backdrop of evolution. Since the great schism which threatens the Church, and therefore the Christian, is the fact that "Christian" and "human" no longer tend to coincide, Teilhard's apologetics of "Christifying evolution" is an effort to see the grandeur of an evolving universe, illumined from within by Christ, "the Evolver."[31] Teilhard seeks to show the Christian that cosmogenesis, the evolution of the cosmos, in all reality is a Christogenesis, the evolution of Christ. For one committed to the person and action of Christ, this "seeing" necessarily invests the world with a splendor and a dynamism it lacks for one who finds Christ mainly or only in the liturgy and personal prayer. (Yet, the central role of liturgy is gleaned from his "The Mass on the World," and *The Divine Milieu* frequently underscores the necessity and value of personal prayer.[32])

Still another way of specifying Teilhard's Christian apologetics is to say that it is rooted in the Ignatian spirituality of "finding God in all things." In the *Spiritual Exercises* St. Ignatius seeks to lead exercitants to an experience of God's presence and action in all aspects of creation. The Jesuit poet, Gerard Manley Hopkins, vividly expresses this drive to experience God:

> . . . and dost thou touch me afresh?
> Over again I feel thy finger and find thee.[33]

Teilhard's innovation is to stress evolution as a most important facet of creation, wherein God and his Christ may be found. In a letter written at the front, Teilhard asks,

Who can say what invincible power it is that sometimes makes
us tremble before the earth, or the sea, or the huge past, as
though we were close to a beatifying presence that still hides
itself from us . . . and who will ever bring about the happy
conjunction of this vague summons, so deeply felt in the heart
of every man at all worthy of the name, and the call of a personal God![34]

In the *Phenomenon's* Epilogue, Teilhard gives the outline of
an experiential answer:

If the world is convergent and if Christ occupies its centre, then
. . . Christ invests himself organically with the very majesty of
his creation. And it is in no way metaphorical to say that man
finds himself capable of experiencing and discovering his God
in the whole length, breadth and depth of the world in movement [evolution]. (297)

Contemporary man, except for periodic vacations, lives out his
life far removed from an experience of the earth or the sea;
he does live his life in the bustling and real extensions of "the
huge past," and he can come to seek and find his God there—
a further facet of what it means to "Christify evolution."

The best summary of Teilhard's apologetics is his own. He
notes three "steps" in his apologetics, each intimately linked to
the others:

1) "a correct physics and metaphysics of evolution," that is,
the hyperphysics of the *Phenomenon*—revealing an evolution
with a direction: towards converging human unification in and
through Omega.

2) A Christology set in an evolving universe, and therefore
stressing Christ as cosmic and evolving Center.

3) An ascetics, or "guruship" of earthly *conquest*, based on
the supernatural value of the terrestrial effort to bring human
evolution to fulfillment *in Christo Jesus.*[35]

Though the first "step" would seem to be specifically for the
"Gentile," there is no question about the Christian's equal need
for hyperphysics' "seeing." Without its placing of man as the

arrowhead of cosmic evolution, there is no possibility of the up-dated Christian theology and spirituality set forth in the second and third "steps."

Since the hyperphysics of the *Phenomenon* is not a completely independent science, it is not surprising that it should be structured in part by the further "steps" of Teilhard's apologetics. A contrast pinpoints the problem. *The Foundations of Metaphysics in Science* by Errol F. Harris is very similar to Teilhard's *Phenomenon* in aim and conclusions. But the difference is also large. Harris, though he admits a direction in evolution, does not press on to the questions of a converging or nonconverging evolution, the existence or nonexistence of an Omega of evolution, and evolution's reversibility or irreversibility. Teilhard's apologetics, however, prodded him to make the hyperphysics as complete as possible. Though hyperphysics has its own method, when Teilhard uses it as part of a higher synthesis it receives a higher direction and structure. *The Phenomenon of Man's* hyperphysics looks beyond itself for the completion of "The Christian Phenomenon."

How much and in what way does "the human phenomenon" depend on "the Christian phenomenon"? A first answer to this exceedingly complex question is that the Christian experience of the growing Body of Christ *was* Teilhard's inspiration for conceiving *The Phenomenon of Man*: "I should never have ventured to envisage [the Omega Point] . . . if, in my consciousness as a believer, I had not found not only its speculative model but also its living reality."(294) We can recall that the monotheism of Einstein was the inspiration for his quest to find a single set of field equations to explain all physical laws. But surely Einstein's general theory of relativity is capable of being judged scientifically, not theologically. The cases of Einstein and Teilhard, however, are not perfectly parallel. Teilhard's hyperphysics moves on to statements about Omega and the future of man, points which Teilhard always recognized as "conjectures and postulates," "vague and misty," without a faith in "the figure of Christ wrapped in the mystery of his Resurrection and Parousia."[36] Mooney agrees with de Lubac's assessment of the relative independence of hyperphysics from Christian faith:

> In a hidden way, his faith in Christ, based on reasons that formed no part of his system, maintained his own effort, even though he did not introduce it into the premises from which he reasoned and even though the conclusions at which he arrived remained independent of it.[37]

This independence is denied by G. G. Simpson, the Harvard paleontologist, who has expressed a great personal liking for Teilhard: "His major premises are in fact religious and except for the conclusion that evolution has indeed occurred, most of his conclusions about evolution derive from those and not from scientific premises."[38] The most questionable point in Simpson's critique is that Teilhard's "premises are in fact religious," but there is more caution in evaluating his conclusions.

On the other hand, Julian Huxley, biologist and non-Christian, is in sympathy with hyperphysics' premises and method, though he admits that Teilhard is more radical in his noospheric convergence and "human rebound" and "out of sight" with his Point Omega.[39] There is obviously no easy theoretical answer to the question of the *Phenomenon's* dependence on Christian faith, only the practical solution of *"tolle, lege"*— take and read and judge.

One final but important point on Teilhard's apologetics is the quality of his rhetoric. Because his apologetics is primarily a personal witness—"this I see, this I feel"—and because the warmth of his person comes through his prose, few readers experience the "arm-twisting" often associated with apologetics. Despite his addiction to a specialized vocabulary, most readers find Teilhard "talking to them—where they are."

The PHENOMENON's *Skeleton*

The Phenomenon of Man certainly is not just a historical

description of evolution going through its various stages. It is this, but it is much more. There is a parallel here with history itself, which is certainly more than a mere account of successive dates and events. True history searches for the unifying significance and intelligibility in the succession of events. It seeks to connect the antecedents with the consequents, the befores with the afters. It tries to develop a unified view of its course.

In the broadest sense, this is what Teilhard attempts in recounting the whole history of evolution. In his readers he wants to generate "seeing things whole," "a *homogeneous* and *coherent* perspective of our general extended experience of man."(35) Put another way, Teilhard addresses himself to the fundamental philosophical problem of the one and the many: how to see the unity, the wholeness, in and of the variegated objects and experiences which comprise our lives.

> Plurality and unity: the one problem to which in the end all physics, all philosophy, and all religion, come back.

> The more I look at it, the more I think that the only knowledge—the one that can be acquired even in all our weakness and ignorance—is the vision of unity in [what is] becoming under and through the incoherent multiplicity of things.[40]

Discovering this unity of the multiplicity is what Teilhard means by faith. "To believe is to bring about an intellectual synthesis."[41] Equally expressive of the same idea is the opening sentence of the *Phenomenon's* Foreword: "This work may be summed up as an attempt *to see* and *to make others see*."(31)

Why is seeing so important? Why is faith so essential to human life? *"To see or to perish."*(31) Long ago Socrates saw that the unseeing life, "the unexamined life is not worth living." Such a life is swamped by multiplicity, subject to the "buzzing, booming confusion" which can be conquered only by a unifying vision or faith. Complete lack of intellectual vision is intellectual blindness. Partial lack of vision grounds the "bewitching by trifles" and leads to "a materiality and ever-increasing multiplicity of experience."

In a technological age, which is characterized by our ability to manage mountains of informational data, there is a tendency to think that the computer can solve our most basic problem: the difficulty of seeing. The gap between factual knowledge and wisdom is solved by nothing less than a unified seeing or a faith, vivifying and illuminating an individual consciousness.

Contemporary existentialist psychiatry seems to validate Teilhard's concern with vision or faith. Existentialist psychiatry is convinced that a patient's cure can be effected, not merely by seeing past causes for his present confusions and distortions, but far more through the construction of a meaningful schema of values and meanings—a *Weltanschauung.*[42] Teilhard saw that, even short of psychoses and neuroses, lack of vision and faith was harmful to human persons, something seen long ago by the prophet Baruch: "so they perished, because they had no understanding."[43]

By a deep and personal preference, Teilhard did not care to analyze the nature of the maladies associated with lack of vision, but concentrated on the positive means of leading others to higher and higher forms of faith. "Because I am conscious of experiencing very intensely the aspirations deep at the heart of my age (as others have its miseries), I feel it my duty to bear this testimony. . . ."[44]

Six years before the composition of the *Phenomenon*, Teilhard wrote *How I Believe,* a short book, more explicitly an apologetics for the "Gentiles" than is the *Phenomenon.* Opposite the title page of this earlier work appears:

I believe that the Universe is an Evolution.
I believe that Evolution goes toward Spirit.
I believe that the Spirit achieves itself in the Personal.
I believe that the Personal Supreme is the Universal Christ.[45]

In a form adapted to Eastern thinkers, this expresses the stages of faith through which Teilhard wishes to lead his readers—

from "faith to faith." In a letter to a Western friend, Teilhard makes more specific the stages of faith: "faith in the world, faith in the spirit in the world, faith in the immortality of the spirit in the world, faith in the ever-growing personality of the world."[46] The first faith embraces the conviction that evolution is governed by a law which manifests a direction—towards ever greater complexity and consciousness. The faith in the spirit in the world implies the insight into the spirituality of man, his transcendence over the limitations of matter. This grounds the further faith in the immortality of man's spirit. The final faith has to do with the corporate growth of men in the realm of the spirit, in the noosphere.

Out of this last faith, Teilhard works to a faith in God—the "Personal Supreme"—and from this to the specifically Christian faith in Jesus Christ as the Alpha and Omega, the beginning and end of cosmic evolution. More often than not, Teilhard felt that his function as an apologete had been performed if he could bring a reader merely to the "threshold of the temple," that is, to prepare the reader so that he is genuinely open to and capable of receiving the revelation of Jesus Christ as the fulfillment and complement of all his preceding faiths. Hence, the sections on Christ and Christianity in both the *Phenomenon* and *How I Believe* are on the sketchy side. To see the full dimensions of this final faith, the reader must consult *Writings in Time of War, Hymn of the Universe* and *The Divine Milieu.*

Traditional apologetics seeks to establish three points: man's freedom, the immortality of man's spirit, and the existence and some attributes of God. In their aim Teilhard's apologetics are traditional, but they are quite new in their method. Starting from the evolutionary views which at first led men astray, he wishes to lead men to "traditional concepts of a God who exercises an intellectual influence on immortal monads [men], distinct from himself."[47] As for immortality, Teilhard asserts that "a world culminating in the Impersonal can bring us neither the warmth of attraction nor the hope of irreversibility (immortality) without which individual egotism will always have the last word."[48] As for the third goal, human liberty, Teilhard takes this very much for granted, doubtless because he never experienced its significant denial. Clearly his apologetics aims at generating the conditions for various acts of faith, which are free acts of free men. Without freedom apologetics would be the nonsense science *par excellence.*

The actual structure and plan of *The Phenomenon of Man* are framed by the questions the author asks: "What does the world-adventure upon which we are embarked look like, when we seek to interpret it both objectively and hopefully in the light of the widest, soundest and most modern concepts of astronomy, geology and biology?" The question is not an abstract one but an inquiry shot through with large personal implications:

> The events we are witnessing and undergoing are unquestionably bound up with the general evolution of terrestrial life; they are of *planetary dimensions.* It is therefore on the planetary scale that they must be assessed, and it is in these terms that I ask you to consider them, so that we may better understand, better endure, and, I will add, better love these things greater than ourselves which are taking place around us and sweeping us along in their course.[49]

The first three Books of the *Phenomenon*[50] paint the planetary panorama of the "huge past" and highlight the "significance of the human phenomenon seen as an effect of the universe's 'convergence on itself by arrangement.' "[51]

Book I of the *Phenomenon* studies the properties of initial matter and how it evolves to higher forms of complexity and organization, from particles to atoms, from atoms to molecules, from molecules to megamolecules—these latter forming the threshold of living matter. It is thus shown that the appearance of life is not an absurd accident but the result of an oriented process or a "cosmic drift" present in matter and its modifications.

Book II details the appearance of life and its historical expansion in quantity and quality, creating around the earth the biosphere, the sphere of organic life. The complexity and consciousness of living things increases, and this constitutes higher and higher forms of living things. Increased consciousness is recognized by using the yardstick of more developed nervous systems and brains—until man arrives.

In Book III the appearance of man is shown to be in continuity with the highly developed hominids. Also shown is man's discontinuity with or qualitative difference from previous animal forms, inasmuch as man possesses *self*-consciousness or "consciousness to the second power." Thus man signifies a definitely new stage of evolution, where the scene of evolution is no longer in the biosphere but in the noosphere, the realm of human consciousness made up of man's intellectual creations, his social, artistic and scientific achievements, his religious activities, his expressions of affection and love.

In the final Book, Teilhard investigates the "fantastic future": the conditions of man's future development in view of the developmental law already discovered in evolution's history. What is the shape of the future we should hope for? How does growth take place in the noosphere? Is there a foreseeable culmination of evolution? After man, what? What are the factors which are necessary for further development of the noosphere? What qualities and actions in man most favor further evolution? Proposed solutions to these questions comprise the bulk of this Book.

In about the last fourth of the *Phenomenon*, Teilhard knows that he has outstepped what is strictly demonstrable by science and has, therefore, transcended hyperphysics.(284) He has entered into the realm of what Mooney calls "philosophic option," a "psychological act of faith" in accord with the requisites of phenomena: "The essential note of a psychological act of faith is, in my belief, to perceive as possible and to accept as most probable, a conclusion which, by spatial extension or by temporal elongation, overruns all analytical premises. *To believe, is to bring about an intellectual synthesis.*"[52] Proceeding from the implications of many psychic factors (the malady of space-time; the modern disquiet; the requirements of freedom, love and the future), Teilhard is able to confront the reader with the necessity of making an option: the world is absurd; *or* it is meaningful in the existence of a personal, attractive center of evolution, who exerts his influence on evolution's forward thrust. This center is Omega or God.

That second stage of apologetics prepares the ground for the final or third stage, faith in Christ. "By itself, science cannot discover Christ—but Christ satisfies the yearnings that are born in our hearts in the school of science."[53] By the specifically Christian act of faith, whose ground was prepared by the two previous stages of "faith in the world," the believer is now able to see Christ as the center of evolution's past, present and future.

> The whole interest and point of the book [the *Phenomenon*] is concentrated toward the end, which must be particularly lucid and carefully done. I hope that the Lord will help me, since it is entirely as an attempt to make His countenance seen and loved that I am taking such pains. . . .[54]

Let us not be deceived; the apologetics of *The Phenomenon of Man* should not be seen as a straight-line analysis proceeding from a scientific investigation of evolution and ending up with Christ as its goal and prime activator. The final and Christian stage is achieved not by reasoning alone, but far more through God's own illumination and the free option of the believer. Further, the truth of Christian revelation is not seen as a mere prolongation of previous reasonings on evolution's phenomena; rather, what Teilhard shows is the "fit," the coherence of a scientific explanation of evolution with a Christian explanation of a cosmic Christ. A reader who has appreciated the full implications of a cosmos in evolution is placed in a position to see and accept a Christ shown in all his cosmic splendor and activity.

READING SUGGESTIONS

1. *Read PM,* Preface, pp. 29-30, Foreword, pp. 31-36.

2. *See Glossary for*: *biological, continuity, hyperphysics, meta-physics, mind, *organic, *phenomenon, physics, *primacy, science.

3. *Passages to be noted*:
   31, "Fuller being is closer union." This is both the conclusion and the premise of *PM*; not only is the whole of cosmic evolution proceeding toward greater psychic union but the consummation of human evolution lies in man's beatifying seeing and therefore union with Omega.
   32-33, "But it is peculiar to man to occupy etc." T. indicates that not only do we have to *see* man at the center of the cosmos, but also in reality man *is* at the center or *is* "the axis and leading shoot" of cosmic evolution. (*PM*, 36) In other words, the universe is self-constructing *in mankind*.
   34, ". . . certain absolute stages of perfection and growth etc." T. is referring to the presence of discontinuities (for example, between living and nonliving and between human and non-human life) within the one and continuous process of cosmic evolution.

4. *Parallel Readings*:
   apologetics: *FM,* 260-269 (272-82); de Lubac, *Man,* 133-149 and *T. Explained,* 7-17; Faricy, 73-100.
   hyperphysics: *VP,* 103-113, 161-174; T. Dobzhansky in *LTF,* 219-227; *de Lubac, *Religion,* 69-77, and *T. Explained,* 62-65; *Mooney, 34-48 (39-55); *Murray, 123-149; Rideau, 38-50; Tresmontant, 13-17; Wildiers, 44-63.
   whole phenomenon: *DM,* 105-111; *MM,* 166-167; *SC,* 11-13 and 43-44.

5. *Critiques*: hyperphysics: I. Barbour, *Issues,* 406-408; Francoeur, *World,* 49-63; Nogar, *Lord,* 111-126; *Rabut, *Teilhard,* 228-244; *Smulders, 13-23.

4

"THE ESSENCE"– TEILHARD'S SUMMING UP

It must be explained immediately why we are leaping from the beginning of *The Phenomenon of Man* to its end. It is rather easy to justify an early reading of Teilhard's own summary, which happens to be placed at the book's end. Predictably this should help the general reader to grasp the book's essential point before its details—to perceive the shape of the forest before studying the individual trees.

Another innovation—suggesting that the reading of the *Phenomenon's* first half be done last—also needs justification. To that end, we may recall Teilhard's own evaluation of the book's different parts: "the whole interest and point of the book is concentrated towards the end."' A further reason is that since the first part of the book is so highly technical, beginning with it could easily discourage the general reader—even if he has a running commentary and glossary. *If* one wants to read the *Phenomenon* straight through, it is easy enough to adapt the *Path* to such a reading. However, experience with readers who have tried both ways points to the superior value of first reading the latter part of the book after the overview from Teilhard's own summary, "The Essence of *The Phenomenon of Man.*"

The *Path's* following chapter, "The Huge Past," will attempt to select the key ideas from the first part of the *Phenomenon* necessary for understanding the latter part. Accordingly, the general reader is urged to defer his reading of the *Phenomenon's* highly technical first part.

Teilhard's Summing Up

Teilhard is certainly not the first author of a difficult book who for one reason or another felt the necessity of drafting his own summary. But Teilhard's summary is much shorter and more clearly titled than, for example, Emmanuel Kant's *Prologomena to Any Future Metaphysics*, a booklength summary of his famous *Critique of Pure Reason*. More basic than brevity, however, is how well Teilhard's summary gives the gist of his principal work.

This writer has three misgivings about the adequacy of Teilhard's summary. The first has to do with his elimination of any descriptive or phenomenological account of "the huge past" in order to concentrate on the *Phenomenon's* three main conclusions. The second misgiving concerns the absence of any advertence to "The Christian Phenomenon" as confirming and completing hyperphysics' account of evolution. And finally, in the summary there is little about what might be called "the ultimate future," the culmination or end of evolution.

On the first misgiving, the lack of an account of "the huge past," well over a hundred pages are devoted by the *Phenomenon* to spreading out the panorama of "the huge past." By means of this, the scientific reader may weigh the evolutionary evidence against the conclusions Teilhard draws from it. In the "Essence," however, there is merely a reordering and restatement of the main conclusions about cosmic evolution. To regret the absence of the empirical data upon which he builds his synthesis is not to overlook the real difficulty of capsulizing such a mass of data within the confines of an eight-page summary. Still, we need the "feel" of that past if we are to catch something of Teilhard's vision.

> If I say the word history, your mind probably races back six thousand years. That's at the most—and that's because you're thinking of history in terms of dates and recorded events. But when you see history in its proper perspective, it's far longer. In the history of the world's evolution thirty thousand years are like a flash. I have concentrated so much on the past, on the earliest phases of the universe before even man existed, because I believe it helps to give us surprising visions of the future. Man is no more static than the world, for he too, like the world, is evolving all the time.[2]

In the *Path's* next chapter an effort will be made to give a picture of these "earliest phases of the universe."

On the second misgiving, it must be said in support of Teilhard's summary that "The Christian Phenomenon" is not an integral part of *The Phenomenon of Man*. Hyperphysics restricts itself to the data supplied by science. There is justice, then, in Teilhard's calling "The Christian Phenomenon" an Epilogue—an essay coming *after* the completion of the book. But given the unity of his vision, the Christian dimension must be added to the scientific investigation of man in order to have a "full and coherent account of the phenomenon of man." (30) Père de Lubac rightly insists:

> His writings undoubtedly form one whole in a way that those of few other writers do, and the imprint of his own personality can constantly be recognized in them. . . . To study the first part [scientific and/or philosophical, for example, the *Phenomenon*] in isolation [from the second part, the mystical and religious, for example, *The Divine Milieu*] is to mutilate Teilhard's thought.[3]

A summary of Teilhard's thought should, then, contain both aspects, the scientific and the religious.

The third misgiving, on the absence of "the ultimate future," arises because the *Phenomenon's* final chapter is devoted to and is entitled "The Ultimate." That Teilhard's summary makes little of this element indicates his high selectivity in summarizing. Three central insights have been selected and there is not space in his summary to develop important connected points.

"The Ultimate" is Teilhard's projection for mankind having reached the limits of terrestrial progress. Then there will be "the overthrow of equilibrium, detaching the mind fulfilled at last, from its material matrix, so that it will henceforth rest with all its weight on God-Omega."(287-8) This is the traditional Christian beatific vision or heaven, but radically recast in the light of an evolving and organic humanity, who together achieve their final end by a common dedication to fulfilling the "spirit of the earth."

Now, in a positive vein, we can ask what is Teilhard doing in his "Essence or Summing Up"? In substance it is no more nor no less than what the *Phenomenon* is all about. What does it take to *locate* man in the universe? How can one make sense of the human phenomenon? Or, in Teilhard's words, how are we to achieve "a full and coherent account" of an evolving universe?

Briefly, what Teilhard proposes in the "Essence" are three critical insights. These are the "seeings" that are essential to making sense of man in an evolving universe. One could say that the three options or hypotheses or conclusions *are* the "new senses" that Teilhard speaks about in the foreword. (33-4) These "new senses" enable us to see the phenomenon of man in a new light, with a new relevance and coherence. The case of Galileo comes to mind. When he became convinced that physical phenomena could and ought to be expressed in mathematical formulae, he was empowered to view physical phenomena in a new and creative light. So, too, in the case of the phenomenon of man: viewed in the light of Teilhard's three options, the whole of evolution and of human life takes on a new meaning and unity.

What is truly curious about *The Phenomenon of Man* is that

the initial presuppositions or hypotheses turn out to be the same as the three concluding propositions. Are we forced to say that Teilhard is such a unified thinker that his beginning is his end and his end his beginning? But is not this the case in science—the verifiable hypothesis ending up as the verified theory?

There is another reason why Teilhard's initial hypotheses should be identical with his final conclusions. Of truths which touch the center of our lives, of truths which are central to a world view or *Lebenswelt*, human choice is decisive. All readers have had sufficient experience of the human condition to possess a suspicion of the truth of the *Phenomenon's* assumptions. After reading its detailed analysis of varied evidences, readers will be in a position to affirm the same propositions as conclusions, but with greater assurance in view of the greater evidence. In both cases, in the beginning and at the end, the affirmations are free.

For each option or conclusion, we will indicate a counter option, one that can be and has been embraced by thinkers looking at the very same evidence as Teilhard. In the face of such a situation, we are almost forced to appeal to human freedom as the decisive factor in the opposing mental stances taken on fundamental issues. Since these are free truths, we must not expect overpowering evidence on either side. Nevertheless, Teilhard has criteria of truthfulness: intellectual coherence (how all the parts of a general theory fit together and fit with the facts); lived coherence (the theory must make life more liveable and loveable); and finally, fruitfulness (the theory must be a spur to significant and vital action).[4]

First Option: An Involuting Universe

Teilhard's first option and conclusion can and must be expressed in many different ways. The evolving cosmos is involuting or convergent. This means, because of the law of complexity/consciousness, the cosmos is always proceeding towards a more unified complexity. The elements, both human and non-human, accomplish this by involuting or coiling ever more closely, folding in upon themselves ever more tightly. "So finally we find the Universe from top to bottom brought within a single, immense coiling movement successively generating nuclei, atoms, molecules, cells and metazoa—the special properties of Life being due solely to the extreme (virtually *infinite*) degree of complexity attained at its level."[5]

Teilhard designates the *Phenomenon's* first conclusion as an option for "the primacy of life in the universe."(306) The importance of this option is made clear by the counter option: life is merely an epiphenomenon in the material universe, not the central phenomenon.[6] Even though life apparently exists only in a minute corner of the universe, even though "its whole planetary duration is no more than a flash" in the course of cosmic time, and even though living substances are of extreme fragility compared to other cosmic substances, life must be affirmed as the central phenomenon in the cosmos. To affirm that life is an epiphenomenon is to say that life is "incidental and accidental."[7] Macbeth gives voice to this view (though he is thinking especially of human life):

> Life's but a walking shadow, a poor player;
> That struts and frets his hour upon the stage
> And then is heard no more: it is a tale
> Told by an idiot, full of sound and fury,
> Signifying nothing.

Many of Teilhard's contemporaries opted for life as an epiphenomenon. "Agnostics such as Sir James Jeans and Marcel Boll, and even convinced believers like Guardini, have uttered expressions of amazement (tinged with heroic pessimism or triumphant detachment) at the apparent insignificance of the phenomenon of Life in terms of the cosmos—a little mold on a grain of dust."[8] Teilhard's option goes directly counter to this: "The fact that Life is so rarely encountered in the sidereal im-

mensity is precisely because, representing a higher form of
cosmic evolution, it can only come into existence in privileged
circumstances of time and space."[9] Life is not an inexplicable
anomaly. It is the rationally expected creation of a cosmic involution or coiling. Life is destined for an irreversible or eternal
consummation through man's noogenesis.

How different is the other option! Sir James Jeans expresses
it in all its starkness:

> To what can life be reduced? An apparently accidental fall into
> a universe which, by all accounts, was not made for it; to re-
> main clinging to a bit of sand, until the cold of death reduces
> us again to brute matter; to strut for a short hour on a very
> small stage, knowing full well that all our aspirations are con-
> demned to a final check, and that all we have made will perish
> with our race, leaving the universe as if we had not existed.
> The universe is indifferent (or even actively hostile) to every
> kind of life.[10]

Teilhard takes his position diametrically opposite to this. For
him life is not incidental to the cosmos; life is a huge and
necessary center of the cosmos. Life is not accidental; the most
basic law of the created cosmos is that it evolves to ever higher
and more complex unities—to ever greater interiority. Life,
with its interior of self-organization, is palpably a higher form
of matter than are inorganic or organic compounds—be they
stars or proteins. Teilhard's statement of his summary's first
point is:

> Regarded along its axis of complexity, the universe is, both on
> the whole and at each of its points, in a continual tension of
> organic doubling-back upon itself, and thus of interiorisation.
> Which amounts to saying that, for science, life is always under
> pressure everywhere; and that where it has succeeded in breaking
> through in an appreciable degree, nothing will be able to stop
> it carrying to the uttermost limit the process from which it has
> sprung. (302)

Some of the greatest theories in science have come from a

thinker who was bold enough to adopt a hypothesis which was exactly the contrary of the received theory. For example, Newton had postulated an absolute space and time for the description of physical events; Einstein, however, asserted that there was no absolute space or time, and, therefore, all events had to be described in terms of a relative space and time.

Teilhard flies in the face of the current theory of astronomers and cosmologists who picture the cosmos as constantly expanding, becoming ever more diffuse and immense. Teilhard does not deny this partial picture but asserts that it is far more significant and fruitful to picture the cosmos as concentrating and involuting, thus producing higher unities. Life is an infinitely richer manifestation of cosmic coiling and involution than are the unities of planets and proteins.

The common conception of matter is of an inert and non-dynamic substance. If one begins his world view from such a conception of matter, there certainly will be no intelligible place or meaning for life and human thought and love. These will be unintelligible, valueless absurdities. However, if one begins, as Teilhard does, with a matter that is actively and dynamically oriented towards bringing forth life, then man has a defined place and a priceless worth. In a genetic view of the cosmos, life is the very impetus of matter towards consciousness and spontaneity. And the fullest expression of these lies in man's reflective consciousness and creative freedom.

Second Option: Man an Ascent from the Ape

It is common enough to describe the evolution of man as a descent from the ape. Since evolution is accomplished by small, almost infinitesimal changes, it has been the fashion to state that man is basically or qualitatively the same as the ape. In other words, the difference between man and other primates is quantitative, a matter of degrees. A few years ago, this writer was told that that was the unanimous opinion of a soiree composed of university personnel at a big ten university. The informant, a cultural anthropologist, embraced the same view.

A popular novel, both in America and in France, is Vercor's *The Murder of the Missing Link*.[11] From the frontispiece—"All man's troubles arise from the fact that we do not know what we are and do not agree on what we want to be"—up to the last chapter, it is made clear that the difference between man and other higher primates is so slight that it is man's free decision which makes a primate into a human or a nonhuman. (One would think that after the gas chambers of Hitler's Germany we were beyond doubting the essential dignity of man; unfortunately, there is too much counter-evidence.)

Another argument against man's essential superiority is drawn from evolutionary facts. Life has evolved in such profusion that there is no choosing among the branches of the tree of life for a privileged shoot like *homo sapiens*: "Is Man really more than a protozoan? It has been possible for the question to be seriously asked and left unanswered."[12] This writer recently experienced a colleague who vehemently affirmed that the question was *unanswerable*; all the varied living species equally solve life's problem, so "Who is to say that one form of life is superior to another?"

To answer the "unanswerable" question, Teilhard almost always centers his analysis on man's power of reflection: "Reflection is . . . the power . . . to take possession of itself *as of an object* endowed with its own particular consistence and value: no longer merely to know, but to know oneself; no longer merely to know, but to know that one knows."(165) This self-reflection man possesses and animals lack, or at least show no signs of possession. As a consequence Teilhard is quite blunt: *"Theorem II. Human Reflection is not an Epi-phenomenon of the Organic World, but the Central Phenomenon of Vitalisation."* Despite the existentialists' nay-saying, human intelligence is "not an anomaly and even a disease of Consciousness."[13]

But how can and do scientists and others come to deny the qualitative difference of human and animal intelligence? By concentrating on similarities and continuities, because science's aim is precisely to find connections and laws. Julian Huxley analyzes the difficulty this way:

> We begin by minimizing the difference between animals and ourselves by unconsciously projecting our own qualities into them: this is the way of children and of primitive peoples. . . . [Science too tends to minimize the difference.] This is partly because we have often been guilty of the fallacy of mistaking origins for explanations—what we may call the "nothing but" fallacy: if sexual impulse is at the base of love, then love is to be regarded as nothing but sex; if it can be shown that man originated from an animal, then in all essentials he is nothing but an animal. This, I repeat, is a dangerous fallacy.
>
> We have tended to misunderstand the nature of the difference between ourselves and animals. We have a way of thinking that if there is continuity in time there must be continuity in quality.[14]

This qualitative superiority of man is capsulized by Teilhard's "the singularity of the human species" or by Huxley's "Man stands alone."[15]

Human reflection is "something new on the face of the earth." It is qualitatively discontinuous with previous consciousness; it is a radically new psychical form. Still, there is continuity between animal consciousness and human self-reflection. Man did arise from lower forms of life and consciousness. Hence, the evolutionary paradox and dialectic: change with permanence, discontinuity in continuity, manyness and unity.

There are many evidences other than the central phenomenon of reflection to ground man's specifically higher "nature." Teilhard appeals to "abstraction, logic, reasoned choice, and inventions, mathematics, art, calculation of space and time, anxieties and dreams of love."(165) Despite this wealth of evidence, he seems quite correct in affirming that man's view of man is the result of choice. Descent *or* ascent from the ape? In order to give a coherent view of man, Teilhard takes his stand on man's qualitative superiority to animals by reason of reflective human intelligence. Michael Murray summarizes it well:

> Physically small, but psychically the superlative result of all the synthetic labors of the stars, man is the spiritual, if not the spatial summit of the cosmos, the hope and instrument of its future consummation. Thus, in Teilhard's hands the theory of evolution, far from diminishing man by relating him to the apes, as so many churchmen used to fear, actually re-establishes him at the moving apex of time-space, well above the fixed central position which he lost in the Copernican revolution.[16]

Third Option: Convergent Spiritual Progress

One may easily enough admit that there has been *evolution*. The "burning question" is: *Is* there evolution *now*? Let us concede the two previous theorems. Evolution has had the significance of bringing about life and human reflection. Is anything significant being brought into existence now?

Teilhard has many equivalent ways of asking the same question. Evolution has always been a process of fanning out or of ramification. Can we say that in the current and human stage of evolution, there is only dispersion into "diverging ethnocultural units," and the culmination of evolution is to be sought in "separate individualities, each within the enclosed sphere of its sensibilities and knowledge representing an independent, absolute summit of the Universe"?[17] Or, if we wish to take notice of the socialization going on, must we not say that this is really an epiphenomenon? That is, is the coming together of men through communication and transportation merely an accidental and incidental phenomenon?

Recently, Rosemary Park, the President of Barnard College, claimed a special obligation for the university administrator: "He must ask the students why they learn so well what they maintain is useless; what they mean by integrity and how they recognize it, and, most important of all, what they think is *going on*."[18] It is the last question, "What is *going on?*" which is identical with Teilhard's questioning of the current "social phenomenon." We easily grant that there are glaring, pressing human needs: work to end wars; help for the racially and physically disadvantaged; aid for the developing nations. But beyond and through the fulfillment of these needs, is there nothing larger, nothing ultimate? If we picture humanity in a car which has obvious mechanical failures, we will agree that these must be fixed as efficiently and expeditiously as possible. But is it wrong to ask—once the car is functional—where humanity is going?

As before, the thrust of Teilhard's option can be best appreciated by contrasting it to other possible answers. First, the answer of individualism. This is the individualism which would seek the perfection of mankind by individual men's distinctness and separation from others "at the extreme limit of, and by the very excess of, their individualisation."(238) There is a sense in which America is the home and breeder of such individualism, by its emphasis on individual freedom and rights but with no corresponding emphasis on fulfillment in and through community. "For each individual the business, the duty and the interest of life consist in achieving, *in opposition to others*, his own utmost uniqueness and personal freedom; so that perfection, beatitude, supreme goodness belong not to the whole but to the least part."[19] That this individualism finds a large American audience is indicated by Ayn Rand's popularity, especially on college campuses. In *Atlas Shrugged* she expresses her philosophy of the "omnipotent individual" through John Galt's words: "I am the first man who told them that I did not need them, and until they learned to deal with me as traders . . . they would have to exist without me."[20]

Many scientists and science popularizers also espouse individualism. This they do by holding that "the tide of Life on earth" has "for [all] practical purposes ceased to flow."[21] If the psychosocial is merely incidental to and not the scene of evolution, then the door is open to an exaggerated individualism, which "threatens to bring matter to fragmentation, dispersion, and consequent return to multiplicity. Everyone tends to neglect the common good. The most natural groupings fall apart. Certitudes slowly gained by the experience and reflexion of ages disappear. A kind of rebellious independence becomes the ideal moral attitude. Intellectually, this dispersion of past efforts and thoughts takes the form of agnosticism."[22] The dour tone of this 1926 essay tends to be muted in Teilhard's later writings. Perhaps he experienced among his colleagues an increase in acknowledgment of the intrinsic significance of the social and collective in human evolution. This was certainly very prominent in the 1959 Chicago University Darwin Centennial Symposium.[23]

Another possible answer to "What is *going on?*" is one which responds by implying "Nothing definitive or substantial." It is easy enough to imagine, as do writers of science fiction, man's endless movement via space travel into the ever broadening realms of space. After a meeting with three Marxist professors, Teilhard reported:

> But suppose we remind him [the Marxist] that our Earth because of the implacable law of entropy, is destined to die; suppose we ask him what will be the outcome allowed humanity in such a world. Then he replies—in terms that H. G. Wells had already used—by offering perspectives of interplanetary and intergalactic colonization. This is one way to dodge the mystical notion of a Parousia [the second coming of Christ], and the gradual movement of humanity towards an ecstatic union with God.[24]

Far from denying the possibility of space travel and colonization, Teilhard again and again entertains man's enlargement by the exploration of space. What he cannot accept is the assumption that the conquest of space is an adequate culmination for human evolution. For him evolution must culminate convergently and irreversibly in a humanity which is super-united and actually immortal:

In order that the end of Mankind may be deferred *sine die*

> [endlessly] we are asked to believe in a species that will drag on and spread itself indefinitely; which means, in effect, that it would run down more and more.

> We cannot resolve this contradiction between the congenital mortality of the planets and the demand for irreversibility developed by planetized life [mankind] on their surface, by covering it up or deferring it: we have finally to banish the spectre of Death from our horizon.[25]

Teilhard sees, then, in the social phenomenon an ascent of mankind towards a collective, culminating and unending coreflection. The terrestrial growth in spirit, noogenesis, is convergent and therefore of limited duration.

That can be and is denied by those who recognize the increased socialization of man but assert that it is only an epiphenomenon:

> That the human particles (because, unluckily for them, they group themselves in crowds and masses) feel the need to arrange themselves thus in order to carry on a tolerable existence, what is this but a most sad necessity? . . . The whole edifice of human relationships and social structures is reduced to the level of a juridical epi-phenomenon, having no value or substance of its own, and therefore no future.[26]

Teilhard finds fault with this view of human socialization because he is convinced that evolution is organic—there is only *one* cosmically integrated evolution. Physical and social evolution are an essential part of this one evolution. And there is *one* law for all of evolution, the law of complexity/consciousness leading to greater unity in greater consciousness.

The evolutionary question of questions is: how is this law to be operative in man's present and future evolution? How is mankind to coil and involute upon itself? Teilhard notes man's growing technical mastery over his environment and man's spirit being sparked by his increasing consciousness of time, space and discovery. Both from without and within, man is pressured by the "cosmic vortex of interiorization" to perfect himself by linking himself to the "All"—to the whole of evolution, past, present and future.

Such a perspective is indeed boundless. Evolution is seen as one thrust within which the primacy of life is superceded by the primacy of reflection, and it in turn by the primacy of social or communal reflection. Evolution and time have a direction: toward ever higher consciousness and communion. There is in evolution meaning and coherence. Evolution is not a "tale told by an idiot," but a drama initiated and fulfilled by a God who is both "Alpha and Omega," First and Last.[27] Teilhard's vision culminates in evolution's culmination in a transphysical communion of a united humanity with "Alpha and Omega."

READING SUGGESTIONS

1. *Read PM,* 300-307, a quite dense and difficult summary but rewarding even prior to a reading of *PM.*

2. *See Glossary for*: centro-complexity, complexity, complexity-consciousness, concentration, convergent, hominisation, interiorisation, *involution, irreversibility, Omega, *reflection ["reflective scales"=men], *socialisation, survival.

3. *Passages to be noted*:
   300, "In the narrow domain etc." T. affirms that the originality of *PM* lies in proposing the law of complexity/consciousness as strictly *universal* and not limited merely to the domain of biology.
   303, "value of a 'threshold' or a change of state" indicates that human reflection is a qualitatively higher form of consciousness than that possessed by prehumans.
   303, ftn. 1, "infinitely complex"=man, in as much as his brain compared to that of lower vertebrates is immensely more complex.

4. *Parallel readings*:

convergent spiritual progress: *FM*, 11-24 (11-25) and 249-259 (261-271).

human soul: Smulders, 60-77.

involuting universe: *FM*, 97-112 (101-17), 214-226 (222-35), 244-249 (255-60).

summaries: *SC*, 86-97; *VP*, 7-25, 51-79; *Murray, 9-26.

5. *Critique*: general: de Lubac, *Religion*, 185-194.

"THE HUGE PAST"

It is "new eyes" that Teilhard tries to give us in the first part of the *Phenomenon*. If we have come to *see* "the huge past," we are ready for the "new hearts" called for by the *Phenomenon's* last chapters.

"To see and to make others see"—such is Teilhard's passion and apostolate. His search is for more life, fuller being; this becomes a progressive search for greater union and communion. Teilhard's own quest for a lived union of his two loves—of the world and of God—was a search for greater union with both. Just as all love is preceded by knowledge, so the union and intensification of the two loves must be preceded by a clearer "seeing."

Perhaps many of us, for one reason or another, are not aware within ourselves of any great conflict between these loves. How do we explain, then, the appeal of Teilhard's writings? To this writer it seems that much of his popularity comes from his ability to strike sparks of love both for the world and for God. Though there is a dizzying and frightening aspect of seeing "the huge past," there is correspondingly a growth of insight into and love for our cosmos and our place in it.

Seven New Senses

In the *Phenomenon's* Foreword Teilhard says that if we are to really see "the huge past," we need seven new senses—geometrical senses of the spatial, temporal and numerical immensity of the cosmos; a sense attuned to the microscopic and macroscopic; plus evolutionary senses to perceive the persistent movement, organic oneness and radical novelty of an involuting cosmos. Pascal, for one, possessed the first four senses, but it was only with the advent of the theory of evolution that men could possess the three evolutionary senses.[1] Teilhard begins using these senses in the first Book of *The Phenomenon of Man*. The French title for this part is *Pré-vie,* "Pre-life," which indicates not only that the *Phenomenon* is a history—an account of a before and of an after—but more importantly that it is the history of a cosmogenesis—the birth or coming to be of a cosmos. What comes *before* life is a real and continuing *process* of bringing life and man to be. Before life, there is a strict genesis—a coming to be of an ordered world, a cosmos which in turn leads to biogenesis—the coming to be of life.

When Teilhard first looks at "The Stuff of the World," it is very much with the eyes of science. We know that, figuratively, we can apply an ever-zooming "microscope" to matter and see it divided into ever smaller worlds, with just as dizzying an effect as astronomy's ever-expanding conceptions of space. Without the benefit of modern atomic physics, Blaise Pascal had an inspired vision of matter, analyzable into ever smaller parts.

> Let a mite be given him, with its minute body and parts incomparably more minute, limbs with their joints, veins in the limbs, blood in the veins, humours in the blood, drops in the humours, vapours in the drops. Dividing these last things again . . . let him see therein an infinity of universes, each of which has its firmament, its planets, its earth, in the same proportion as in the visible world; in each earth animals, and in the last mites, in which he will find again all that the first had. . . .[2]

Unlike Pascal's poetic guess, Teilhard's vision of "elemental matter" is based on contemporary science's entry into the molecular, atomic and subatomic worlds. The early Greeks who coined the word "atom" understood it as "the indivisible." Modern science paradoxically is spending much of its energies on dividing "the indivisible," the atom, and splitting subatomic particles—"a new abyss."

This view of science we know. But the complementary view is found less in scientists and more in poets, philosophers and mystics. Let matter be divisible and analyzable to the limits of our imaginations. At the same time, matter is even more *indivisible* because it is essentially *one*. Newton's theory of universal gravitation postulated that the heavens are of the same material makeup as the earth; there is *one* material system. What is more to the point is that every material body has an influence on and is influenced by every other body in the one cosmos.

We are aware of this influence when we step forward from a small wagon or boat. We move forward and it moves backward. By Newton's third law, we are constrained to say that when we walk forward, the earth moves backwards—albeit infinitesimally. Teilhard's "cosmic sense" is truly cosmic:

> Through Physics, a homogeneity and a solidarity without limit are discovered in the mass of Matter. "All is connected with all." . . . The world constitutes a *Whole*. . . . To my eyes, to express it differently, there are no more things in the World, there are only *elements*. . . . I am brought to think that man possesses, by the very condition of his being in the World, a special *sense* which discovers for him, in a manner more or less confused, the Whole of which he is a part. There is nothing astonishing, after all, in the existence of this "cosmic sense." Because he is sexed, man possesses the instincts of love. Then as he is an element, why should he not sense obscurely the attraction of the Universe?[3]

One could multiply Teilhardian expressions of this cosmic sense of the unity, the wholeness of all parts and times of the cosmos. One thinks, too, of the cosmic unification wrought by an astroidal rose in Antoine de Saint-Exupéry's *The Little Prince*. Poets, like Blake, proclaim this individualness and relatedness of all parts of the one cosmos:

> To see a world in a grain of sand,
>   And a heaven in a wild flower,
> Hold infinity in the palm of your hand,
>   And eternity in an hour.

The philosopher A. N. Whitehead expresses, in more difficult language, the same concept:

> For each relationship enters into the essence of the event; so that, apart from that relationship, the event would not be itself. This is what is meant by the very notion of internal relations. . . . The scheme of relationships as thus impartially expressed becomes the scheme of a complex of events variously related as wholes to parts and joint part within some one whole. . . . So the whole is evidently constitutive of the part.[4]

When we ask what it is that holds the teeming multiplicity of matter together in one whole, science responds, "Energy." By the collective bonds of energy, each particle of matter is related to, is acted upon by, and acts upon all other particles. "There are no more things": unrelated, nonintegrated parts; "there are only *elements*": integral parts of one whole, one cosmos, one "gigantic 'atom.' " Energy is the source of the intrinsic tendency of matter to evolve; at the same time, it is the reason for the fundamental coherence or "hanging-togetherness" of the universe. But energy is not, according to Teilhard, the ultimate reason for the universe's unity and coherence. If it were, then we would have to accept without qualification the dismal "final equilibrium" of a heat-death as the end state of cosmogenesis. Rather, as he suggests somewhat vaguely in an early section of the *Phenomenon,* we must look for the ultimate source of the universe's unity and coherence as coming "from above." (43) Already, we note Teilhard's qualified acceptance of science's analysis, which seeks ultimate explanations in the elemental origins of the universe. Such analysis tends to give us a picture of a static universe; as a consequence we find Teilhard insisting even more on the dynamic, durational, evolving aspects of the universe. In this view the finish line or goal is far more important than the starting line or the origins.

Biological Space-Time

Repeatedly in Teilhardian writings we read of the change wrought in contemporary man's cosmic view by the discovery of space-time. Initially the reader wonders if he will have to master the intricacies of relativity physics in order to understand the *Phenomenon.* Though Teilhard's concept of space-time bears similarities to relativity physics', he makes it clear that he is talking about *biological* space-time. (218-19)

In order to understand Teilhard's space-time, we have to see the evolution of the very concepts of space and time. Before the sixteenth century, space was an arbitrary organizing category. Space was used in order to locate objects and events—up, down, right, left. That such spatial location is arbitrary is discovered in the fact that if we turn around, right becomes left and vice versa. Further, space was characterized by "proximity": the nearness and smallness of space. The cosmos, it was thought, is made of a series of spatial spheres, the last of which is not very far away, and beyond it—nothing. Finally, space and things placed in space were perfectly fragmentable and transferable; they could be broken up into parts and moved to other sections of space *without any change.*

What has happened to this conception of space? It has evolved into a radically new idea of space. Now, space is no longer arbitrary. It is not an accident that the earth, this spot in space, is the scene of the origin of life. The whole of space is needed to explain why the earth is the privileged space for life. The telescope's discovery of space's immensity and boundlessness has caused the idea of space's proximity to be discarded. At the same time, the microscopic immensity of space was explored to the infinitesimal and seen to descend ever lower and lower. Space became boundless both in the direction of the infinite and the infinitesimal.

The conception of time has also undergone a like evolution and transformation. Originally time was very small: the earth had existed for a few thousand years and probably would exist for a few thousand more. Time as a measure was a purely arbitrary instrument; things, events, even persons, could be juggled around in time. "Socrates could have been born in place of Descartes, and vice versa."⁵ Also, people did not conceive time as having any direction; that which is always being repeated, that which is cyclical, is basically proceeding without any meaning. With the advent of a sense of history and evolution, time has undergone a radical evolution. Time is not "proximate," small, finite or comfortable. Time now extends endlessly into "the huge past" and into "the fantastic future." Time is now *real* time, duration; it has irreversibility and direction. Descartes could *not* have been born in the time of Socrates. What it takes, both physically and spiritually, for a Descartes could happen only *after* all the genetic and intellectual changes between Socrates and Descartes. Time is no longer conceived as cyclical but as linear—moving in a direction, irreversible and with a meaning. Time is boundless, extending both backwards into the past and forwards into the future. [Almost always Teilhard will insert a cautionary proviso: "to a future that, *at first sight,* has no limit."(47) Before we have seen the pattern of complexity/consciousness operative in time, we cannot know that time and evolution are convergent, coming to a culmination and consummation. If that is so, time is *not* infinite in its future extension.]

The greatest transformation, however, is not the "infinitizing" of both time and space, but their union into "one container," one instrument for the description of phenomena. Before evolution we could think that we had described sufficiently a particular species or an individual of a species by saying that it existed in such a place and at such a time. From an evolutionary perspective, such a description is quite deficient. To really "locate" a species or an individual, we must "fix" at the same time the course of events which preceded that which we are seeking to locate. This individual or this species is what it is because it was preceded by these individuals and these species in these places and these times. And that involves the *whole* of evolution! There is no "simple location" of any event.[6] Time and space are woven together to form one immense framework to locate and describe the *whole* of an evolving material universe. (217-9) "The mesh of the universe is the universe itself." (45)

Biological space-time is, then, the framework by means of which we can organize our experiences with phenomena. Just as from atomic physics we know that matter is not static, so from the discovery of evolution, we know that species and their individuals are totally immersed in the duration of a real genesis or evolution, which affects all matter, all space, all time.

Biological space-time differs therefore from relativity space-time. There *is* a privileged way of looking at the phenomenal word, and it is from the evolutionary viewpoint. It is from the viewpoint of a real process: birth, growth and death. It is from the viewpoint in which something is really *going on*; we are not trapped in a meaningless world of endlessly repeated cycles. Our world has a *directed* duration, directed in the same sense that the growth of a fertilized ovum or of a child is a directed process. The perception of biological space-time or of duration (Teilhard equates the two) is the perception that we live in a world *on the move* in a direction that makes sense. (220-1) Something is *going on*.

What is going on, the direction of evolution, can only be discovered by an analysis of evolution's law (complexity/consciousness) and its main implication (a *convergent* noogenesis). Yet, present and operative in the universe is another law, the law of entropy, which casts a somber shadow upon all of evolution's movements and creations.

The Specter of Entropy

Any hyperphysicist who studies the phenomena of an evolving cosmos is constrained to face the many implications of entropy. In thermodynamics, the branch of physics which deals with energy exchanges, entropy signifies, first, the quantity of energy which becomes permanently unavailable for further energy exchanges. In chemical or physical changes, it "costs" to go against friction or inertia, to establish new chemical bonds or to produce radioactive exchanges. There is a permanent and irreversible "cost" to boiling potatoes, accelerating electrons, forming a new molecule of nylon. Since the world is conceived to possess a finite quantum of energy, the conclusion from the "law of entropy" is that in a finite time, the initial quantum of energy available for all change, evolutionary and otherwise, will be exhausted, and the universe will reach a "heat-death," a state of absolute and uniform coldness or lack of energy. In this state no further changes or activities are possible because the cosmos' quantum of "free energy" will have been expended. Entropy can, therefore, refer to the final, energyless state of the cosmos.

Teilhard "bought" the theory of cosmic entropy: "A rocket rising in the wake of time's arrow, that only bursts to be extinguished; an eddy rising on the bottom of a descending current—such then must be our picture of the world. So says science: and I believe in science. . . ."(52) But Teilhard immediately adds a question: Is this the *full* picture?

Some cosmologists, such as H. Bondi, T. Gold and F. Hoyle, propose a "steady state" cosmos that would be nonentropic. The energy of the cosmos can be postulated as constant, either by the constant "creation" of matter/energy, or by the pulsations of a cosmos which now is expanding only temporarily and is therefore, in a diminishing state of energy concentration; this would be followed by a contracting state with increased energy, and so on *ad infinitum*. Thus far such theories are little accepted and seem to be contradicted by recent evidence from radio astronomy.[7]

One might, though Teilhard does not, question the law of entropy, which is certainly verified for small, limited systems, but on the cosmic plane, the law is an immense extrapolation, which lacks sufficient evidence for certainty. Teilhard, like most scientists, takes the law of entropy as a "given" in the explanation of the cosmos. Quite obviously entropy is a non-optimistic "given": the universe is "a rocket rising . . . that only bursts to be extinguished."

The laws of energy include not only the law of dissipation of energy, entropy, but also the law of the conservation of energy. The latter law teaches that there is no creation of energy, but that the cosmos uses up its initial energy quantum. (This, of course, would be denied by the steady state theorists.)

The apparently logical conclusion from the laws of the conservation and dissipation of energy is a dismal one: "the death of the materially exhausted planet," and so the cessation of evolution and of evolution's creations.(289) Teilhard, with many other thinkers, cannot accept this as a final or complete picture of the cosmos. His way of both accepting and correcting the picture is a probing questioning of the fundamental assumption, the nature of energy: "A rocket rising in the wake of time's arrow, that only bursts to be extinguished. . . . Such then must be our picture of the world. So says science: and I believe in science: but up to now has science ever troubled to look at the world other than from *without?*"(52) Thus does Teilhard raise the question of the nature of energy and the possibility of a higher law than the law of entropy.

Bifaced Energy—Tangential and Radial

When early in the *Phenomenon* Teilhard introduces the concept of the two kinds or "faces" of energy, it does not strike the reader immediately how bold an innovation this is. For one thing the way is gently prepared by the earlier description of the "within" of all things. The reader is then in a position to see that there must be an energy of the "within," radial energy. If we see this with Teilhard, we have gone a considerable distance beyond science's usual conception of only one energy, which is basically physical and manifests itself by gravitational, electromagnetic, chemical, radioactive effects. Teilhard, in what at first seems a direct contradiction of science, goes "hyperphysically" beyond science to "assume that, essentially, all energy is psychic in nature; but add that in each particular element this fundamental energy is divided into two distinct components: a *tangential energy* which links the element with all others of the same order (that is to say of the same complexity and the same centricity) as itself in the universe; and a *radial energy* which draws it towards ever greater complexity and centricity—in other words forwards."(64-5)[8]

A truly and almost incredible assumption: all energy is basically psychical, that is, productive of psychic activities, such as concept formation, thinking, knowing, desiring, hoping, loving. The whole thrust of science points to all energy being basically physical. Whose assumption shall we choose?

But do we have to choose? It would seem not. Hyperphysics and science are not looking at the same data nor are they trying to explain the same phenomena when the one assumes that all energy is basically psychical and the other assumes that all energy is basically physical. Hyperphysics is trying to explain the *whole* phenomenon of evolution, especially man, while individual sciences are trying to explain only very partial and limited changes. Hyperphysics is trying to explain "the huge past" and "the fantastic future," while science is trying to explain some limited segment of temporal mutation. Teilhard with his assumption of the "within," radial energy, consciousness, is adopting what he feels is a necessary instrument of explanation for the *whole* process of evolution. Individual sciences concentrate on the "how" of one particular state leading to another particular state, but hyperphysics seeks to explain the genesis of man from preatomic particles. Hyperphysics is not a science which in its hypotheses and laws considers man as nonexistent or as merely marginal. It is "a science of the universe that embraces man as such" and requires explanatory instruments, which unite the origin and activities of human thought with the beginning and the whole course of evolution.[9]

Before the functions of radial and tangential energies are explained, it is important to see that these lie at what might be called the second level of explanation. In *Man's Place in Nature*, which Teilhard playfully called a "rehash" of the *Phenomenon*, there is no mention of the two energies, perhaps because he discovered that the theory of the two energies created more problems than it solved. From the absence of this theory in *Man's Place in Nature*, one certain conclusion can be drawn: Teilhard's synthesis does not stand or fall with the existence or nonexistence of the two energies. In both books, however, there is the same insistence on the *fact* of one evolutionary movement towards higher complexity and, accordingly, to higher consciousness or centeredness, especially as concerns human self-reflection. In the *Phenomenon* the theory of two energies is proposed as an explanation of the *how* of a directed evolutionary movement towards higher complexity and consciousness.

Using only the one energy of science, tangential energy, we are at a loss to explain evolution's direction and man's place in nature. Tangential energy alone can account only for chance physiochemical interchanges, leaving unexplained the growing unification and centeredness of evolving matter and finding no definable place in the cosmos for man.

By postulating a radial or centering energy in matter, one can explain the increasing complexification of matter. This radial energy accounts for the imponderable action whereby matter arranges itself, under pressure of the environment's scattered tangential energies, into more complex arrangements and, therefore, into more centered unities. The presence in matter of a self-organizing energy explains both the direction of evolution and the very centeredness or unity of atoms, molecules, cells, animals and men.

Considerable support for Teilhard's bifaced energy is to be found in Errol Harris' *The Foundations of Metaphysics in Science*.[10] Alfred North Whitehead points to science's difficulty in trying to explain the whole phenomenal world by means of tangential energy alone.[11]

Neither of these philosophers is so bold as Teilhard in postulating that all energy is basically *psychical*—but with two faces, tangential and radial. This bold assumption certainly undercuts the perennial problem of dualism, the sharp break between matter and spirit, body and soul. In the *Phenomenon* Teilhard does little to justify his assumption. We can suggest two reasons, which were probably operative in his thinking. Psychical energy is prime because evolution seems bent on engendering ever higher forms of psychisms and psychical activity, all the while tangential energy decreases in quantity. The second reason for the primacy of psychical energy comes from the revelation of God as spirit and creator, certainly implying that the divine psychical energy is primordial in the cosmos. The first reason seems quite implicit in Teilhard's hyperphysics, while the second manifestly transcends it.

Many details of Teilhard's "energetics" are not essential to his argument at this present level. He ends his discussion of energy by placing three questions, which all involve in their answers the energy of the Omega Point—divine energy—as the principal operative. 1) By what special energy is the cosmos' movement directed to higher complexity/consciousness? 2) Is there a limit to the development both of the individual (man) and of all united radial energies (men)? 3) Is the final form of radial energies reversible through entropy or, if irreversible (immortal), through what causality?[12]

Orthogenesis—The Direction of the "Huge Past"

The very technical early parts of the *Phenomenon,* comprising most of the chapters on Pre-life, Life, and Thought, are devoted to using the "new senses" on the whole sweep of evolution. From this examination Teilhard wants the reader to see the one movement and the one law of evolution. Though there is extreme variety in "the huge past" of evolution, underneath and through all the change there is but one all-encompassing movement, the movement expressed by evolution's one law. "The huge past" is, then, a movement towards ever greater complexity in organization coupled with ever greater centeredness and consciousness.

What the vast quantity of scientific detail in the *Phenomenon's* early part indicates is that through all the variations and ramifications there is a *general* direction. It is this direction or axis which throws light on the meaning and value of contemporary man and which opens up, at least partially, the vista of mankind's future.

The Phenomenon of Man frequently is criticized for presenting biological explanations which are invalid and for advancing anthropological hypotheses which are no longer held. Probably much of the criticism is merited; we could say the same of most scientific books written twenty-five years ago. The question is not whether there are scientific errors or inadequacies in the *Phenomenon*, but rather whether its fundamental thesis is so dependent on these that it is no longer tenable. There are many reasons for replying in the negative. The most important reason is that the *Phenomenon* is basically directed toward seeing that evolution is one directed movement and not toward what science is most interested in—for example, seeing precisely *how* the eohippus evolved into the contemporary horse.

True as that answer may be, it is too facile. Before man can accept a radically new fact, he is in almost essential need of an explanation of the fact. Before Darwin there were proponents of evolution who presented confirmatory evidences for evolution. But they were not heeded. Darwin *was* heeded because he not only proposed the evolutionary theory together with confirmatory evidence, but also with a plausible explanation of evolution's mechanism. Some criticisms of Teilhard's science and of certain aspects of his theory indicate, then, that just as for Darwin, he leaves us as much to do as he himself has done.

In his explanation of "the huge past," Teilhard tries to do justice to the tension or dialectic between chance and antichance factors. If he were to attempt an explanation which restricted itself to chance factors, there would be next to no explanation for the obvious overall direction of evolution. If there is nothing but a blind groping and competition, perhaps individual segments of evolution may be explained, but certainly not its comprehensive movement. On the other hand, if Teilhard were to appeal only to inner factors—the "within," consciousness, spontaneity—he would certainly explain evolution's directedness but he would leave unexplained the vastness of time and of the near infinity of "blind alleys" involved in evolution's past. In general Teilhard tries to steer a course between the Darwinian or chance explanation and the Lamarckian or inner-directedness explanation. In part he does this by his concept of "groping," which is a trying of every possible avenue to higher forms. But inasmuch as "groping" is not completely blind, there is, at the very least, some preexistent inclination to accept and utilize the avenue which is *not* a blind alley.

To some critics Teilhard seems to be denying the constant tension between chance and antichance factors in evolution when he repeatedly affirms that evolution is *orthogenetic*. For the life scientist, orthogenesis signifies "a tendency for evolution to continue steadily in the same direction over indefinitely prolonged periods of time regardless of influences directly involved in the interaction of organism and environment."[13] That is G. G. Simpson's definition, and he is correct in asserting that such orthogenesis is scientifically nonexistent. But what escapes many critics of Teilhard's orthogenesis is that he uses the word for a related but different meaning. (Almost certainly it would have been better if he had avoided the word. Since "orthogenesis" has such pejorative connotations for most scientists, it was and is almost impossible to rehabilitate the word for some other, and different, usage.) For Teilhard orthogenesis signifies that evolution *on the whole* is progressive, that there is a direction towards increasing complexification and consciousness.

Such a meaning of orthogenesis is not what most biologists understand by the term. Theodosius Dobzhansky, a noted geneticist, has pointed out that Teilhard's use of orthogenesis is not in the usual biological sense, but "in a philosophical and mystical sense."[14] One final point is that in the ordinary realm of biology, orthogenesis is a useless concept, since no functional definition can be formulated whereby it may be tested by empirical data. It is, in other words, a useless concept in the limited areas within which biology usually operates because it cannot explain in the way biologists want explanation. When, however, one is looking at the whole of "the huge past" through a hyperbiology, orthogenesis indicates a structural concept, which is essential to an explanation of the data.

Panconsciousness

One of the most troublesome points in the early part of the *Phenomenon* is Teilhard's assertion that consciousness "has a cosmic extension, and as such is surrounded by an aura of indefinite spatial and temporal extensions."(56) Positively, this means that *all* matter is and has been endowed with some degree of consciousness, "within," or psyche. Negatively, it connotes the nonexistence of "absolutely brute matter"(57); consciousness is not to be restricted to the higher forms of life.(55)

These are "hard sayings," but before we reject them, we will do well to understand Teilhard's thought on panconsciousness, the existence of consciousness in *all* material beings. Teilhard first appeals to the well-known fact that though velocity *apparently* does not influence a body's mass, and chemicals and mountains and stars are *apparently* stable, the truth is that increased velocity does cause increased mass, that all chemicals are basically instable due to radioactivity, and that mountains and stars are essentially changing and impermanent. From these examples Teilhard tries to show the reasonableness of projecting consciousness backwards from ourselves, where it surely exists, into all the stages of evolution's ascent. A phenomenon such as consciousness has "an omnipresent value and roots, by reason of the fundamental unity of the world."(56)

Because of this assumption, Teilhard is often accused of panpsychism: *all* things have souls, are living, perceiving beings; this seems to fly right in the face of all available evidence. This writer has encountered many readers of the *Phenomenon* troubled by this point, so much so that he felt impelled to make a close study of "consciousness" as applied to preliving matter and to prehuman living things. The results of this study were surprising for it revealed that Teilhard was very cautious (with one exception, p. 57, footnote 1) in his attribution of consciousness to *all* matter. He clearly does *not* say that preliving things have a faculty of knowledge or perception, though that is what we immediately think when we are told that all matter possesses the property of consciousness. Rather, Teilhard points to the *dynamism* within organized units of matter whereby they tend to higher, more complex organization and thus come to greater unity, centeredness, immanence and spontaneity. Through consciousness, organized units are better able to benefit from what is transiently done to them. Instead of being completely at the mercy of transient and chance influences, "consciousness" implies a leaning (Aristotle's "natural appetite") towards higher forms of existence and, therefore, a certain "freedom" or spontaneity in appropriating or rejecting environmental influences.

Teilhard would have avoided a great deal of misunderstanding if he had used a word more neutral than "consciousness," which for most of us signifies some active power of knowing. In the later version of the *Phenomenon, Man's Place in Nature*, Teilhard does this by using "centeredness" or "centricity" instead of "consciousness" to indicate the antichance factor within evolving matter. Without "consciousness" or "centeredness," evolution would have to be explained by chance alone—which would be no explanation at all—or by God's action alone—which would mean the abolition of science.

Another aspect of panconsciousness is that throughout the whole of evolution there is no absolute beginning of anything; there was always consciousness, or at least preconsciousness. So there was always life or at least prelife. Does this mean that evolution is a process of continual changes wherein there are no real discontinuities, no qualitative differences? Am I no different, a little different or radically different from a fleck of dust or a drop of tap water?

"Discontinuity in Continuity"

The *Phenomenon* in diverse ways seeks to aid us in seeing *one* cosmic process governed by *one* evolutionary law. The continuity and the organicity of the evolving whole point to the meaning and value of "what is *going on.*"

At the same time that Teilhard would have us possess a "sense of movement" and a "sense of the organic" in evolution, he underlines our need for a "sense of quality, or of novelty."(34) He would have us see the "discontinuity in continuity."(169) Negatively, he does not wish us to be blind to or to blur the radical changes or discontinuities in evolution's continuous past.

There is the story of a young man who successively dates his employer's oldest marriageable daughter, whom he discovers to be "just a little bit bowlegged," and the next oldest, who is "just a little bit neurotic," and finally the youngest and prettiest, who is "just a little bit pregnant." What grounds the story's incongruity is the recognized absurdity of the unexpressed assumption: all differences are alike; they are just differences in degree or quantity. Because evolution is a continuous process wrought by minute changes through immense periods of time, there is a strong temptation to see and to assert that evolution's products do not differ radically but "just a little bit."

To do full justice to evolution's phenomena, Teilhard proposes that we must use "a sense of quality, or of novelty, enabling us to distinguish in nature certain absolute stages of perfection and growth, without upsetting the physical unity of the world."(34)[15] He would have us see in evolution's immense history not only minute changes and minute differences, but also some radical or qualitative changes and differences. The two radical changes he singles out in evolution's course are the changes from nonliving to living and from nonhuman to human.

Why does Teilhard spend so much effort in trying to highlight these qualitative differences? One reason is that he experienced fellow scientists who stressed only the continuity between living and nonliving and between human and nonhuman. He shows himself sympathetic with science's intrinsic and necessary drive towards discovering continuity. One can only frame a law of recurrence for that which is connected and continuous. For example, we can express mathematically, as Hooke did, the relationship between the stretch of a spring and the weight applied to it because it varies in a continuous way. But if we lived in the Wonderland of Alice, six pounds might stretch it two inches, now seven inches, while twelve pounds might stretch it two inches, now five inches. In such a world, there is no continuity between antecedents (weights applied) and consequents (stretches of spring), and hence, no laws of recurrence are discoverable. In Wonderland there is no science.

Since continuity in nature's operations and manifestations is at the center of science's venture, it is not difficult to appreciate scientists' instinctive bias against discontinuity. Still, phenomena, *all* phenomena, must be looked at and evaluated fairly.

First, the phenomena of life. Teilhard stresses the extremely long preparation for the evolutionary appearance of life. It is true that we lack and almost certainly will continue to lack for primordial chemical evolution much of the direct sort of evidence we have from paleontology for biological evolution.[16] But we do possess the indirect evidence of atoms and molecules "falling towards" certain types of higher complexities. We have mentioned the experiments with very simple molecules (water, methane, ammonia and hydrogen) subjected to "perculation," electrical discharges and ultraviolet light, synthesizing to form very complex amino acids, the building blocks of living organisms. These efforts at reconstructing the primitive earth's chemical condition point to the increasing chemical complexification of matter.

Teilhard's principal point is not on *how* life came from prelife, but on the simultaneous continuity and discontinuity of life with prelife. He would have us see primordial life "as something *at one and the same time* both the outcome of long preparation and yet profoundly original."(80) Though the difference between the nine-pound, newly-born infant, who could not distinguish his own limbs, and this writer's present self are striking enough, they *are* to be explained in terms of a gradual and *continuous* evolution. In the appearance of life, however, Teilhard stresses not only the continuity between living and nonliving, but also the discontinuity—like that between nonpregnancy and pregnancy, where there is no room, strictly speaking, for "a little bit of pregnancy."

Hyperphysics, since it deals only with appearances, can best visualize the evolutionary transition from prelife to life as the crossing of a threshold, a passage through a critical point, a change of state. While it is only figurative, the carrying of the bride over the threshold points to the beginning of the radically new life on the other side of the threshold. In the case of boiling or freezing, there are critical points—0° C and 100° C—where water is no longer continuously cooled or heated, but undergoing a dramatic "change of state"—passing from a liquid into a solid (ice) or into a gas (steam). Such are the visual models Teilhard would have us use to picture the passage from prelife to life and from nonhuman to human. Only thus can we do justice to all the phenomenal data, some of which point to a strong continuity and some of which point to a strict discontinuity.[17]

The first living organism certainly possessed a specific bodily form and structure, grew and developed, exercised metabolism, and reproduced. Though none of these characteristics was wholly lacking in some nonliving things, all living things possessed these characteristics while most nonliving entities lacked them.[18] The perplexing existence of borderline entities does not detract from our clear knowledge of a specific or qualitative difference between living and nonliving. Rather, our difficulty in classifying borderline cases (for example, virus, DNA) points rather to the imperfection of our criterion of classification, which, though it handles with ease well over ninety-nine percent of all instances, is not sufficiently refined to handle *all* instances.

A connected and very provocative point is that life began *only once* in the history of the earth's evolution. Teilhard is led to this position by the paleontological evidence which does not show life beginning in various geological ages, but only in one, the Cambrian. Perhaps even more forceful for Teilhard is the argument that "the very emergence of a biosphere so disturbed, impoverished and relaxed the primordial chemism of our fragment of the universe that the phenomenon [of the appearance of life] can never be repeated (unless perhaps artificaly)." (102) Or, as Teilhard puts it another way, "the most convincing proof to me that life was produced once and once only on earth is furnished by the profound structural unity of the tree of life." (97)

After stressing the continuity in the evolution of life, despite the profuse ramifications of living things, Teilhard expends considerable effort to delineate the radical discontinuity between man and his predecessors. "Between the last strata of the Pliocene age, in which man is absent, and the next, in which the geologist is dumbfounded to find the first chipped flints, what has happened? And what is the true measure of this leap?"(164) The answer to these questions hinges on "whether the human psychism differs specifically (by 'nature') from that of man's predecessors or not."(164) Teilhard's answer to this question is unmistakable, unambiguous: man's consciousness possesses what animal consciousness possessed and possesses not at all: the power and the activity of self-reflection—"the power acquired by a consciousness to turn in upon itself, to take possession of itself as of an *object*."(165) The power of self-reflection further manifests itself by "abstraction, logic, reasoned choice and inventions, mathematics, art, calculation of space and time, anxieties and dreams of love." (165)

Because of the specific difference between man and animal, between human consciousness and animal consciousness, Teilhard makes the further point that historically the passage from animal to man was *not* done by steps or grades but in one stroke—"an infinite leap forward."(169) This position flies in the face of what unreflective imagination, guided by evolutionary images, would project: consciousness rising by degrees in the same way in which the eohippus developed into the contemporary horse. Not so, says Teilhard. Evolution, in passing from the humanoids to the human, underwent "a critical transformation, a mutation from zero to everything." (171)[19] The birth of human thought cannot rightly be pictured as slowly increasing in thousands of individuals ("missing links"). "We are forced to admit that [human self-reflection] appeared *between* two individuals," the one, an anthropoid, lacking a consciousness "leaping and boiling in a space of supersensory relationships" and "perceiving itself in the concentrated simplicity of its faculties," and the other, a human being, possessing those prerogatives, capable of the self-reflective grasp of his own "I"—and of everything.[20]

Thus we must picture, evolving out of "the huge past," the appearance of man, inaugurating "an entirely new biological plane" (172)—the plane of the noosphere.

READING SUGGESTIONS

1. *Note.* This chapter of the *Path* sought to bring together from the earlier part of *PM* (37-211) the ideas essential to a profitable reading of *PM*'s final chapters. It is strongly suggested that the reading of this portion of *PM* be postponed until the latter part been read. The following places in *PM* are given for the reader who at this point wishes to gain greater depth on one or other point: seven new senses, 31-34; space, 41-42, 43-47; time, 77-78; space-time, 83-84, 216-221; entropy, 50-52, 66, 271-272; tangential and radial energies, 62-66, 88-89, 168-169; orthogenesis, 108-111, 140 *n.*, groping, 109-110, 118; panconsciousness, 54-61, 71-74, 87-90, 164-174; discontinuity in continuity, 78-79, 83, 169.

2. *Parallel readings*:
   history of huge past: *AM*, 210-230; **MPN*, 26-78; *AM*, Preface by R. T. Francoeur.
   evolution is a whole: *MM*, 144-146.
   space-time: *FM*, 82-88 (85-92); **VP*, 127-132.
   complexity/consciousness: **Smulders*, 27-44.
   orthogenesis: *MPN*, 17-25; *SC*, 44-48; *VP*, 248-255 and 268-274; Faricy, 33-72; Tresmontant, 18-39.

3. *Critiques*: panconsciousness: Francoeur, *World*, 98-114; de Lubac, *Religion*, 166-167; Rabut, *God*, 49-57 and *Teilhard*, 33-68; Nogar, *Lord*, 111-126. Time: Chaix-Ruy, 219-226.

6

CONTEMPORARY EVOLUTION: NOOSPHERIC, CONVERGENT AND ANXIOUS

In the two earlier chapters of Book III, Teilhard has shown what happened to evolution when man appeared. "The step to reflection," the transition to man, was accomplished in one stroke—"an infinite leap forward."(169) The dimensions of this stupendous transition are explored by first tracing the ramifying or branching out of prehistoric man. Then, in historical time the meaning of the changes in civilizations is examined. This leads to the insular-sounding conclusion that the "principal axis of anthropogenesis has passed through the West."(212)

What Teilhard aims at in the third and final chapter is an investigation of the *within* of human evolution: what it has achieved in modern mentality, what qualities and configurations it has formed in man's spirit. The changes worked in man's heart and mind by evolution create a double problem: first, of seeing himself as he now is, and not falsely, through some outmoded perspective; and then of possessing sufficient orientation and generosity to give himself actively to pushing forward "the building up of the earth," to continuing cosmogenesis.

Because Teilhard is now dealing with the consciousness of man, and since this is in good part open to a descriptive or phenomenological investigation, there is a real shift in his hyperphysics. Previously, it concentrated principally on the without of evolving things, noting only such manifestations of rising consciousness as were observable in their external expressions. With the advent of man, however, and with the scene of evolution now situated right in man's consciousness, hyperphysics is in a position to investigate directly the data of consciousness itself. One could say that prior to this point, the *Phenomenon* focused on the objective side of reality. Now it turns to the subjective side, to the human, knowing subject, and especially to the changes wrought in his knowledge and feelings.

Also, this point in the *Phenomenon* marks a shift in Teilhard's apologetics. Prior to this he could only speak of a more or less probable convergence or unification for evolution. With the advent of modern man, Teilhard can propose an actually convergent evolution, one which requires an actually existent Omega. With this shift Teilhard is able to lay the groundwork for a contemporary posing of the Christological problem: Is the actually existent and risen Christ identical with the postulated Omega?' Though it is not until the Postscript that he will actually ask and answer the Christological question, it adds perspective to see that the ground is now being prepared.

"A Veering"

In speaking of "The Modern Earth," Teilhard is not yielding to the "sin" of those vain and thoughtless classifiers who want to build up egos by showing that we are "not like the rest of men," but "bigger and better" because we are modern. Teilhard points to many evidences to verify that truly our age *is* a new age, which has been brought about by a sharp veering from, but not a break with, preceding ages.

There are specifics whereby one can distinguish the baby from the child, the child from the adolescent, et cetera. So

Teilhard can point to the economic, industrial, intellectual and social changes which have radically modified not only our environment but, far more importantly, our ways of thinking and feeling. We are somewhat like adolescents—in the middle. We know that there were other forms of mentality before our present one, and we recognize that change is going on within our minds and hearts, bringing about some future and unexperienced mental powers and outlooks.

Many questions arise in our minds. What sort of spirit do we possess now? What is our progress doing to us now? Where have we been, and more importantly, where are we going?

"Where have we been?" is the easiest question to answer. We only have to analyze the mentality of our great-great-great grandfather to know that we are "somewhere else." He was "perfectly at ease in a cubic space where the stars turned round the earth, and had been doing so for less than 6,000 years."(216) Then with Galileo, space is made immense, and man is made infinitesimally minute. Then with Darwin, time begins to be immense in its labors to form the present; in comparison to the length of the "huge past," the present is now seen to be an infinitesimal point. Then with biology, space-time indicates the irreversible coherence—the bound-together-ness—of all that exists; time and space are united organically in order to give birth to and weave together all that exists. Then, all fields of knowledge—chemistry, physics, sociology, mathematics, philosophy, theology, history—expand the space-time viewpoint of evolution, whereby any existent must be explained not in itself but by means of the total genesis which preceded its appearance.

Is evolution a theory, a system or a hypothesis? It is much more: it is a general condition to which all theories, all hypotheses, all systems must bow and which they must satisfy henceforward if they are to be thinkable and true. Evolution is a light illuminating all facts, a curve that all lines must follow. (219)

Evolution, then, creates in us a whole new intellectual universe because our consciousness is constrained to see all things in its light. Perceiving a new universe ushers us into a new age, in which we are unable any longer to divide up time and space into self-contained wholes. Rather, we see that reality is a single organic evolutionary flowing.

And we do not, cannot, stand outside of evolution's current. We might be tempted to think that only our bodies are immersed in the flow of evolution, while our spirit somehow totally transcends the influence of the current.[2] That this is an illusion is manifest, because the flow of evolution is now clearly seen to be operative precisely in man's spirit, in the realm of the noosphere. Now, "the movement of our souls expresses and measures the very stages of progress of evolution itself. Man discovers that *he is nothing else than evolution become conscious of itself.*" (221)

That the noosphere is the scene of current evolution is seen in man's spirit and its creations forming the "last-born, the freshest, the most complicated, the most subtle of all the successive layers of life." (224)

By looking backward and seeing noogenesis' continuity with the earlier biogenesis, Teilhard is able to identify evolution's present milieu. Both in man's spirit and in earlier forms of life, he discovers similar structures, similar mechanisms and similar laws of operation or movement. Evolution, he concludes, merely has shifted the scene of its activity to man's spirit. Some readers may feel that Teilhard too facilely "discovers" similarities and makes connections. Such readers may remember that finding no connections between biogenesis and noogenesis means that the process of evolution has halted and that man therefore is an absurd and "erratic object in a disjointed world." (34)

Teilhard connects the vertebrate growing extra limbs, covering itself with feathers and the aviator providing himself with wings. He also joins the interplay of human likes and loves with the gravitational attraction between bodies and with the instinctual attractions of animals. These provide some evidence for the one same structure pervading both prehuman and noospheric evolution. Especially in the creation and dissemination of languages, technological improvements, and religious and philosophical doctrines, Teilhard finds the prolongation and culmination in the noospheric of the earlier biological ramifyings and propagations.

In both biogenesis and noogenesis, Teilhard also sees the identical mechanism of "groping" and "invention" used as the means to higher forms of existence. Though in the earlier stages "groping" is blind and "invents" or finds higher viable forms of life by a prodigious number of trials and errors, "groping" and "invention" in man mainly are accomplished by means of intelligence gaining insight into the better and higher forms. But since the same mechanism is operative in both, "the instinctive gropings of the first cell link up with the learned gropings of our laboratories." (224)

Besides a unity of structure and mechanism, Teilhard shows that evolution possesses also a unity of movement: evolution is the upsurging and expansion of consciousness. To understand man we must understand evolution's movement. "Man is not the [spatial] centre of the universe as once we thought in our simplicity, but something much more wonderful—the arrow pointing the way to the final unification of the world in terms of life." (224)[3]

This rising movement of synthesis or unification is accomplished by means of heredity, the passing on of acquired gains to progeny. In the case of biological evolution, the role of heredity may be minimized or doubted, but in noospheric evolution there is indubitable hereditary transmission. Man is capable of storing up and communicating his cultural and moral riches in and through a collective memory and intelligence, that is, in and through a noosphere. By means of the noosphere, spiritual heredity passes the spiritual treasures gained by previous generations.

By pointing out the organic unity of similar structures, similar mechanisms, and similar laws of movement for both biogenesis and noogenesis, Teilhard identifies man's spirit as the present scene of evolution. In its earlier biological phase, evolution did not come to a halt with the appearance of man. Rather, there has been a veering in evolution's course; it has entered into the noosphere. This sphere we must investigate in more detail.

The Noosphere

At the center of Teilhard's vision of mankind's future is the present existence and future development of the noosphere. Though it certainly stretches our minds and imaginations to try to see what Teilhard sees when he looks at the noosphere, it is not his most difficult innovation. In some of the implications of the noosphere, however, many readers will likely experience difficulties.

Julian Huxley has no trouble in seeing the reality of post-biological evolution being now "primarily a psychosocial process, based on the cumulative transmission of experience and its results, and working through an organized system of awareness, a combined operation of knowing, feeling, and willing." (27) This is a quite good description of both noogenesis and the noosphere.

Teilhard coined the word "noosphere" in 1925. What it means for him can be discovered in part by seeing the world as a geologist sees it: constructed of a series of successive layers composed of different materials. Without specialized training as an artist, it is difficult, if not impossible, to have the artist's sensitivity to color and form; so without specialized training in geology, it is difficult to see the earth as a geologist sees it. We see a hill; he sees a whole series of layers and thinks of the events that brought them to exist in this particular form. Nevertheless, just as any one of us can become more sensitive to color and form, so we can become more "seeing" of the various spheres which go to make up our earth.

In the central sphere of our earth, the barysphere, there are probably very simple, superheated metals. Above the barysphere is the lithosphere, the sphere of various sorts of rocks, quartzes, sands, et cetera. Above this is the hydrosphere—"the zone of water and carbonic acid, enclosing the silicates in an unstable, mobile and penetrating envelope"—constituting the earth's surface.(68) Above the hydrosphere is the atmosphere and above that, the stratosphere, each with individual characteristics.

When Teilhard encounters the reality of the psychosocial interchange among men all over the world, it is very easy for him to see and speak of another sphere, of a "thinking layer," of the noosphere, which is literally the sphere of mind. He uses the word to signify "an envelope of the thinking substance," a *"sphere of consciousness* (and of collective consciousness)."[4] It is a sphere which preserves and communicates "everything precious, active, and progressive" contained in this earth's previous evolution.(183)

On a small scale, we recognize the reality and influence of an impoverished "noosphere" on children brought up in the ghetto of the inner city. The IQ's of such children can be advanced significantly if they are placed in a culturally and intellectually richer "noosphere." It is quite reasonable, then, to think of an all-embracing noosphere, which includes all partial "noospheres" and which is capable of continuing expansion in richness and fruitfulness. Finally, we are assured that those who live in a richer noosphere will have greater potentialities for heightened knowledge, love and creativity.

Most of us, however, would be ready to admit that the existential reality and importance of Teilhard's noosphere is not something which comes easily within our intellectual grasp. Barysphere, yes; biosphere, yes; atmosphere, yes—but a sphere of spirits and their creations? This concept is not easily comprehended and affirmed. Hence, it will be helpful to give some of the empirical evidence available to both Teilhard and ourselves.

His experience of war for four years in the trenches was ambivalent. On the one hand, he felt the obvious disunity and disharmony of men as well as the apparent futility and waste of human efforts and lives. On the other hand he experienced the "display of mechanical and moral energy" in the united "going over the top." And there were supranational experiences. On the day after a memorial service for the regiment's dead at Verdun, a performance was given by the "actors with the forces"; "Parisian actors playing under the village chestnut trees to an audience of Senegalese, Martiniquans, Somalis, Annamites, Tunisians and French. . . . I brought back from it the very definite conviction that, among other results of the war, will be that of mixing and welding together the peoples of the earth in a way that nothing else, perhaps, could have done."[5]

Marguerite Teillard-Chambon, the favorite cousin to whom the wartime letters collected in *The Making of a Mind* were addressed, correctly sums up Teilhard's experience of the war: "In it he saw a crisis of evolution which had to be gone through. Civilized nations, at grips with one another in a merciless struggle, were moving against the great life-current, which he already saw as an irresistible progress towards unification of the human race."[6] In a victory of the French in Alsace, Teilhard could sense the type of spiritual union which is the heart of the noosphere: "and above all there was something you so seldom find, the confluence and meeting of countless spiritual energies—the whole soul of a country that finds itself again, to join up with that of another country."[7] Two weeks later, following another victory celebration in Strasbourg, Teilhard writes:

I've never seen anything like it. What was most impressive in this celebration, and moved some hardened *poilus* to tears, was

the presence, beneath this popular gaiety, of a very deep, somewhat ill-defined but still real, feeling. It will be a long time
before such a scene is witnessed in Alsace again; for it was
natural, in no way organized or artificial. You can't give orders
to the soul of a people (even less than one can to one's own).
And yesterday it was the whole soul of a province that was
profoundly happy and gay.—On such occasions, however little
one consciously looks for it, one *feels* the reality of the extra-
individual world, of the world which takes shape through a
union of souls. The feelings you experience and that animate
the crowd with one mind, are definitely of a higher order than
those experienced in the private life of an individual. You
would have to be blind not to see that such an expansion is
possible for our own individual souls, and what hopes it opens
up for us. I can assure you that yesterday, within this unanimity,
I really understood heaven better, and 'yearned' for it.[8]

"An extra-individual world . . . which takes shape through a
union of souls"—another description of the noosphere. Note
also how Teilhard specifies heaven as the culmination of the
possible expansion of individual souls within the "extra-
individual world." His investigations of noogenesis and of the
noosphere seek to explore as far as possible the *terrestrial*
potentialities for such expansion of souls.

A more positive source of evidence for the reality of the
noosphere is the unity of scientists in the pursuit of new truths.
When Teilhard first went to China in 1923, he was "initiated"
into a cosmopolitan coterie of scientists. Americans, Chinese,
Frenchmen, Englishmen, Swedes, Russians, all had the same
spirit and the same mind; all were engaged in research to
further man's knowledge. Here there were no barriers or divisions of nation, race, creed; men were united by their common search, by a single soul.

More and more we see science becoming less the work of
one man and increasingly the work of a team. The team itself
tends to grow larger and larger, often becoming international
in scope. Scientific research, more than any other human activity, depends on communication, union and cooperation—

witness the 1957 International Geodesic Year, the International Atomic Agency, Euratom, Eurochemistry, et cetera.

By the double revolution in communications and in transportation, it can be seen that man is creating a nervous system for the noosphere, which enables individual men to be present with all other men, despite barriers of land, sea or space. We witnessed a dramatic instance of the coreflection which Teilhard predicts as the specific activity of the noosphere at the time of President Kennedy's death. With the development of the noosphere, Teilhard predicted that all men would be put into a position to know and feel together in one psychic act. Many observers noted the new quality of their knowledge and feeling at the time of President Kennedy's death.[9] Television made it very clear that the sense of loss and grief was not merely a private or a national one. Rather, Americans were genuinely in communion with the whole human race, which cosuffered a common tragedy.

The development of more sophisticated machines is another instance of the reality and evolution of the noosphere:

> Every new tool conceived in the course of history, although it may have been invented in the first place by an individual, has rapidly become the instrument of all men . . . by being adopted corporatively by all men together. What started as an individual creation has been immediately and automatically transformed into a global, quasi-autonomous possession of the entire mass of men. . . . Consider the locomotive, the dynamo, the aeroplane, the cinema, the radio—anything.[10]

More and more it is not the individual inventor or the isolated machine but the team that produces the new machine—and by means of other machines.

Speaking of the development of the atom bomb during World War II, Teilhard notes:

> Through the non-fortuitous conjunction of a world crisis and an unprecedented advance in means of communications, a planned

scientific experiment employing units of a hundred or a thousand men had been successfully completed. And very swiftly. In three years a technical achievement had been realised which might not have been accomplished in a century of isolated efforts. The greatest of Man's scientific triumphs happens also to be one in which the largest number of brains were enabled to join together in a single organism, the most complex and the most centrated, for the purpose of research.[11]

When Teilhard visited Berkeley in 1952 and saw the cyclotron, this new product of the noosphere sparked still further thoughts.

I could not help feeling and perceiving, beyond and around this electromagnetic whirlwind, the concentric and convergent flowing of another and no less formidable radiation: that of the Human sucked in on me, in a vast wind from the four corners of space. . . .

Before my distraught eyes, the Berkeley cyclotron had completely disappeared. And in its place, my imagination saw the entire noosphere, which, coiled in upon itself by the breath of research, formed a single enormous cyclone, whose property it was to produce, not nuclear energy, but psychic energy in a continually more reflective state, in other words the ultrahuman itself.[12]

At the end of the *Phenomenon,* Teilhard indicates that he was able to formulate his ideas of the noosphere and its Omega Point because as a Christian he had already experienced "not only its speculative model but also its living reality." (294) What this enigmatic affirmation expresses is that because he had experienced the reality of the communal Body of Christ, the union of Christians with Christ in one body or sphere, he was spurred to discover its natural counterpart—the noosphere. Just as grace builds upon the individual human nature, Teilhard probably reasoned, so the corporate Body of Christ must build upon the corporate and natural union of men in the noosphere. Just as Christ is the head of the Mystical Body, so is Omega at the center of the noosphere. Christ's great desire and prayer, "that they may be one," has its parallel in the noospheric dynamism towards ever greater union in knowledge, love and creativity.

Finally, the reality of the noosphere seems to be more and more accepted, as can be seen by the articles of anthropologists Hallowell, Steward and Kroeber in the report on the University of Chicago Centennial of Darwin.[13] McLuhan too projects a noospheric union.[14]

In tracing the developmental history of the noosphere, Teilhard shows us that in the very beginning of the noosphere, with primitive peoples, communications were limited to exchanging some objects and a few ideas. With the rise of great civilizations, though, communications included "the dissemination of languages . . . the development and specialization of new industries . . . the formulation and propagation of philosophic and religious doctrines."(223) From his survey of the great civilizations, Teilhard makes what, at first hearing, sounds like a very provincial conclusion: "all the peoples, to remain human or to become more so, are inexorably led to formulate the hopes and problems of the modern earth in the very same terms in which the West has formulated them." This is so because "the principal axis of anthropogenesis [and, therefore, noogenesis] has passed through the West." (212)

It is the Western world which has been the most active in the realms of transportation and communication, bringing about a profound revolution in psychosocial evolution. Prior to this, groups of men were not only physically but also psychically isolated from the rest of mankind. Now, however, "each individual finds himself henceforth (actively and passively) simultaneously present, over land and sea, in every corner of the earth."(240) We are now truly world citizens; the noosphere is actually an organic envelope, which surrounds the whole earth and unites the whole of mankind's psychical efforts and achievements.

As we have seen, the mechanism used by the noosphere to promote the organic expansion of consciousness is a psychic form of heredity. By education and imitation, the riches of the noosphere are transmitted to the human elements who make up the noosphere. Not only that, but the noosphere serves as a "collective memory and intelligence" of mankind in which are collected the spiritual treasures gained by psychic powers and activities:

> Under the free and ingenious effort of successive intelligences, *something* . . . irreversibly accumulates, according to all the evidence, and is transmitted, at least collectively by means of education, down the course of ages. The point here is that this 'something'—construction of matter or construction of beauty, systems of thought or systems of action—always ends up by translating itself into an increase of consciousness. (178)

Evolution in the noosphere, though a prolongation of the previous biospheric evolution, differs from it in a major way. Biological evolution was not under the free choice of the living subjects undergoing mutations. Noospheric evolution, on the other hand, *is* subject to the free control and choice of mankind. Perhaps the most dramatic way Teilhard puts this is negatively: "The last century witnessed the first systematic strikes in industry; the next will surely not pass without the threat of strikes in the noosphere." (230) When man experiences industrial grievances, he goes on strike. Teilhard forecasts cosmic grievances:

> It is a terrifying thing to have been born: I mean, to find oneself, without having willed it, swept irrevocably along on a torrent of fearful energy which seems as though it wished to destroy everything it carries with it. . . . I am afraid, too, like all my fellow-men, of the future too heavy with mystery and too wholly new, towards which time is driving me. Then like these men I wonder anxiously where life is leading me.[15]

If life is too filled with meaninglessness and the future too lacking in hope, then there will surely be "strikes in the noosphere."

Because man is in evolution and because man is free, the

present and future growth of the noosphere is dependent upon humanity's use of its freedom. For the gigantic task of developing and consummating the noosphere, man must be motivated deeply, if he is to give completely of himself. This motivation must include the grounded hope "of achieving, through something of itself, a supreme consummation—without which it would rightly feel itself to be stunted, frustrated and cheated. By the nature of the work, and correlatively by the requirement [*exigence*] of the worker, a total death, an unscalable wall . . . are thus 'incompossible' with the mechanism of conscious activity. . . ."(231)[16] For man freely to choose to give himself entirely to building up the noosphere, he must be sure of a double immortality: his own and the noosphere's. However, certainty about these immortalities does not come simply from the evidence available. The evidence we possess provides at most "rational invitations to an act of faith."(233) To see that evolution has thus far succeeded in a magnificent way suggests strongly that it will succeed in the further evolution and final consummation of the noosphere. Certainty, however, must come from some other source.

Convergence of the Noosphere

Teilhard now begins to investigate the intrinsic requirements for further progress of the noosphere. The cardinal point to be established is whether noospheric progress is convergent or not, that is, does noospheric evolution tend towards higher and higher forms of unity? The importance of establishing noospheric convergence is evidenced by his formulation of the question towards the end of his life (1952):

> It is on this fundamental question . . . and not on the reality of a general evolution of the universe, nor on the reality of a secondary or partial cosmic flow towards greater complexity and greater consciousness—it is, I repeat, on the fundamental question of the convergence on itself (in a reflective form) of this consciousness-current that the great battle will soon, I believe, be fought.[17]

This quotation indicates that at least as far as popular acceptance goes, the battle for evolution has been won, for all practical purposes. Evolution is now an accepted fact and it is governed by the law of complexity/consciousness. Teilhard implies, however, that many fellow scientists are not ready to affirm the convergence of the noosphere.

There are several good reasons for their reluctance. For one thing Teilhard's analysis of the noospheric convergence ultimately leads him to affirm the existence of a transcendent, personal Omega Point—God. This line of thought is clearly outside of science as it is usually understood by scientists. The next chapter will take up this problem.

Other reasons for difficulty with the convergence of the noosphere are: 1) its investigation is almost entirely in the realm of the spirit; 2) it considers the whole social phenomenon of man; and 3) it mainly concerns itself with the future development of the noosphere. Why scientists, who have a restricted concept of science's ambit, have difficulty on these scores should be evident: 1) science is conceived to be primarily, if not exclusively, an investigation of matter and its properties, not of spirit and its characteristics; 2) science can master the total situation by breaking it down into its analytical parts, but the noosphere must be considered as an indivisible whole; 3) science deals with past or present phenomena, and since the future does not yet exist, it exhibits no phenomena and, therefore, seems to be outside the pale of science.

In Teilhard's favor, however, is the logical continuity of his procedure. He started with what were certainly scientific phenomena and showed how, by evolution, these led to higher and higher phenomena, and that, especially, human psychic phenomena are an integral part of the whole process. There is no logical point wherein to halt one's investigation once the viewpoint of hyperphysics has been adopted. There is no justification for a "thus far and no further." On the contrary, the

very dynamism and continuity of evolution insistently urge the
scientific thinker to investigate man and his future in order to
give meaning to the whole of evolution. Michael Murray
correctly assesses the validity of hyperphysics' investigations
here.

> At this point Teilhard ceases to reason inductively from observed
> phenomena and begins to deduce their probable future mani-
> festations by extrapolation on the basis of the principles already
> inferred. This too is a common and legitimate scientific pro-
> cedure so long as the approximate nature of such predictions is
> recognized and tested as new data becomes available.[18]

In the present section of the *Phenomenon,* then, Teilhard
concentrates upon the noosphere as the natural culmination of
biological evolution, continuous with it by reason of a common
structure, mechanism and movement. Like the living individual
who is a whole which is greater than the sum of its parts,[19] so
the social organism of the noosphere is a whole irreducible to
its parts. Both as a social phenomenon and as the highest result
of convergent evolution, the noosphere is necessarily an organic whole destined for some type of superconvergence.

As an initial definition of convergence, we suggested that it
is the movement of one or many beings toward higher unities.
Divergence, on the other hand, is the movement towards dispersion, separateness and isolation. The concept of convergence
is contained in the law of complexity/consciousness, which implies that evolution tends towards more conscious, more centered, more unified beings. The use of the concept "convergence," however, makes explicit this inner dynamism of evolution towards unification. Since at all levels of evolution
unification is possible, both within an individual being and
among a whole group of individuals, it is obvious that the
term has many different nuances.

The concept of convergence is rooted in the fundamental
presupposition of science: the cosmos is intelligible. To under-

stand something complex, such as the cosmos, we know that there must be unities which bind together and make intelligible the multiplicity and variegatedness of the universe's component parts and activities. If the scientist could discover no unifying and converging threads, he would have to give up his search for meaning.

It is for this reason that we find Teilhard so opposed to all forms of cosmic divergence. Though he gained from his reading of Bergson valuable orientations and insights, he refused to accept Bergson's basically divergent evolution, which flowered not in the unity of persons but in the dispersion of individual "heroes" and "saints." Like Plotinus, Bergson has unity at the beginning and dispersion at the end; if there is to be a "conversion," a return of the many to the one, it is generally in a pantheistic way, by the destruction of the reality of the individuals who make up the many.[20] For Teilhard, however, the reality of the many is equally as primordial as the reality of the one. (The simultaneous existence of a trinity of persons in the unity of the Godhead is the theological ontology which underpins Teilhard's conception.) The law of complexity/consciousness points to the higher forms of unity made possible precisely by means of higher forms of complexity.

Communism also postulates in its dialectical materialism a process of convergence—to the classless society, where as a band of brothers "the free development of each is the condition for the free development of all."[21] Teilhard appreciated (some would say, overappreciated) the valid aspects of communism's projected convergence: its love of this earth, its desire to bring this earth to perfection, its faith in the future, its desire to rid man of his alienation and settle him forever in a classless society. He also saw the deficiencies, which can only be mentioned at this point. Marxism depersonalizes man by emphasizing the determinism of history as necessarily moving him to his final state. It lacks motivation, which appeals to and respects man's freedom. Communism's tendency is to "defraud man of his future" by stressing *well-being* rather than *more-being*. Finally, without a transcendent pole of super-love—Omega—communism lacks both sufficient motivation for and a focus on the final consummation of which man is capable.[22]

Why is convergence so important in Teilhard's synthesis? The past movement of evolution towards higher unification demands, by reason of scientific completeness, an investigation of the shape of future noospheric convergence. Teilhard's noospheric predictions are not given for prediction's sake but rather to satisfy a profound human need: to know and to desire the shape of the future he can and should bring to be.[23]

In prehuman evolution convergence was far more manifest in the centered unity of the new and higher beings brought forth. Every higher level of consciousness—whether within the atom, the molecule, the macromolecule, the cell, the insect, the vertebrate—was a mark of a higher unification or convergence of the multiplicity of elements which went into the higher unity. When many individuals of the same species converge and join, as in the hives or anthills of insects, there is a dim foreshadowing of the socialization which will characterize human convergence. Dim, because in the insects consciousness becomes extraverted and frozen, and individuality is absorbed by the communal whole. (153-5)

Fundamental to Teilhard's outlook is an understanding of this cosmos as not having been created in a finished or near-finished state. Rather, it is a universe "passing from *State A*, characterized by a very large number of very simple elements (that is to say, with a very poor *within*), to *State B* defined by a smaller number of very complex groupings (that is to say, with a much richer *within*.)"(61) In other words, ours is a convergent universe.

Another consideration tends to confirm this. From the manifest noninterference of God with what creation can do of itself and for itself, we see that God respects the natures of secondary causes or of creatures; He allows them to effect their proper results. Since matter, even in a most dispersed condition, has the natural potentiality for even higher forms of unity, it is most consonant with God's respect of creatures that he allow matter to reach of itself these higher forms of unity. In other words, a convergent universe seems more in harmony with God's known mode of acting in this world than a nonconvergent universe, where the higher unities would be immediately created by God and not caused at all by creatures.[24]

The convergence of the noosphere is, then, a true continuation of the universal tendency towards unification. A new factor, however, is now operative: in noospheric convergence we have self-reflective consciousness or spirits at work. Since man's consciousness is the new and highest form of centeredness or unity, one can reasonably expect that its potentialities for still higher forms of unity would be remarkable.

Man's self-reflective consciousness raises two main questions with regard to the future noospheric evolution and its convergence. The first is: What sort of progressive unification and convergence should we look for in the noosphere now and in the immediate future? The second is: Should we look for an ultimate state to be achieved through progressive convergence? Noospheric convergence involves, then, both the present and ultimate meaning of human creativity and activity. In the fourth Book of the *Phenomenon*, Teilhard explores the future possibilities of noospheric convergence, but as a prelude to this, he explores in the final chapter of the third Book the modern mentality as it faces the future of evolution.

Evolutionary Anxiety

In the chapter on "The Problem of Action," the future of the noosphere is broached in terms of man's psychic requisites. What motivation is necessary for modern man so that his noospheric action be undertaken with joy, and continued with courage and persistence?

Put negatively, what are the psychic diseases or maladies

which would greatly diminish or prevent human action for the ultimate development of the noosphere? Teilhard isolates two diseases: the malady of space-time and the disease of pessimism.

"The malady of space-time" is experienced first as a feeling of being crushed and therefore helpless in the face of the "enormities of space" and time.(227) The enormity of space we perhaps realize somewhat better than Teilhard; our first probings of space reveal that even when we get to Mars, we will not have left the narrow confines of our "space backyard."[25] The planets of our solar system are merely the very near specks in our own galaxy. What of the "galaxies whose distance apart runs into hundreds of thousands of light years"?(227)

Consider the enormity of duration of the "great past"—it is almost impossible to think of the origin of the universe some thirteen to twenty billion years ago, the origin of our earth five billion years ago, the first fossil beds dating back six hundred million years, and men having existed for about a million years. What is our own momentarily short span of life compared with these immensities?

Corresponding to the enormity of space-time is the hugeness of the number of galaxies, stars and planets which go to make up our cosmos. And if we merely restrict our gaze to fellow-men on this earth, how can we find a place for ourselves amid the mass of three billion human beings, or, as Teilhard states, "merely in a crowd"?(228) One can, of course, refuse to think of one's material setting, but whoever tries to face reality in its immense dimensions will necessarily experience the feeling of being crushed into insignificance and worthlessness—unless we see that all this matter in all its spatial extensions and throughout all of its duration has moved in a directed way. The immensities of space and time *are* crushing unless we have a perception "of an evolution animating those dimensions." (228)

To completely counteract the malady of space-time, we must see that cosmic evolution is now in the stage of noogenesis.

Each human being, as an integral part of the noosphere, has meaning and value because of the contributions he or she can make to the enrichment of noogenesis. Man may be small quantitatively and numerically, but considered in a deeper and more significant way, that is, qualitatively, he is seen to be "the axis and leading shoot of evolution."(36) Seeing himself as he really is, the vanguard of the whole of cosmic evolution, he cannot feel himself lost or insignificant. He discovers himself as the core and carrier of the cosmos' meaning and value.

The second malady, which tends to cripple mankind's gift of himself to furthering noogenesis, is what might be called the malady of meaninglessness and determinism. It is not the outer world of the macrocosm which here frightens and oppresses man, but the inner world of man himself, the microcosm, who realizes the dread consequences of the meaning he can freely give or refuse to give to himself and his cosmos. Though the *Phenomenon* was written before the postwar wave of existentialist angst, Teilhard poses the problem very much as do the existentialists. It is the answers of Teilhard and the existentialists which are diametrically opposed.

"When the first spark of thought appeared upon the earth, life found it had brought into the world a power capable of criticizing it and judging it. . . . There is a danger that the elements of the world should refuse to serve the world—because they think."(230) Man's liberty is not a trifling or insignificant thing; he recognizes that all is won or lost through it. His very meaning is constituted by the nature and quality of his fundamental option: "It is man with the freedom to give himself to effort or draw back from it, man with the frightening power to criticize life and take its measure."[26]

It is especially in deciding whether the future holds forth an absurd void or the vivifying vision of *"a suitable outcome"* that our liberty is put to the critical test. Freely our liberty can leap to a faith in the future. This would "give us the strength or even the joy to accept the prospect of it and bear its weight."

Without this faith there is "the sickness of the dead end—the anguish of feeling shut in."(229) The whole meaning of man and further evolution in the noosphere is bound up with his future: Is it meaningless and absurd, or is it filled with promise?

Quite clearly Teilhard recognizes that the answer to this question lies beyond the boundaries of science, even though the logical extensions of evolutionary history both urge the question and provide "rational invitations to an act of faith." (233) Hyperphysics urges the question because in detailing the history of evolution's increasing complexity/consciousness, it instinctively asks, "What does the future hold?" This question gives way then to the question, "Is there a future?" Though we must freely decide the answer to these questions, hyperphysics loads the dice in favor of faith over despair. "If it [an evolving cosmos] undertook the task, it is because it can finish it, following the same methods and with the same infallibility with which it began." (233-4)

In order for us to give ourselves unreservedly to furthering noospheric evolution, we must be assured that there is *"a suitable outcome"* for the efforts of men committed to building up the earth. We must be attracted by "a precious future with which all our efforts and our industry co-operate, an intimate bond of union in matter and in the transformation that makes us evolve as one being,—a destiny that is not artificially imposed but organically based on our capabilities."[27]

There are, then, two aspects of this "precious future" which must be established. These constitute the subjects of the fourth Book of the *Phenomenon*. First, it must be determined "that there is for us, in the future, under some form or another, at least collective, not only survival, but also *super-life*." (234) Since evolution has always been towards higher forms of being, the future must hold up to men some superior form of life and activity. We must foresee something of the shape of this future life to motivate a full commitment to the progress of the noosphere. From the fact that there is possible now both individual and social progress, both individual and corporate consummation, we are justified in our faith in the noospheric future.

The second point, which must be explored, is the "how" of our reaching the "superior form of existence" which the future can promise us. The general clue, which Teilhard proposes to exploit, is to follow out evolutionary vectors of the past to their point of "maximum coherence" in the future. From the patterns revealed in past and present evolution, he seeks to project the future state of the noosphere and what would constitute its consummation and perfection.

READING SUGGESTIONS

1. *Read PM,* 213-245.

2. *See Glossary for*: change of state, critical points, *duration, *element, emergence, faith, *genesis, *groping, *outcome, physiognomy, *radial, recoil, *reflection, *space-time, *survival, *tangential, within, without.

3. *Passages to be noted*:
   220-221, "From the very first pages etc." The point of this and the two following paragraphs is that because man's soul or spirit is observed as a product of the space-time web of matter's evolution, man's soul or spirit is increasingly the principal scene of cosmic evolution. Cosmogenesis has become noogenesis. Hence, recent and present evolutionary progress is measured by the "movement of our souls," by the psychosocial progress of mankind.
   221-226, *"C. The Illumination,"* i.e., evolution's illumination of our psychosocial progress as a *continuation* of biological evolution because of their similar structure, mechanism and movement.
   229, "Here only, etc." marks hyperphysics' transition from science, as ordinarily conceived, to "faith," the necessary extension or prolongation of science.
   239, "to combine their 'radial energies' in bundles," that is, to unify by means of psychic energy into higher and more potent unities.

243, "The coalescence of elements, etc." is a dense but very adequate summary of the preceding fifty pages.

4. *Parallel Readings*:
   veering: *FM*, 227-237 (236-47).
   noosphere: *AM*, 230-244; *FM, 155-184 (161-191); *MPN*, 79-95; *VP*, 61-79.
   convergence: *FM*, 196-213 (204-21); *SC*, 137-150; Tresmontant, 50-57.
   freedom in development: *FM*, 37-60 (39-63), 140-144 (145-49), 244-259 (255-71); de Lubac, *Religion*, 108-120.
   evolutionary anxiety: *WTW*, 226-231; *Mooney, 13-33 (18-39); Rideau, 31-38; Smulders, 89-99.

5. *Critiques*: convergent noosphere: Benz, 205-241; Speaight, 273.

7

THE FUTURE OF MAN: "HUMANITY"

The question of man's future is truly a burning one. The past and the present are fixed; only the future is open to the impact of human freedom and foresight. Further, it is the quality and quantity of the future that are critical: What kind of future, and how much future is in store for man? If the future holds only nothingness both for individual men and for the human race, human motivation must run at a low ebb. On the other hand, if the future holds a promise of the preservation and vitalization of the past and present, of the individual and of the race, man faces life's challenges with far more enthusiasm, courage and hope. Any treatise which professes to deal with "the *whole* phenomenon of man" must address itself unblinkingly to the future of man. This the fourth Book of *The Phenomenon of Man* does.

In a still larger framework, this final Book is seen as describing the third and final stage of evolution: the planetization of Mankind, the coming together of men into one "planet," or "atom," or "organism":

First the vitalisation of matter, associated with the grouping of molecules; then the hominisation of Life, associated with a super-grouping of cells; and finally the planetisation of Mankind, associated with a *closed* grouping of peoples: Mankind, born on this planet and spread over its entire surface, coming

gradually to form around its earthly matrix a single, major organic unity, enclosed upon itself; a single, hyper-complex, hyper-
centrated, hyper-conscious arch-molecule, co-extensive with the
heavenly body on which it was born.[1]

Teilhard de Chardin: Pilgrim of the Future

Even before World War II, Teilhard's interest in the past
had waned, and his intellectual involvement in the future had
waxed.[2] When he first experienced Mongolia in 1923, he wrote
the prophetic evaluation of himself: "I am a pilgrim of the
future on my way back from a journey made entirely in the
past."[3] The final book of the *Phenomenon* bears this out both
in itself and in Teilhard's own estimation of it: "the whole
interest and point of the book is concentrated towards the
end," which deals with the future of man.

Already in 1926 the seed of *The Phenomenon of Man* was
germinating in Teilhard's mind. The following represents his
dream of the book-to-be in which the future of man is obviously
central.

I contemplate in fancy a kind of "Book of Earth," wherein I
should let myself speak, not as a Frenchman, or as belonging to
any separate category, but as Man, or simply as "Planetarian."
I should undertake to express the confidence, the ambitions, the
fruition, and the disappointments too, the insecurities, and
the feeling of dizziness, of one who has realized what destiny
awaits the Earth (mankind) as one complete whole. I should
not be concerned to reach agreement with any of the accepted
currents of thought, but only with expressing what I myself experience; I should try to communicate my faith in human en-
deavour and in human unity, and my impatience with all the
petty barriers that divide and isolate minds whose true future
lies in coming together; I should like, too, to picture the frustra-
tion we feel at finding ourselves imprisoned on one little sphere
which will soon have nothing more to offer us, and our desola-
tion when we realize that we are, all of us equally, alone in
starry space.

Here, I believe, we have an immense psychological domain of

thought and feeling that no one enters because it seems altogether too fanciful. In fact it is as rigorously objective as any concern with family or society. If I could get such a book written it would be, in a way, the book of my life.[4]

Teilhard shows himself to be truly "a pilgrim of the future." Cuénot reports an evaluation of that pilgrim: "Paradoxically, here is a scientist whose specialty is the past, but who is interested only in the future."[5] Why this shift in Teilhard's interest from the past to the future? Why is the *Phenomenon's* last Book on the future of man?

A true but less than satisfactory answer is that systematic completeness, to which Teilhard was greatly attached, demands that man be considered not only in the past but also in the present and in the future. The more important consideration is, however, the pressing need (*exigence*) man experiences in the realm of action: How can man be sufficiently motivated to fullness of activity unless he knows the shape of his future and the "suitable outcome" of his work? Again and again in Teilhard's thought, we see this same concern reappearing. It is not that man, without a knowledge of the future of Humanity, would do nothing, but he would certainly do very little of what he is capable of and, as Teilhard sees it, very little of what is now required by the very process of evolution so that it may keep progressing.

Of Humanity's future Teilhard insists most of all that it will be convergent or collective—all together. On this he experienced considerable opposition from various thinkers. His Jesuit confrere, Jean Daniélou, said, "I can base my life on the hope of individual salvation, but not on the certitude of universal survival. Some imbecile may drop the bomb."[6] This represents a Christian form of the "pluralism" which is opposed to Teilhard's "monism." The future of man is pictured by "pluralism" mainly in terms of individual perfection and salvation. To the reality and value of a collective perfecting and consummation of Humanity, "pluralism" is largely blind. If the "pluralist" is right—

if mankind were destined to achieve its apotheosis, if Evolution were to reach its highest point, in our small, separate lives, then indeed the enormous travail of terrestrial organization into which we are born would be no more than a tragic irrelevance. We should all be dupes. We should do better in that case to stop, to call a halt, destroy the machines, close the laboratories, and seek whatever way of escape we can find in pure pleasure or pure nirvana.[7]

Teilhard, as a "monist," appreciates the necessity of trying to get others to *see* the concrete reality of the evolving human collectivity and the sort of outcome rightly to be hoped for it. Whereas the "pluralist" suffers from too little motivation for giving himself to the building up of this earth, the "monist" has the problem of preserving the value of the individual. In the *Phenomenon's* next Chapter, we shall find Teilhard laboring to show how a correctly conceived and ordered collectivity of man constitutes a personal and personalizing universe in which the value of the individual is not only preserved but enhanced.

Humanity's Body and Christ's Body

During the first World War, Teilhard had a quite developed idea of the coming together or coalescence of human elements to form the whole Body of Christ. But at this time he does not seem to see what is prominent in the *Phenomenon* —the noosphere, a *natural* correlate of Christ's Body—though he was clearly groping for this insight and its formulation:[8]

You see, the more I think of it (as I've done a great deal during these recent marches), the more I feel the necessity of defining and organizing the *total* natural human effort. Individual lives carry on from day to day;—political foresight never goes beyond short-term economic or territorial ambitions . . . . Every one, every life, proceeds *at random*. . . . But what positive, progressive, precise end are we to assign to human efforts? In what natural direction are we to advance? To what tangible end should we unite, *all of us*?

By the very fact of its appearance, thought is an element of disorganization, of decomposition, for the living stem. The monads refuse any longer (rightly or wrongly) to submit to the laborious task of extending life blindly with docility.—Either they look only for enjoyment, and follow the line of least resistance; or else they try to break the links that attach them to others: they have of their nature a constitutional urge to exist proudly and selfishly. . . . The appearance of reason necessarily marks an organic crisis. The former cosmic framework no longer suffices to contain [to satisfy] the new activities born with the human soul. Thus the equilibrium of the universe urgently demands that all men should be given a transcendent interest and outlook and thus with the cohesion imposed by the new ties be prevented from frittering themselves away.—Isn't this the obvious place for the liberating function of the body of Christ . . . ?[9]

In the development of Teilhard's thought, there can be little doubt about his theological insight into the Body of Christ as the stimulation for seeing also a natural body of men, a noosphere, Humanity, "that Great Thing," a superindividual, "the spirit of the world." This organic unity of men is so clear in the *Phenomenon*:

some great body which is being born—with its limbs, its nervous system, its perceptive organs, its memory—the body in fact of that great Thing which had to come to fulfil the ambitions aroused . . . by the newly acquired consciousness that he [man] was at one with and responsible to an evolutionary All. (246)

There is no question that Teilhard's mature thought was quite certain and specific about the existence of the noosphere, the natural analogue of the Mystical Body of Christ.

As we know, the belief that the human individual cannot perfect himself or fully exist except through the organic unification of all men in God is essential and fundamental to Christian doctrine. To this mystical super-organism, joined by Grace and charity, we have now added a mysterious equivalent organism born of biology: the 'Noospheric' human unity gradually achieved by the totalising and centrating effect of Reflection. How can these two super-entities, the one 'supernatural,' and the other natural, fail to come together and harmonise in Christian thought; the critical point envisaged by science being simply the physical condition and experimental aspect of the critical point of the Parousia [of Christ] postulated and awaited in the name of Revelation?[10]

The certainty that "noospheric" human unity will be brought to some form of completion comes in (greatest?) part to Teilhard from the Christian certainty of Christ coming to "full stature" by the time of his Parousia or appearance at the end of time. There are, of course, natural grounds which contribute to this certainty; the largest of these grounds is evolution's past success, which bodes well for human evolution coming to whatever fulfillment lies within its potentialities.

The Reality of "Humanity"

The achievement of the noospheric unity of all men can be frustrated by a large proportion of mankind committing itself to an individualistic philosophy of life. It is difficult to imagine devotees of Ayn Rand's individualism seriously considering the possibility and needs of "an organic super-aggregation of souls." The same could be said of the followers of an existentialism such as Jean-Paul Sartre's. For one thing, the reality of the noosphere demands a permanence or irreversibility of both evolvers and evolution; such permanence is diametrically opposed to the total-death hypothesis of most non-Christian individualisms.

The other form of individualism which Teilhard considers is the group individualism of racism and/or totalitarianism. When he wrote the *Phenomenon*, totalitarianism had not yet shown its complete visage; hence, we can understand his brief discussion of this type of individualism. (256-7) However, in several of the post-war essays collected in *The Future of Man*,

Teilhard shows himself quite sensitive to the possibility that the universal noospheric collectively might be as dehumanizing and depersonalizing as the forms of totalitarianism recently or currently experienced.[11] It is for this reason that we find him in these later essays exerting more effort to show that a true totalization of Humanity is the one composed of *all* men. As such it is intrinsically perfective of each and every individual who gives himself or herself to it.

The adoption of individualistic philosophies may be considered as an extrinsic, because freely adopted, counterforce to a convergent evolution. Teilhard adverts again and again to the intrinsic counterforces of repulsion and materialization. It is in view of these forces that so many moderns are unwilling to admit the fact of any significant psychosocial evolution in man. "What do you mean, human progress? Oh, I'll grant you that we have improvements in communications and transportation, in gadgets and data processing. But the real question is: Are *men* better? Is there really more justice and love abroad now than a thousand years ago? Are men more moral now than at the time of Christ?" To reinforce a negative answer, the questioner has only to point to two world wars in the last sixty years, the genocides and massive repressions perpetrated by totalitarian regimes, the extensive racial injustice, the grinding poverty and lack of opportunity both in the ghettos and the underdeveloped countries, the continuing threat of the immoral and frightening use of nuclear warfare, the assassinations of the two Kennedys and of Dr. King.

Teilhard puts the question bluntly: "Does it not appear, on the contrary, that social totalisation leads directly to spiritual retrogression and greater materialism?"[12] After World War II he noted:

A thick fog of confusion and dissension is at present drifting over the world. Indeed one might say that men have never more vehemently rebuffed and detested one another than they do now, when everything drives them closer together. Is this state of moral chaos really to be reconciled with the idea and the hope that we are advancing towards *unanimity* [one-souledness] through the closer contact of our bodies and minds?[13]

Though he perhaps pays too little attention to all such negative factors, Teilhard does not, to this author's knowledge, assert that our present age is morally better than earlier ones. In fact, he states that we exist in ignorance about this:

> We cannot claim as individuals to be more moral or saintly than our fathers.

> That man, with the passage of time, has become "better" or "worse"—I just don't know what those words mean and I don't concern myself with the question. But that Humanity can be considered, right now, as a species which is dispersing or as a species which is static [*plafonne*], that is what I absolutely deny. [The editors add to this: that man becomes "better" or "worse" is really an ambiguous question. For Père Teilhard, as for every Christian, the moral value of a man is a mystery which God alone judges and which therefore is not the concern of a thinker.][14]

Teilhard denies, therefore, that evolution is necessarily tending to a morally better humanity, though this is what many critics interpret him as saying. The truth is that hyperphysics operates on an entirely different plane, the plane of what is *observable* in the human species. By legitimate extrapolation or extensions, Teilhard investigates the collective future of man—the coming superconsciousness and superunion of mankind. Even though many of the current social ills are the result of complexification, he is convinced that evolution will ultimately lead to higher consciousness and personality. It is in view of that future that he tends to minimize the negative forces of repulsion and materialization.

Concerning repulsion, Teilhard recognizes that there are "individual and collective forces of dispersion" in mankind.(243) Evolution is anything but a straight-line progress of unification by forces of attraction and harmony: "thinking units do not seem capable of falling within their radius of internal attraction . . . men are hostile or at least closed to one another . . . deep down men exclude and repel one another with all their might. . . ." (256)[15]

But all this cannot slacken Teilhard's hope. A Sartre, on the other hand, pessimistically "accepts" the tragic and eternal repulsion of mankind. "Hell is—other people! . . . For ever, and ever, and ever."[16] Teilhard, however, is realistic about the ambiguity of human affectivity:

> If the pressure of some great common need should succeed in overcoming our mutual aversion and in breaking the icy barriers that isolate us, who can tell what well-being and tenderness would not emerge from our harmonized multitude? When men feel that they are really alone in the world, then (unless they turn and rend one another) they will begin to love one another.[17]

What, then, for Teilhard is the ultimate and necessary remedy for human repulsion? The innate egoism and dissension in man calls for—if humanity is to be truly convergent—a divine focus of love, an Omega who must be "supremely present . . . supremely attractive."(269)

The second counterforce is that of materialization. Teilhard does not embrace the mass coming-together of Humanity as an unmixed blessing and an unalloyed fulfillment of the noosphere. As man increases in density upon the face of the earth, he is ever more subject to the depersonalization of "massification." Marshall McLuhan welcomes and feels at home in this totalizing earth:

> Ours is a brand-new world of allatonceness. 'Time' has ceased, 'space' has vanished. We now live in a *global* village . . . a simultaneous happening. We are back in acoustic space. We have begun again to structure the primordial feeling, the tribal emotions from which a few centuries of literacy divorced us.[18]

Teilhard, it seems, takes better account of the ambiguity of the contemporary scene. He sees that a constricting conformity "makes us slaves of the obscure seethings of the human mass." We have now " 'the Million' scientifically assembled. The Million in rank and file on the parade ground; the Million standardised in the factory; the Million motorized. . . ." (256)

The mere physical coming together of large numbers by means of improved communications and transportation does not seem to necessitate a coming together into a love-inspired union and communion. The fears of George Orwell's *1984* and Aldous Huxley's *Brave New World* are hardly offset by the shaky optimism of B. F. Skinner's deterministic *Walden II*. The contemporary fact seems to be that as men are more closely linked and interdependent with all other men, they feel the linkage and relationship less and less.[19] This is connected with Durkheim's pessimistic prediction: the more men are capable of controlling their environment by their cooperative coming together, the less interest they have in living.[20]

It is not enough to say, as Teilhard does, that the materialization and depersonalization coming from mass pressure and culture are "the sign of and the price paid for progress." (256) Few of us are stoic enough to embrace the diminution or destruction of our personalities in the cause of progress. We feel all too deeply that *we* must grow with the growth of Humanity —so, too, Teilhard.

Accordingly, though a huge number, a "legion," is necessary for mankind's advance, still more necessary is the "personalizing action of the Centre of centres"—Omega. (271) Without such a transcendent focus, there is every reason to fear a *1984* depersonalized mass society in place of the personalized community we dream of and which Teilhard projects as the goal for a converging and totalizing Humanity.

The truth or falsity of the projection of the coming to be of an organic union of all mankind cannot be settled by the listing of authorities, but rather in terms of seeing—seeing that this idea is consistent with the phenomena, with our other concepts, and with our hopes. To note, however, the variety of thinkers who also see the coming to be of some superunion of men shows that Teilhard's thought is not strangely singular. The American philosopher Josiah Royce sees the need for a universal unanimity:

> The moral insight, insisting upon the need for the harmony of all human wills, shows us that, *whatever the highest human good may be, we can only attain it together, for it involves harmony.* . . . Either the highest good is for humanity unattainable, or the humanity of the future must attain it *in common.* Therefore the sense of community, the power to work together, with clear insight into our reasons for so working, is the *first* need of humanity. Not what good thing men may hereafter come to see, but how they shall attain the only sense whereby they can ever get to see the good, is the great present human concern.[21]

The Catholic theologian Emile Mersch in setting forth the natural substrate for the Mystical Body notes the many natural bonds which go to make mankind one.[22] The British biologists, Julian Huxley and J. B. S. Haldane, both propose ideas which closely parallel Teilhard's. Quoted early in the *Phenomenon* and later referred to is the remarkable sentence of Haldane: "Now, if the cooperation of some thousands of millions of cells in our brain can produce our consciousness, the idea becomes vastly more plausible that the co-operation of humanity, or some sections of it, may determine what Comte calls a Great Being." (57) We have already mentioned the philosopher of mass media, Marshall McLuhan, and we can add (from many other possibilities) Lecomte du Noüy whose *Human Destiny* has been an immensely popular justification of spiritual and communal values in an evolutionary world.[23] At the very least, this small selection of "like-thinkers" with Teilhard indicates that he was anything but alone in his proposing the noosphere as bringing about the reality of Humanity—"the harmonised collectivity of consciousnesses equivalent to a sort of super-consciousness." (251)

The Unification of "Humanity"

How will the unification of Humanity come about? Teilhard sees two general causes at work: the geographic curvature of the earth and the psychic curvature of men's spirits. The very roundness of the earth forces men to cover the earth. *If* the earth were flat and boundless, men would constantly spread out and diverge, not converge. The physical unification effected by the earth's roundness and by improved communication would never of itself be enough to bring men together into organic unity, because this is a unity forced on them from without. True human unity must proceed from man's inner freedom and liberty.

The spirit of man has not only the property of self-reflection, of coiling upon itself, but, by its basic dynamism towards the other through knowing and loving, has a need of uniting with other persons in order to fulfill itself. Its progress in self-unification is directly proportioned to its unification with other spirits and ultimately with infinite spirit. This is what makes mankind a unique species; instead of finding its perfection in ramifying into other and new species (and therefore in isolation from the others), man shows the remarkable characteristic of an entire phylum coalescing upon itself. This does not deny the invention of the new in the human phylum. Obviously there is human creativity, but it is not achieved by biological or physical ramification. Rather, the new things discovered in the realms of science and art become instruments to unify further mankind. (242-3)

This phenomenon points to the psychic curvature of spirit; such curvature marks spirit off from matter. It is also called "psychic permeability," the second factor which Teilhard indicates as instrumental in the building up of the "spirit of the earth." Through psychic permeability human elements are able to penetrate one another; by this interpenetration "their minds (mysterious coincidence) are mutually stimulated," and cause a "corresponding expansion in each element," so great is the power of psychic penetration and interpenetration.(240) In the realm of the spirit, there is "interfecundation at every level, the blending of genes, anastomoses of races in civilisations or political bodies," and all of this makes possible a "radical perfectioning" and concentration in the realm of spirit. (241-2) Therefore, Teilhard can look forward to an advanced stage of human megasynthesis, when the noosphere will constitute a single closed system "in which each element sees, feels, desires and suffers for itself the same things as all the others at the same time." (251)

It is certainly not illegitimate to raise here the question contained in each morning's news. Given the continuous account of "wars and the rumors of wars," of man's continuing inhumanity to his fellowman by various acts of violence, intrigue, racial and national repression, gross neglect, et cetera, have we any right to hope for the coming to be of a union of men that would be characterized by "unanimity" or one-souledness? It is here that extrapolation from the law of complexity/consciousness has considerable force in making the coming to be of an organic and perfected "Humanity" seem not only possible but highly probable. Since the past of evolution is seen as the production of ever higher unities of matter, we have the right to project for mankind a higher form of unity which corresponds to his particular psychic potentialities. At lower levels, the couple, the team, the religious order, the social organization, the nation, show the real possibilities of men coming to higher perfection through higher and more complex social unions. Why cannot this be extrapolated to the truly universal—the union of all men "in the act of a single unanimous reflection"? (252) For the Christian there can be "not merely a probability but a certainty" about this "eventual biological success of man."[24]

Of the interpenetration that this would involve, we already have some evidence. Maurice Blondel, the French philosopher with whom Teilhard had considerable contact, expresses the organic unity of men strongly: "we are literally made of one another without ceasing to be individual personalities.[25] Teilhard indicates in a graphic way the present interdependence and interpenetration of all men: "each man demands his daily ration of iron, copper and cotton, of electricity, oil and radium, of discoveries, of the cinema and of international news. It is . . . the whole earth which is required to nourish each one of us."(245-6) These strong economic and cultural links give intimations of even higher links that are possible for all mankind: links of personal knowledge, feeling and love which become universalized. As a result of the projected superunion of men, mankind appears anything but small, insignificant and fragile. Rather, he is seen as destined for a most substantial, significant and immense existence by reason of the megasynthesis which is under way now.

Humanity's Unifiers: Science and Unanimity

Teilhard singles out the two principal means for advancing towards the superorganization of mankind: science and unanimity. The first aspect of science which he emphasizes is the elaboration of "an over-all and completely coherent perspective of the universe."(248) This is, as the reader immediately recognizes, a description of what Teilhard is attempting in a pioneering way by the hyperphysics of The Phenomenon of Man. That such a perspective is needed for the superunion of men should be fairly obvious, since it would provide a common outlook, a common hope. Seeking this service from science seems reasonable.

There has been much discussion of C. P. Snow's thesis of the two contemporary cultures of science and of the humanities. By their noncommunication with each other, Snow believes our civilization is rendered schizophrenic. Jacques Barzun, however, in his Science, The Glorious Entertainment, makes what seems to be a more valid point and at the same time a radical criticism of Snow's thesis: there is only one culture, and it is scientific.[26] Hence, to look to science to frame "Humanity's" world-view seems a legitimate expectation, if we remember that "as soon as the field of vision extends to the whole . . . science, philosophy and religion are bound to converge as they draw nearer to the whole." (30)

The other role of science which Teilhard emphasizes is the power of science to work upon *human* matter through psycho-chemistry, genetics, et cetera, to bring it to the highest level of material organization, thus providing a base for still higher consciousness and, accordingly, for still higher spiritual unity. Science, by mastering the "ultimate energy," thought, will make available to Humanity the excess of energy needed to pass through the threshold to a new and higher form of consciousness, superconsciousness.

This section on the mammoth evolutionary role of science Teilhard closes by noting what science cannot do—"give to each and every element its final value by grouping them in the unity of an organized whole."(250) (Both human liberty and the activity of Omega's superunity are required for the element's ultimate value.) Even with this restriction, there are aspects of this section which tend to disturb some general readers and perhaps some scientists too. Placing so much confidence in man and especially in science—"the twin sister of Humanity"—has a Promethean or Faustian ring.[27] Teilhard, in other writings, shows an awareness of this. It can be said in general that he would vastly prefer to "sin" on the side of hoping too much rather than too little. Nonetheless, the general reader can wonder why no specific evolutionary role is assigned to various forms of humanistic knowledge, for example, historical, philosophical, artistic, literary, et cetera. In other writings Teilhard does acknowledge the evolutionary role of human creations, for example, philosophy and art.[28] We must remember, however, the intended readers of the *Phenomenon*, Teilhard's fellow scientists. Mindful of these we are able to understand more easily the omissions and emphases of this section.

The other means which Teilhard postulates for the superorganization of mankind is unanimity, or, literally, one-souledness. By projecting from the law of complexity/consciousness discovered in evolution's past, Teilhard sees that individual human consciousnesses in mankind's future will become a harmonized, living unity, a superconsciousness in which individual consciousnesses grouped together and reinforcing one another, will know in a single act of unanimous reflection and will love in a single act of harmonized affectivity. We are persuaded to the real possibility of such unity by recalling how atomic particles, achieving sufficiently ordered complexity, form the new and dynamic unity of an atom. A corresponding phenomenon is noted in the higher unities of the molecule, the macromolecule, the cell, the animal. In the light of the evolutionary past, Teilhard finds every reason for projecting a superunity of men, the head of evolution's arrow.

Unanimity involves not only a "common act of vision" and a "common power of action" but what makes these possible—"a living union of reflective particles," animated by a "super-soul." This is the "still unnamed Thing which the gradual combination of individuals, people and races" is bringing into existence. (251)

To summarize the various causes which are at work, bringing about the coalescence of a "vast grain of thought on a sidereal scale," we find:

1) The geographical curvature of the earth which together with human multiplication exerts a pressure from without to unify men, at least physically and spatially. This has led to further and higher unification through revolutions in communications, transportation and technology. (239-40)

2) The psychic curvature of man's within, or spirit, works not only towards individual integration and unification, but the human spirit's openness to permeation and penetration by other spirits means also that fulfillment and completion of the individual comes from "an advance of *all together*, in a direction in which *all together* can join and find completion."(244-5)

3) The very curvature of the whole of evolution has produced

ever higher complexities which are more centered and unified; thus the multiplicity of men is clearly the scene of current evolution. If evolution follows the law of its "huge past," mankind is destined for a superunity in the realm of spirit.(243-4)

4) The convergence of Christ's Body, not yet broached in the *Phenomenon*, is discussed in the Epilogue. Since Christ's Body is evolving toward "full stature" and completeness by means of the dynamic ingrafting of men into its being, there is reason to believe in a natural unification which would be influenced by Christ's unifying and cosmic power. It is in this context that Teilhard can speak of men acquiring "the consciousness, without losing themselves, of becoming one and the same *person*."[29]

Critical Reflections

In connection with the above, Teilhard's critics pose two questions. One, has Teilhard overestimated or misstated the physical reality and union of Christ and his members in his Mystical Body? Second, is Teilhard "dreaming false dreams" when he projects, through increasing socialization, a superorganism of all men, productive of a superconsciousness?

On the first question, competent theologians, who know Teilhard's thought well, find no difficulty with his views of the Mystical Body. Mooney notes the marked contemporary trend in scholars to emphasize St. Paul's strong realism in expressing the unity of the Body of Christ.[30] Teilhard would almost certainly agree with J. A. T. Robinson's desire: "one could heartily wish that the misleading and unbiblical phrase the 'mystical' body had never been invented."[31] Pius XII's 1943 encyclical, *The Mystical Body of Christ,* is influenced mainly by dogmatic theologians' emphasis upon the collectivity of Christians as an organization. Pius warns that there are those "who neglect the fact that the Apostle Paul has used metaphorical language in speaking of this doctrine, and failing to distinguish the physical from the social Body of Christ as they should, out of their fancy draw some deformed kind of unity."[32] Giving a precise explanation of and formulation to the union of Christ and Christians is no easy matter, though we earlier explored some of its facets.[33] Scriptural scholars, however, rooted in the thought and expression of St. Paul, emphasize that *body* is person and that Christ is a corporate personality. For Paul "all union is a surrender of the body of the Christian in the Semitic sense of self to the body-self of the risen Savior, thus forming with him only one body."[34]

Teilhard loses, however, most of his scholarly support for the thesis that was important in his world-view. Is human evolution convergent, forming by socialization a natural super-organism? The nineteenth chapter of de Lubac's *The Religion of Teilhard de Chardin*, "The Legitimacy of Teilhard's Extra-polation," is devoted to a searching questioning and criticism of his thesis. Rideau also rejects for the most part Teilhard's projections of a human superorganism. Mooney seriously questions the possibility of valid knowledge about the natural future of mankind.[35] Julian Huxley follows Teilhard to this point of collective convergence and then "loses him." (19)

Why do Teilhard's friendliest critics "cop out" on noospheric convergence? The simplest and most fundamental answer is: it is a revolutionary idea, and it meets, therefore, the resistance that the revolutionary ideas of Galileo, Copernicus and Darwin met.[36] "The concept of human convergence on itself seems to me as revolutionary a step (for all human thought and activity) as ever was that of a 'revolving' earth or of biological evolution. . . . I have no illusions about the incredible element in my hypothesis."[37] His critics might perhaps mitigate their criticism in view of the fact that much of Teilhard's popular appeal is precisely his boldness in facing the future. To answer the question, "What is *going on?*" we are inevitably led to ask, what can man hope for man? Deliberate ostrich-like refuge can be taken in non-looking at the future of man. Or, one could appeal to the dimness of man's vision, or could claim that looking into the ultimate future of man would take us away from seeing the immediate tasks and needs. "Man does not live by bread alone."

In addition to the revolutionary character of noospheric convergence, there is also large counterevidence to a future superunion of men—evil in all its faces. Teilhard's special and particularized experience of the "absolutely *complete* union that research in common can establish between the most dissimilar ethnological elements" as well as the intimate brotherhood he experienced as a Jesuit could be put forth as reasons for an insufficient evaluation of the *de facto* disunion between men, races and nations. Perhaps, but what is clearer is that the presence of evil makes the future of the story of man totally inscrutable for most of Teilhard's critics, especially so when this future is projected as an optimistic superunion of mankind. In addition most critics feel that in order to safeguard man's freedom, we must not project the future outcome of the human project. Christian critics, however, will accept the surety of a mysterious and final communion and consummation *in Christo Jesu*, but they feel that no extrapolation can be made from this *datum* of faith to the phenomenon of evolving man.

Teilhard recognized his role as a prophet—unheeded in his own time and by his own people. This did not silence his voice nor dim his hope:

> It requires no great gift of prophecy to affirm that, within two or three generations, the notion of the psychic infolding of the earth upon itself, in the bosom of some new 'space of complexity,' will be as generally accepted and utilised by our successors as the idea of the earth's mechanical movement round the sun, in the bosom of the firmament, is accepted by ourselves.[38]

Noospheric Critical Point

Teilhard foresees that there will surely be a critical point in the development of the noosphere, and it will present severe problems for mankind. In recent times we have discovered the two symptoms of such a critical point: 1) the mass-formation

of mankind, that is, the ever-increasing compression of mankind upon himself; and 2) the upsurge of freed energy coming
from technological gains. This excess of energy leads to the
"super-heating of thought." Though he cannot see clearly what
lies beyond the critical point, he chides us for timidity in our
projections and hopes. The newness beyond the critical point
will certainly mean more than a peace achieved by settling
international disputes, more than a vastly increased leisure.
Coming are radically new opportunities for psychic experience
and expansion "in an interior totalization of the world upon
itself, in the unanimous construction of a *spirit of the
earth*." (253)

At this point in parallel writings, but not in the *Phenomenon*,
Teilhard indicates the insufficiency of science and unanimity to
effect the transition to superconsciousness. "It is not *tête-à-tête*
or a *corps-à-corps* that we need; it is a heart-to-heart."[39] Thus
we are led to a discussion of the necessary role of love and
"the rise on our inward horizon of a cosmic spiritual centre . . .
the *rise of a God*."[40] These are the subjects of the next Chapter.

READING SUGGESTIONS

1. *Read PM,* 245-253.

2. *See Glossary for*: *affinities, biosphere, concentration, confluence, consistent, *element [grains of thought (251) = individual men], homogeneous, hyper-organic, *issue, *Mankind,
   *mind, neo-life [probably (247) = true or real], planetisation,
   rebound, recoil [reflective beings or particles = individual men],
   reflection (250) = 2nd definition, sidereal, totalisation, *unanimity, unanimous.

3. *Passages to be noted*:
   246-247, "Mankind was a fragile etc." A unified Humanity appears as a transitory accident or even as a groundless dream unless Humanity is seen as an intrinsic and integral continuation

of cosmic evolution.

247-248, *"Physical Stuff."* T. is insisting that Humanity is as much a physical and collective reality as an evolving phylum of, say, Equidae, though in the next paragraphs, *"Specific Nature,"* he argues for Humanity as a special and higher kind of collective reality.

248, "confluence of human thoughts"=shorthand for the coming together and unification of human thinking *and* thinkers.

4. *Parallel Readings*:
   a new humanism: *FM*, 89-96 (92-100).
   reality of Humanity: *FM*, 185-192 (192-200).
   unification of Humanity: *FM*, 124-139 (129-44), 281-288 (295-302), 289-297 (303-11); *MPN*, 96-112; *SC*, 152-164.
   science as unifier of Humanity: *SC*, 199-205, 214-220.
   summaries: *Murray, 27-42; Wildiers, 83-108.

5. *Critiques*: I. Barbour, *Issues,* 403-406; *de Lubac, 206-220.

8

OMEGA: SOURCE OF "INVERSE GRAVITATION"

Given the fact of evolution's having brought forth man, the question of questions is: what is the next stage of evolution? Have we any way of extrapolating from past evolution to what should be expected of it in the future? What we can do immediately is rule out one possibility of further evolution—one which suggests itself so readily to those who ponder questions about the future of evolution.

Evolution's Future

Bluntly, the future of evolution is *not* to be looked for in the realm of biological transformations in or of man; qualitative or radical changes in the realm of biology are almost certainly at an end. This is quite well agreed to by contemporary scientists, but the nonspecialist, perhaps rendered uncritical by science-fiction, frequently balks at it.[1] We can, however, look for some quantitative or minor modifications which will improve man biologically, but the essential hope for further evolution cannot be placed in biology.[2] Foreseeable biological modifications are just that, modifications which are minor and less significant when compared to what evolution has already

140

achieved in men: self-reflection and the power for its further evolution.

It should come as no surprise, then, that scientists believe that the scene of evolution is now in the psychosocial sphere, in cultural evolution. Teilhard phrases it this way: "The question of whether the Universe is still developing then becomes a matter of deciding whether the human spirit is still in process of evolution."[3] Or, put in his technical terminology, has cosmogenesis and biogenesis become noogenesis in a noosphere?[4]

If then it is agreed that evolution is now in the realm of man's spirit, a further question is: What higher form can human consciousness take? In a letter written during World War I, Teilhard seemed to think that this question was not explorable by scientific means. "What advance could there be upon thought? As I was saying, the liberation of matter [matter evolving to spirit] is an extra-transformist phenomenon [concept], which belongs more to idealist philosophy than to a scientific examination of things."[5] But when he later developed a consistent and total "physics" of man, he saw that it necessarily included an investigation of the future progress of human thought.

Because he is so sensitive to emotional biases which tend to cloud the speculative questions he wishes to investigate, before considering the hyperpersonal future of man, Teilhard finds it necessary to consider the discouragement produced by certain counterevidence. *Is* mankind proceeding to a universal unification in thought and affection? Perhaps the signs are to be read that we are really *regressing,* not progressing? There are many pessimists (frequently calling themselves realists) who are able to marshall evidence for their pessimism. There are numberless individual conflicts, mass selfishness, class struggles, racial antagonisms, national warfares, the phenomena of communism and totalitarianism. Is this unanimity? Is this progress?

Hardly sufficient to remove the verdict of pessimism, but a help towards balance, is Teilhard's reminder that we are scarcely through the second century of realizing that all men should unite in thought and affection. Given the immense periods of time involved in previous evolution, to expect human solidarity overnight is scientific nonsense. Evolution, especially to those who are part of the process, is necessarily slow, and next to, if not totally, imperceptible. (Note how we are unaware of the *growing* of our fingernails and hair but become aware of growth only after they have *grown*.) Whether there is progress or regress is far less a matter of evidence and far more a "leap" to optimism or pessimism.[6]

Further favoring the stance of pessimism are many evidences of a basic repulsion—"deep down men exclude and repel one another with all their might"—and there are forces of materialization, forces which in the process of joining men together introduce determinisms or limitations of their freedom. But when we see human unification gone awry, as in totalitarianism, we know that it is not from a lack of unifying energy, but from some perversion of the rules of noogenesis. And Teilhard takes heart from this! The energy is present, but it is not rightly directed: "The great human machine is designed to work and *must* work—by producing a super-abundance of mind."(257) And why has noogenesis gone wrong? Because it failed to give proper place to the value and significance of the person and to the forces of personalization. This is the backdrop for the consideration of the nature and properties of person, of Omega, and of the characteristics of the energy of love—the essential forces for a rightly directed noogenesis.

The Evolution of Persons

What are the conditions for a genuine growth and culmination of human personality? First, tackling the question negatively, Teilhard notes that we surely will not construct a correct theory if we make physical energy the basic reality and reduce the human person to some mere modification of energy. This is, as Teilhard states, to locate the Impersonal "at the world's

Omega, as at its Alpha."(258) Such a theory misses the value of the human person and destroys every dream of personal fulfillment. Positively, what Teilhard implies here is that the root and ground of human existence as of all being must be Personal. At the beginning of World War II, confronted by the magnitude of human conflicts, he located the "source of the conflict . . . the root of the evil . . . not in the apparent conflicts but very far away from them, in the inner fact that men have despaired of God's personality." Hence, it should come as no surprise that when his hyperphysics proceeds to "prove" the existence of God, it will "prove" not a "First Mover" or a "Necessary Being" but a Personal Omega, "Someone Loving and Loveable." The personality of God, however, is not arrived at in a contrived way. Rather, it is necessarily connected with Humanity's need for an evolving and *personal* unification and fulfillment.

The value of the human person may be negated by stating that growth in personality is accomplished by growth in isolation and individualism. What is generally clear in the present Western milieu is that man is fulfilled in his person by friendship, human communion, interpersonal relationships—and not otherwise. But as we encounter more and more the influence of Eastern cultures, we may be attracted to the theory that personal completion is to be achieved by absorption in the All or in the Collectivity. This, too, Teilhard rejects in view of his philosophy of person.

His analysis of what he believes to be a true theory of personal development and fulfillment is quite straightforward.

1) Evolution is an ascent or growth in consciousness. (The argument might be amplified by seeing, as Teilhard does, that evolution proceeds to higher and higher forms of complexified *unities*, for example, the atom, the molecule, the macromolecule, the cell, the animal, man—and what next?)

2) Therefore, evolution must culminate in a supreme form of consciousness (or, following the above parenthesis, in a

supreme form of human unity exercising hyperconsciousness).

3) This supreme form of consciousness will be accomplished in a way similar to that in which previous higher forms of evolutionary unity have been achieved—by aggregation of individual elements into a new and organic whole.

That this totalization should happen with regard to consciousness is also seen by an analysis of human consciousness itself. Because it is capable of centering all other things upon itself, and centering itself upon itself, human consciousness is capable of coming into psychic union with all other consciousnesses, human and divine. The probing question can be asked: What is the limit of friendship—one person, ten, a hundred? All will agree to the expansion of human personality by deep interpersonal relations, certainly at the level of the couple and the family. Are there intrinsic limits to the possibilities of this enrichment?

4) This convergence or coiling of all human persons in the noosphere demands that there be a center upon whom they converge, Omega, the Center of all human centers. (At this point in his dialectic, Teilhard leaves the identity of Omega quite vague—hence his use of the neutral mathematical symbol, Omega, fitting enough for the scientist, but for the Christian it probably will recall, in the light of the *Apocalypse* or *Book of Revelations*, Christ Himself as the "Alpha and Omega.")

Why must Omega be the actually existing and autonomous Center of centers? Since consciousness is essentially a power of centering, supreme consciousness will be the supreme center of the collectivity of all human consciousness. An actually existing and autonomous Center can alone assure the success of such centering. If the center were merely an ideal, a hope, the fortunes of evolution would be problematic. Another point, which Teilhard makes later, is that because of the ambivalence of human persons, drawn to unity and yet "hostile or at least closed to one another," a supremely attractive Center is needed in order to ensure both the growing and the consummated unification of men.

5) In a personalizing universe, there is accordingly no conflict but rather great harmony between the Universal and the
Personal. The value of the individual consciousness is not lost
in the Universality of the Noosphere, if we admit that man's
power of knowing and loving increases to the point of being
able to embrace through Omega-Center the whole of mankind
and the whole of the world. Is not this what should be projected
for the evolution of the human spirit? To those who think that
a universal knowledge and love is impossible, Teilhard retorts:

> How can we account for that irresistible instinct in our hearts
> which leads us towards unity whenever and in whatever direc-
> tion our passions are stirred? A sense of the universe, a sense
> of the *all* . . . a cosmic affinity [attraction] and hence a cosmic
> sense. A universal love is not only psychologically possible; it is
> the only complete and final way in which we are able to love.
> (266-7)

6) The future of mankind is then a Whole, rendered one,
organic, and hyperpersonal in and by the Omega Point. This is
the ultimate perfection of evolution because it is the ultimate
perfection of men and of their deepest personal powers:

> For men upon earth, all the earth, to learn to love one another, it
> is not enough that they should know themselves to be members
> of one and the same *thing*; in "planetizing" themselves they
> must acquire the consciousness, without losing themselves, of
> becoming one and the same *person*. . . .
> And what does this mean except, finally, that the planetization
> of Mankind, if it is to come properly into effect, presupposes,
> in addition to the enclosing Earth, and to the organization and
> condensation of human thought, yet another factor? I mean the
> rise on our inward horizon of a cosmic spiritual centre, a supreme
> pole of consciousness, upon which all the separate consciousnesses
> of the world may converge and within which they may love one
> another: *the rise of a God*.[8]

The future, then, of the individual lies in an internal deepening and universalization of consciousness and love, while the future of Humanity is situated in the formation of a Whole with a collective consciousness, which makes coreflection and coloving both possible—and actual.

For this reason Teilhard sees a serious shortcoming in the Marxian projection of the classless society, which will hoard the works of earlier consciousnesses but *not* the consciousnesses themselves. Teilhard's criticism has force:

> Our works? But even in the interest of life in general, what is the work of works for man if not to establish, in and by each one of us, an absolutely original centre in which the universe reflects itself in a unique and inimitable way? And those centres are our very selves and personalities. The very centre of our consciousness, deeper than all its radii; that is the essence which Omega, if it is to be truly Omega, must reclaim. . . . The conclusion is inevitable that the concentration of a conscious universe would be unthinkable if it did not reassemble in itself *all consciousnesses* as well as all *the conscious.* (261-2)

Hence, for Teilhard the future of evolution must be projected as the personalizing of a personal universe.

Some Clarifications

Teilhard, in this section of the *Phenomenon,* uses the term "Omega" in two distinct senses: first, as the state of collective coreflection or hyperreflection achieved at the term of evolutionary process, and second, as the Center of centers, whose attractive action assures the success of that process.[9] Omega, being the last letter of the Greek alphabet, aptly expresses both meanings, and yet Teilhard makes it clear in another essay that it is God as Center who is the "one and only true Omega."

> Unless it is to be powerless to form the keystone of the noosphere, "Omega" . . . can only be conceived as the *meeting-point* between a universe that has reached the limit of centration, and another, even deeper, centre—this being the self-subsistent centre and absolutely final principle of irreversibility and personalisation: the one and only true Omega.[10]

Two observations now may be made for the Christian reader. First, the existence of God as the Omega of evolution is rendered ultimately *certain* by means of divine faith in Jesus Christ, "the Alpha and Omega" of revelation. "This pole Omega is reached only by extrapolation; it remains of its nature an assumption and conjecture . . . which nourishes our hope on traits that are vague and ethereal."[11] "But instead of the vague center of convergence envisaged as the ultimate end of this process of evolution, the personal and defined reality of the Word Incarnate, in which everything acquires substance, appears and takes its place. Life for Man. Man for Christ. Christ for God."[12] Teilhard is insistent on the source of certainty about evolution's ultimate success.

> For a Christian . . . the eventual biological success of Man on Earth is not merely a probability but a certainty: since Christ (and in Him virtually the World) is already risen. But this certainty, born as it is of a 'supernatural' act of faith, is of its nature supra-phenomenal: which means, in one sense, that it leaves all the anxieties attendant upon the human condition, on their own level, still alive in the heart of the believer.[13]

Hyperphysics, therefore, attains Omega only as "a conjecture and a postulate" of hominization, but a humbling certainty is granted through Christian revelation.

The second observation is that the Christian doctrine of the Trinity provides the model or paradigm *par excellence* for the ultimate perfection of evolution, a human Whole which personalizes and perfects the elements composing it. In the one perfect substance of the Godhead, there exist the three most distinct Persons: Father, Son and Holy Spirit. The closeness of their union diminishes not at all, but rather heightens their personhoods. There is reason, then, for Teilhard's parallel claims for the noospheric whole personalizing the elements. However, it must be noted that it is difficult to document Teilhard's dependence on a specifically Trinitarian insight.[14] The more proximate pattern or paradigm for noospheric completion is the Body of Christ and the Communion of Saints. Of these we shall have more to say when we consider "The Christian Phenomenon."

"Union Differentiates"

Why the "law of union," which states that "in every organized whole, the parts perfect themselves and fulfil themselves," assumes such a central place in Teilhard's synthesis is that it rids us of false fears and it grounds justifiable hopes. In some unions we can think of, there are grounds for fearing either a depersonalization or even the very loss of our whole persons. In a totalitarian union or in the union of the assembly line or in the huge industrial organization, there are legitimate reasons for fearing that our persons shall be diminished. In these unions there is certainly differentiating specialization, but that is not what the "law of union" intends. The whole which is being formed must be an *organic whole,* that is to say, one which is somehow rooted in the natural dynamism of evolution, and forming a union which has a genuine and intrinsic life of its own. It is to be contrasted to an artificial whole, which can certainly be highly organized, but whose principle of unity comes from without and so must be superimposed upon the elements. Mark the difference between marriage unions: one in which the parties freely will the marital union, and one in which the union is willed by the parents and rejected by the "spouses."

"To become personalised under the creative influence of Union, they must not . . . join up together anyhow. . . . It is centre to centre that they must make contact and *not otherwise*."(263-4)[15] Herein lie the seeds of failure of many unions to personalize; the motivating force for the union is not personal, nor are the goods sought in the realm of the spirit but rather tied all too strongly to materiality.

> But so far how have we gone about the business of unification? A material situation to be defended; a new industrial field to be opened up, better conditions for a social class or less favoured nations—those are the only and very mediocre grounds on which we have so far tried to get together. There is no cause to be surprised if, in the footsteps of animal societies, we become mechanised in the very play [activity] of association. (265)

In nonartificial or organic wholes, the outcome is otherwise. The differentiation involved in such unions is genuinely perfective of the individual elements. The hand of the human is not a replaceable and amorphous protuberance on the body, but a highly individualized and differentiated organ, perfect in itself and perfective of the whole.

When we proceed to the realm of spirit, still another factor is operative, the immiscibility or nondisappearance of human consciousness. The autonomy and permanence of the individual human consciousness positively precludes a union which blots out the definiteness and incommunicability of spirit. Matter and that which is intrinsically dependent upon matter necessarily are subject to radical changes, which spell the end of the original being. The human spirit, however, has its existence so firmly in its grasp that no change can rob it of its personal center. At the same time, spirit has an openness to the other and a capability for union with all others, but only on condition of accentuating "the depth and incommunicability of their *egos*. The more 'other' they become in conjunction [union], the more they find themselves as 'self.' "(262) This is to say that, in the very act of union, they are differentiated, become more themselves, are personalized, and heightened in that which is deepest in their beings. This we see, on the small scale, in privileged marriages, where the closeness of the interpersonal relation does not at all diminish but heightens and accentuates the personality of individual partners. On the large scale of the noosphere, why, instead of personal diminishment, cannot there be a similar growth in individuality and personality?

Love-Energy: The Noosphere's "Gravitational Force"

Love-energy is the answer to the question of how noospheric personalization is going to be achieved. And though we suffer from a cultural weakness which tends to reduce love to "only the sentimental face of love, the joy and miseries it causes us" (264), we must, if we want to see the face of the future, penetrate the heart of love.

This Chapter's title identified Omega as the "Source of 'Inverse Gravitation,'" that is, the ultimate source of love-energy. We generally experience gravity as drawing things downwards, towards the center of the earth. Love can be described as "an inverse form of gravitation," because cosmogenesis in the final stage of noogenesis is an ascent of Humanity "upwards," towards the immaterial, towards Spirit, towards superunion. Man is drawn or gravitates "up" to these heights under the influence of the love-energy or love-attraction of Omega. Another similarity between the gravitation of love and of bodies is the universality of the attraction. From Galileo and Newton, we learned that not only does the distant moon exert an attraction upon the oceans but that *we* exert an attraction upon the moon. Especially in *The Divine Milieu* does Teilhard point out the cosmic value of the human element's least activities and achievements.

However, at the middle of this Chapter of the *Phenomenon*, Teilhard is concerned more with the cosmic roots of human love. For this reason, and following his usual pattern, he first locates the source of love in the primordial "attraction of being to being." We notice how similar this is to his finding the roots of human consciousness in the radial energy of preatomic particles. Human love, on the other hand, has its own special characteristics and imperatives. In Teilhard's definition, love is "the more or less direct trace marked on the heart of the [human] element by the psychical convergence of the universe upon itself."(265) The psychical "gravitational" convergence of the whole of evolution is mirrored in the individual element's gravitation to every other element and to the whole.

We are ready enough to say "yes" to the question, "Does not love every instant achieve all around us, in the couple or the team, the magic feat, the feat reputed to be contradictory, of 'personalising' by totalising?" At the microlevel we see well enough that unions or totalizations do personalize and perfect the personalities of the uniting elements. But are we as ready to reply affirmatively to the question, "And if that is what love can achieve daily on a small scale, why should it not repeat this one day on world-wide dimensions?"(265) For Teilhard evolution leads far beyond the merely collective grouping of men, which we possess now by means of a spherical earth, economic dependencies, cultural communications, et cetera. Because evolution is the ascent to ever higher forms of unity, he describes the future of human evolution as a hyperpersonalization brought about by an intensification and universalization of human love. In the end an element will embrace not only another element or a few elements, but the totality of elements and the Center which makes such a love non-Utopian. Is there not considerable reason for seeing the evolution of human loving "developing until it embraces the total[ity] of men and of the earth?" (266) Teilhard is most affirmative: "a universal love is not only psychologically possible; it is the only complete and final way in which we are able to love."(267)[16] We have been told to "think big"; Teilhard's message is to "love big."

Omega—Source of Love-Energy

In recognizing the impersonalness that the universal naturally tends to conjure up for us, Teilhard is sensitive to a widespread fear. Accordingly, unless the universal convergence of Humanity and the world is vivified and impregnated with the love and personality of Omega, men will cling to extremely limited views of their power of loving and will refuse to think about a general culmination and consummation for the whole process of evolution.

Yet the very drive or *élan* of evolution forces us to take thought. Humanity must converge and totalize, but it must be done in a personalizing way. Grasping the very real and human obstacles to such progress (fear of the impersonality of the universal, tendency to isolation, antipathy, misuse of freedom, et cetera), Teilhard sets about showing the necessity for an *autonomous* Center of noogenesis. Two points are involved: an autonomous Center is not brought into existence by noogenesis and therefore is not dependent upon it; secondly, an autonomous Center is an independent and self-existent principle.

Teilhard first shows that Omega is not dependent upon the whole process of evolution, but that it is just the other way round. The noosphere's very real need for a unifying energy greater than its own leads the argument to the existence of Omega. It is an autonomous Omega who supplies the love-energy necessary for the successful personalization and consummation of Humanity. Thence we are led "to accept the possibility, indeed the reality, of some *source* of love and *object* of love at the summit of the world above our heads." (267)[17]

> Energy taking on Presence. And so the possibility appears, opens out, for man not only of believing and hoping but (what is much more surprising and much more worthwhile) of loving, co-extensively and co-organically with all the past, the present and the future of the universe in process of concentrating around itself. . . .
>
> Evidence, too, of the contagious power of a form of Charity in which it becomes possible to love God not only "with all one's heart, and all one's soul" but with the universe-in-evolution.[18]

That last paragraph indicates a point not so clear in the *Phenomenon*: the autonomous Omega is not only a necessity for the consummation of the process of cosmic noogenesis, but equally an ontological and psychological necessity for the individual element. "Our reach *is* greater than our grasp." We dimly but really recognize our power to love and to be loved as transcending this person, this family, this organization, this nation. Ultimately the depths of our beings have not been invoked until we experience the love-attraction of an autonomous Omega and the accompanying possibility of giving ourselves in a way impossible with finite lovers. Certainly the union to which we want love to lead us is not a thin and perishable union. Hence, what ultimately corresponds to our powers of loving is nothing less than an autonomous Center of centers, Someone *supremely* "Loving and Loveable."

Perhaps Teilhard does not develop this side of Omega for fear of continuing the propagation of an individualistic love of God. As an antidote for such individualism, he is correct in insisting on the universal aspect of our love of God:

> My present great discovery (?!) is: 1. that the whole human problem comes down to the question of the love of God; but also, 2. that the legitimacy, the psychological possibility (everywhere questioned, to my great surprise), and the triumph of this love depend upon the compatibility (or, better, the essential association) of the two terms *universal* and *personal*. . . . By and large, our world denies the personal and God, on the grounds that it believes in the whole! Everything tends to show on the contrary, that it must believe in the personal precisely because it believes in the whole.[19]

It is on this precise point that Julian Huxley, in the Introduction to the *Phenomenon*, finds difficulty and admits to faltering in his understanding of Teilhard:

> Here his thought is not fully clear to me. Sometimes he seems to equate this future hyperpersonal psychosocial organisation with an emergent Divinity: at one place, for instance, he speaks of the trend as a *Christogenesis*; and elsewhere he appears not to be guarding himself sufficiently against the dangers of per-

sonifying the nonpersonal elements of reality. Sometimes, too, he seems to envisage as desirable the merging of individual human variety in this new unity. (19)

It is easy enough to see how one with Huxley's convictions would find difficulty on these points, since even the committed Christian frequently experiences bafflement over related points.[20]

To take only Huxley's last point, "the merging of individual variety in this new unity," Mooney seems correct in suggesting that Huxley's difficulty comes from failing to "recognize the central importance of love in Teilhard's explanation of evolution."[21] The mysterious truth involved in the union of love is that there *is* a sacrifice of self and of individual human variety to the "other," but, at the extremes of the paradoxical, the lover in this sacrifice finds himself more himself, more individualized. It is the language of the mystics to speak of love as "becoming lost in the greater than himself," but as Teilhard asks rhetorically, "where is it written that he who loses his soul shall save it?"[22] In this matter perhaps St. Augustine has the last word: *"Da amantem"*—give me a lover, and he will understand the paradoxes of love.

It is precisely love itself and the love of God that painfully puzzle Screwtape in C. S. Lewis' classic. The "Enemy" is, of course, Christ, since the writer is Screwtape, the demonic uncle of Wormwood.

> For we must never forget what is the most repellent and inexplicable trait in our Enemy; He *really* loves the hairless bipeds He has created and always gives back to them with His right hand what He has taken away with His left.
> One must face the fact that all the talk about His love for men, and His service being perfect freedom, is not (as one would gladly believe) mere propaganda, but an appalling truth. He really *does* want to fill the universe with a lot of loathsome little replicas of Himself—creatures whose life, on its miniature scale, will be qualitatively like His own, not because He has absorbed them but because their wills freely conform to His. We want cattle who can finally become food; He wants servants

who can finally become sons. We want to suck in, He wants to give out. We are empty and would be filled; He is full and flows over. Our war aim is a world in which Our Father Below has drawn all other beings into himself: the Enemy wants a world full of beings united to Him but still distinct.[23]

Teilhard recognized that the evolutionary importance of love-energy was, in the elaboration of his own thought, a "late-comer" but the most essential of all the elements in a coherent explanation of evolution.

> Never before, perhaps, did I perceive so clearly the possible meaning of the deep evolution of my internal life: the dark purple of the universal matter, first passing for me into the gold of Spirit, then into the white incandescence of Personality, then finally (and this is the present stage) into the immaterial (or rather supermaterial) ardour of Love.[24]

This account is something of a summary of the dialectic thus far presented in *The Phenomenon of Man*. But as a report of the evolution of Teilhard's own thought, it lacks an essential element: the person of Jesus Christ and the love of his human heart as the overarching and ever present focus of unity and unification. That this is so will be revealed only haltingly in the *Phenomenon's* Epilogue, but is abundantly manifest in a work like the *Hymn of the Universe*.

Omega—"Prime Mover Ahead"

More can be said of Omega than that he is an autonomous Center of elements' centers. Starting from the same premises which yield the autonomy of Omega (a convergent evolution of self-reflective consciousness), Teilhard adds two motivational needs which man possesses in order to give himself wholly to the evolution of the noosphere. If the Center of centers were autonomous but fragile, he would not be able to insure the permanence of the noosphere's acquisitions nor, more importantly, the individual element's continuance and growth in existence and personality. If our efforts to build up "civilisation, humanity, the spirit of the earth . . . rest with all their weight on the earth, they will vanish with the earth."(269-70) No man is going to give his whole self to the construction of the fragile and ephemeral. Hence, so that man may be fully motivated for the legitimately expected consummation of Humanity, Omega must be irreversible, "independent of the collapse of the [fragile and material] forces with which evolution is woven."(270) Not only is Omega immortal and eternal of himself, but he assures the success of noogenesis by immortalizing and eternalizing Humanity's personalities and personalizations.

If Omega were autonomous but distant, again motivation would be insufficient to continue the huge burden of noogenesis. Since love-energy is the mainspring of converging reflection, Omega, to initiate and maintain his influence upon all the elements and upon the whole of evolution, must be "loving and loveable *at this very moment*"— not someone distant by reason of existing in the past or the future. Human love demands that its beloved exist in the present; love's fires languish when its object recedes into the past or future. "For love to be possible there must be co-existence. . . . To be supremely attractive, Omega must be supremely present," actual and attracting. (269)

The fourth and final property of Omega is transcendence, that is, existing beyond and not being subject to time and space and matter's corruptibility. If Omega were totally immanent in matter, the question of sufficiency of motivation would return: Would man be drawn sufficiently by the merely temporal and by the certainly corruptible? To that a man might give "half of himself." Such motivation is scarcely adequate when one is speaking of a noogenesis destined to consummate Humanity at the peak of its spiritual potentialities and achievements. Nothing less than a complete dedication of man's efforts is required to hasten and bring about Humanity's consummation. For this reason, then, Teilhard concludes that Omega must be transcendent, capable of gathering and solidifying all the fragile victories and achievements of men in time and evolution.

By his analysis of evolution, therefore, it is inferred that Omega is autonomous, actual, irreversible and transcendent, and that the love-energy with which He attracts the minds and hearts of men participates in the same qualities. As "Prime Mover Ahead," Omega exercises "inverse gravitation" by the hyperattraction of divine love-energy, drawing Humanity "up" to an evolutionary completion and fulfillment in an irreversible love-union.

But what is the consummation of noogenesis? What is the final state of the converging elements? Already, Teilhard has given a glimpse of his answer to these, the largest of questions: "The final state of a world undergoing physical concentration would be . . . a system whose unity coincides with a paroxysm of harmonized complexity."(262) Clearer yet is this answer: "The end of a 'thinking species': not disintegration and death, but a new break-through and re-birth, this time outside Time and Space, through the very excess of unification and co-reflection."[25] But since more may be said about evolution's final stages and about the final state itself, Teilhard's final chapter is devoted to considering these.

READING SUGGESTIONS

1. *Read PM*, 254-272.

2. *See Glossary for*: *affinity, *centre [centre of centres (271) = Omega], concentration [consumes (259) = perfects or consummates], *convergence [determinism (256) = lack of spontaneity and freedom] [divine focus of minds (271) = Omega], element [elementary centres (259) = individual men], *emerge, *emersion, *entropy, envelope [granular (262) = made of many individual men], hominisation [human particles = men], hyper-personal, involution mind, noogenesis, neo-matter, play, punctiform [reflected (259) = human knowledge],

super-matter, totalisation, *unanimity.

3. *Passages to be noted*:
    255, "transposition of values remains etc." To proceed from the interpretation of phenomena of an earlier stage to an interpretation or valuation of later phenomena.
    256, "thinking units do not seem etc." Men, even though pressured together by geography and by psychological influences, do not seem to be entering into each other's zones of attraction, i.e., experiencing the lovableness of one another.
    257-8, "Unlike the primitives, etc." T. in this and the following paragraph portrays what is for him a false vision: brute energy at the beginning and end of all creation, together with man as a freak in nature or as something to be swallowed up in a totalitarian society.
    259, "the birth of one single centre etc." T. later says this is only a first and halting approximation and basically erroneous. On page 262 T. says the centre, Omega, is *not* "born of [human] elements," but is rather "a supremely autonomous focus of union."
    260, "beyond our souls," i.e., towards something transhuman, not subhuman.
    260, "totalised grains of thought" = men totally unified.
    260, "the two movements," i.e., the movement of the individual and the movement of all men, Humanity.
    261, "phyletic value," i.e., its value for the further noospheric evolution of Humanity.
    261, "To communicate itself, my ego etc." As a person I must continue to exist in the very act of relinquishing or giving myself to another.
    266, "It may be said etc." This is an objection which T. answers in the following paragraph.
    262-270. The four properties of Omega are explained:
    autonomy, 262-3, "Thus, under the influence etc."
    actual, 269, "First of all, the *reason of Love.* Etc."
    irreversible, 269-270, "In addition, the *reason of survival,* etc."
    transcendence, 270, "Actuality, irreversibility. There is only etc."
    271, "we must add that etc." The sense is that though Omega *appears* to us as emerging out of the rise of cosmic consciousness, Omega also *reveals* itself as already existing, before and independently of cosmic evolution. The latter is the true situation.

4. *Parallel Readings*:
   arguments for Omega's existence: *AM*, 271-273; *FM*, 91-96 (94-100), 120-123 (125-128), 187-192, *LTF*, 31-33, *SC*, 160-173; de Lubac, *Religion*, 173-184 and *T. Explained*, 41-58; Rideau, 146-152; Tresmontant, 58-63.
   Omega as personal and universal: de Lubac, *Man*, 13-19 and *Religion*, 143-151.
   love-energy: *VP*, 205-215.

5. *Critiques*: T.'s argument for Omega: Nogar, *Lord*, 72-81; Rabut, *Teilhard*, 115-142; Rideau, 245-248.

9

EVOLUTION'S FINAL OUTCOME

Quickly and graphically Teilhard sketches the final stages and final state of the earth and of man, of cosmogenesis and noogenesis. But, since he perhaps goes too quickly for us, let us consider the sketch in "slow motion."

The Communion of "Elements"

Teilhard first notes the obvious—the individual deaths of men: "All round us, one by one, like a continual exhalation, 'souls' break away, carrying upwards their incommunicable load [acquisition] of consciousness."(272) Individual death is a fact which must be fitted into a fully coherent explanation of the universe. Just as evolution's final outcome is necessary for explaining the earlier stages of evolution, so too is the corporate and universal term of evolution necessary for an understanding of individual terms or deaths: "One by one [men die], yet not in isolation. Since for each of them, by the very nature of Omega, there can only be one possible point of definitive emersion—the point at which . . . the noosphere . . . will reach collectively its point of convergence—at the 'end of the world.' " (272) By "one possible point of definitive emersion," Teilhard is stressing that both for the individual and for the whole race of man there is one point ("the end of the world") and there

160

is one being ("the noosphere [having reached] collectively its point of convergence") which give meaning to and shape the very being of every element and of their union.

For a Christian reader, a comparison between the end of noospheric evolution and the Parousia of Christ at the end of time should help to clarify Teilhard's thought. In writing for Christian readers, he develops the interconnections between these two events, but for obvious reasons the *Phenomenon* is silent on these.[1] Scripture presents the Parousia, the appearance of Christ at the end of time, in two radically different ways. St. Peter presents the end of the world, apparently, as a dissolution of the earth and the heavens in a cataclysm, whereas for St. Paul the Parousia signals not the annihilation of the earth but its transformation in and through Christ.[2] Teilhard combines these two traditions in his use of the concept of change of state with its resulting emergence. In an evolutionary process, there comes a point wherein there is no possibility of further development along the same line. Through increasing tension the process reaches a critical point in which there is a "leap" to a specifically new and higher level of existence and development. Examples of this are the transformation of nonliving forms into living, and of nonhuman forms into human. Teilhard insists that these changes took place instantaneously, even though their preparations may have required millenia.

At the end of terrestrial time and evolution, there will likewise be a change of state: "This essentially convergent movement will attain such intensity and such quality that mankind, *taken as a whole*, will be obliged . . . to abandon its organoplanetary foothold so as to shift its centre on to the transcendent Centre of its increasing concentration."(287)[3] Just as the living being leaves behind the limitations of the nonliving, and just as the human transcends the limitations of the nonhuman, so at the end of time, mankind as a whole will leave behind the limitations of time, space and matter ("organo-planetary foothold"). This does not mean, however, that *all* of matter is left behind, though this impression can easily be generated by some of Teilhard's expressions, such as "matter which vanishes," and "the death of the materially exhausted planet." (272, 289) Just as the living being in evolution is continuous with and preservative of the perfections of the nonliving, so is the final cosmos continuous with the pre-final cosmos; hence, something of matter and of material perfection passes over into the post-Parousial state. "By assimilation to the Body of Christ, some part of matter is destined to pass into the foundations and walls of the heavenly Jerusalem."[4] "Beneath our efforts to put spiritual form into our own lives, the world slowly accumulates, starting with the whole of matter, that which will make of it the Heavenly Jerusalem of the New Earth." Perhaps the clearest expression of matter's future is, "This movement [of evolution] must have its term; one day the whole divinisable substance of matter will have passed into the souls of men; all the chosen dynamisms will have been recovered; and then our world will be ready for the Parousia."[5]

Not only matter but everything that has been achieved in matter's past, present and future, "the whole divinisable substance of matter," will be transformed at the definitive point of the noosphere's complete convergence. But how are the achievements of an individual element, who dies before this definitive point is reached, a part of the final transformation? Teilhard's answer is rooted in his fundamental conviction:

"All is connected with all." In this elementary expression, the faith in the World does not differ sensibly from the acceptance of a scientific fact. . . . For all men who think, the Universe forms a system [a whole] interminably connected in Time and Space. . . . Over the cosmic system of beings and phenomena, I sense the idea of total Reality whose condition is to be more consistent, more rich, more assured in its advances, than any of the particular *things* which it envelops. To my eyes, to express it differently, there are no more things in the World, there are only *elements*.[6]

This sense of the organic unity of all the elements that go to make up the cosmos is one of the most distinctive aspects of Teilhard's synthesis.

The feeling for the "All," the Whole, is anything but a purely speculative outlook on Teilhard's part. Its personal repercussions on life's activities are clear:

> 'I' is not an entity isolated from all relations: it is, in a way, the whole universe centred on me, *whose destiny* (in a very true sense) *is played out in me* (in God's eyes isn't every soul worth the whole world, isn't it the whole world? . . .). Thus, in this essential confrontation of God and me, I feel *every* creature *behind* me.[7]

For this reason there can be the "hominisation of death itself," that is, animal death is transformed into the genuinely human death.[8] "Strictly speaking, there are no separated souls; there are only souls which change their 'sphere' in a world where everything is related to everything else."[9] What Teilhard strives to show is that death does not separate the individual man from the evolution of Humanity: "*They are not able to grow without changing.* Hence the pain of losing themselves in the prodigious mass of Humanity—or the even greater pain of escaping, by the slow or rapid dissolution of the body, from the whole experimental framework within which we were born."[10] Death, "the escape from the whole experimental framework," is then the means for entry into a new realm of existence and activity. For this reason Teilhard affirms that in the definitive act of noogenesis "the full consciousness of each individual man will be sustained by that of every other man, not only the living but the dead."[11]

"The mass of humanity," the new "sphere," transcribed into specifically Christian terms, would refer to the Communion of Saints, the union of all the redeemed, including the living, the dead and angel spirits. All that the noosphere connotes, this Communion embodies: an intimate union and communication of interest, affection and aid. Like the noospheric union of Humanity, the Communion of Saints is not a system constituted by feeble relations, but is a dynamic whole, organically integrated and interactive.

Does Evolution Have a Term?

Thus far we have been presupposing that evolution has for the totality of its process a term, a suitable outcome. But this is such a fundamental problem that it must be faced again, even though the latter part of *Phenomenon's* Chapter III seemed to settle the matter. Perhaps Teilhard returns to the question of a "suitable outcome" because it is answered not by cold reason but by human option. The more angles from which the question is investigated the more chances readers will have to opt for evolution's *issue* or successful outcome.

There is no blinking at the fact: many there are who have made the pessimistic option. They divide into those who see a dismal end for the world and, therefore, no *issue*, and those who see neither an end of the cosmos nor a suitable outcome. Taking the first group of pessimists, Teilhard outlines their general outlook:

> All pessimistic representations of the earth's last days—whether in terms of cosmic catastrophe, biological disruptions or simply arrested growth or senility—have this in common: that they take the characteristics and conditions of our individual and elemental ends and extend them *without correction* to life as a whole. Accident, disease and decrepitude spell the death of men; and therefore the same applies to mankind. (275)

George Gamow in his popular *Biography of the Earth* says that in ten billion years or so, "we will find the dying Sun surrounded by its family of rapidly cooling planets. There will be no observer to watch this sad picture."[12] One could multiply the contemporary affirmations of this pessimism almost *ad infinitum*, starting with Willy Loman, in Arthur Miller's *Death of a Sales-*

man, spending his life "ringing up zero," continuing with Walter Kerr's assessment of Broadway in which he says "man's case is hopeless, man is impotent," and perhaps capping it with C. P. Snow's reflections:

> Most of the scientists I have known well have felt—just as deeply as the non-scientists I have known well—that the individual condition of each of us is tragic. Each of us is alone: sometimes we escape from solitariness, through love or affection or perhaps creative moments, but those triumphs of life are pools of light we make for ourselves while the edge of the road is black: each of us dies alone.[13]

Snow goes on to state that nearly all these people see no reason "why, just because the individual condition is tragic, so must the social condition be."[14] If there is optimism here, it is certainly bound to and restricted by an indefinite but *limited future* of scientific and social progress. No reason is given why such progress will not have an ending just as tragic as that of the individual.

Two of the most discussed theories of the origin of the universe, the steady state theory—new matter is constantly being "created" to keep the expanding cosmos at a constant density—and the pulsation theory—we are in an expanding phase now, but this will be followed by a contracting phase, and so on without end—deny a beginning and therefore, by projection, an end. A third theory, the most commonly accepted one, has the universe beginning with a "big bang," thereafter constantly expanding, and ending in the "whimper" of complete dissociation. Recent astronomical evidence seems to favor the "big bang" theory which, without any hyperphysical additions, inclines to a pessimism about any suitable outcome for cosmic evolution.[15]

The other group of pessimists (who should logically hold either the steady state or pulsation theory) see no end to the cosmos or say nothing about it. Rather, they talk about "indefinite" progress of man in the future. One of the "death of

God" theologians, Thomas Altizer, seems ready enough to deny in some real sense the existence of God in order to have a doubtfully "ultimate yes-saying to the world."[16] Charles Frankel lists as one of the four essentials for a "liberal conception of history . . . the doctrines of 'the indefinite perfectibility of man.' "[17] This certainly means that there is no assignable limit to the progress man can make, and it is exceedingly likely that Frankel would exclude as unreasonable a hope for infinite time in which to pursue this progress. Julian Huxley also seems to belong to this second group of pessimists. Though convinced of the end of a habitable universe, he does not want to hear of a projected outcome for evolution.[18] Such an attitude probably proceeds in part from legitimate scientific caution; however, it would be difficult to rule out a fundamental option which controls the pessimistic conclusion, just as Teilhard's conclusion about a completed and suitable outcome for evolution flows from an option.

Teilhard does what many contemporary writers on cosmic evolution do not do: he faces squarely the question of whether there lies before us finite or infinite terrestrial duration. He flatly affirms that the future holds only "a strictly limited cycle of geogenesis."(273)[19] He denies therefore that there is to be "an indefinite progress, which is a hypothesis contradicted by the convergent nature of noogenesis."(289)[20] Scientifically it seems that Teilhard has the evidence on his side, that is, that noogenesis will proceed only for a finite duration. (286)[21] Further, there are many reasons for agreeing with him that some projected but limited period of a "Golden Age, a period of euphoria and abundance . . . a 'bourgeois' paradise" is insufficient to satisfy our legitimate hopes for Humanity.[22] True optimism, then, must be built not only on the existence of an end to noogenesis but even more on a *suitable* fulfillment or outcome for the process.

The Christian parallel once again may be averted to, not because it is the immediate evidence which Teilhard uses for the *Phenomenon's* optimism, but because it is part of the whole of his thought. The Christian has the most historical of beliefs; his central belief, the Incarnation, is rooted in a most specific historical—and transhistorical—event. Also, the Christian believes in a creation of the universe in time; hence, the universe has existed for only a finite period of time. Finally, the Christian is convinced that the future of man's existence on earth is also of a strictly finite duration, to be terminated by a revealed event, the second coming of Christ, which will take place when man shall have "come to full stature." That the outcome of this temporal process will be suitable and consummating is assured by Christ's own resurrection and the immediate control he exercises as Lord of the universe.

The End that Is a Beginning

Almost irremovable ambiguity infects speaking about the end of the world or the end of noospheric development. All too readily, "end" suggests to us the complete and final termination of all that went before. This is true for the individual and for the whole. Since the thrust of the *Phenomenon* is towards a total explanation of human evolution, Teilhard's main concern with "the ultimate earth" is to demonstrate that the convergent nature of noogenesis demands not only an end, but more importantly, an end that is a beginning. In this there should be no astonishment. We experience that the end of being a baby is the beginning of being a child; the end of being a child is the beginning of being an adolescent, and so on. Likewise, the end of the world and the end of time mark the beginning, the emergence of a radically new existence.

The end of the world is structurally identified as the moment when the noosphere's continuing convergence has achieved a maximum of psychic temperature and tension. This second critical point in reflective consciousness is like the moment of transition from animal consciousness to human self-reflection: "This critical point of collective maturation will be a point of paroxysm and ecstasy, by which mankind will emerge into a state of consciousness 'beyond the time-space matrix of the universe', and it 'coincides concretely with the point called the Parousia of Christ'."[23] Just as the point of death marks for the individual an "emergence" into a new and higher state, so the critical point of noogenesis initiates the "passage, by Translation or dematerialisation, to another sphere of the Universe: not an ending of the ultra-human but its accession to some sort of trans-humanity at the ultimate heart of things."[24] The Christian parallel is, of course, heaven, whose beatifying, knowing and loving are conceived not in individualistic terms but in organically corporate dimensions.

Propellants of Noogenesis

Given that the evolution of the human spirit, noogenesis, is proceeding to a critical point of final and collective emergence into "the transcendent Center," it is inevitable to ask, what human initiatives are conducive to this "suitable outcome"? "*Along what lines* of advance . . . are we destined to proceed?"(278) The point must be made that Teilhard is not giving a comprehensive survey of human activities calculated to promote noogenesis, but rather a selection of some activities from "among others." The basis of selection seems to be what fits in better with scientific readers and with the present stage of the *Phenomenon's* dialectic.

Other very important human activities are not mentioned. Surely, all manner of humanistic ventures—artistic creations, literary works, together with interpersonal activities of human friendship, love, and religious achievements—are very important in Teilhard's mind for increasing noogenesis. In the *Phenomenon,* however, he concentrates on the role of science.[25] If a reader forgets this, he could easily—and unjustly—reproach Teilhard for making science into the unique instrument for humanity's further evolution.

In his own practice, though, we find Teilhard with a decided bent for working with scientists. In the interdisciplinary projects of his last years, he manifested a strong preference for physical and life scientists. "My (convinced) opinion is that *only* biologists, physicists and geologists should be admitted to it [a projected symposium in Paris]. . . . *Not* historians, nor sociologists, nor 'cultural' anthropologists." Teilhard's reason for this selectivity is that his experience had led him to believe that at the present time it is only the biologists, physicists and geologists who are "capable of studying man in his *ascent* from the atom, the protein, the cell, the species."[26]

Having written the *Phenomenon* for scientific readers, it is understandable that he selects three scientific human instruments to push forward human evolution: the organization of research, the scientific discovery of the human object, and the union of science and religion. For the first activity of research, Teilhard insists on the value of pure research—scientific knowledge sought for its own sake and, unlike most current research, unsubordinated to industry and armaments. The possibilities suggested by the new discoveries of science never ceased to spark his imagination and hope. One could never accuse him of dreaming small dreams of science's contributions to man's future development—"fathoming everything, trying everything, extending everything." (279)[27]

"The discovery of the human object" represents the second instrument for current evolution. Science, Teilhard says, must discover man as a specific object for its inquiry because "he represents, individually and socially, the most synthesised state under which the stuff of the universe is available to us . . . He is at present the most mobile point of the stuff in course of transformation."(281-2) Until now science has been slow to consider the whole as a proper object of scientific investigation. Such expansion is a necessary development of science because of science's own intrinsic dynamism and of humanity's evolutionary needs. The science which considers the *whole* of man from the phenomenal viewpoint is, of course, a hyperphysics—

irresistibly led to concern itself with the ultimate future of mankind.

Science which has discovered the human object will concern itself with the improvement of the human body by means of eugenics. Perhaps Teilhard would not have used the word "eugenics" if he had realized what sinister connotations it carries for many readers. Eugenics as "perfecting the continuance and fulfilment of the species" need not be accomplished by a totalitarian violation of man, but can and ought to be achieved by a persuasion which uses increased genetic knowledge and respects human freedom and dignity. Teilhard is careful to note that the new biology to control life must be "suitably subordinated to other values," and thus become a "nobly human form of eugenics."[28] However, it is in the realm of the social and the psychological that science can make its greatest contributions to further evolution: "the distribution of the resources of the globe; the control of the trek towards unpopulated areas; the optimum use of the powers set free by mechanisation; the physiology of nations and races; geo-economy, geo-politics, geo-demography; the organisation of research developing into a reasoned organization of the earth."(283) Such contributions by science are obviously and critically necessary for humanity's further development.

Beyond this function Teilhard, especially in the latter part of his life, looked for the creation and expansion of a "science of human energetics." This science would concentrate upon an "energetics of the mind [spirit]"(290) which would necessarily encompass a "comparative study of physical and psychical energy."[29] (Mystical energy constitutes a special division of psychical energy, one of special interest to Teilhard but out of place within the *Phenomenon's* self-imposed limits.) The "science of human energetics" is just as necessary to the further development of the noosphere as was the science of physical energy for the development and utilization of atomic potentialities. One particular field to be investigated would be that of extra-sensory perception (ESP) and telepathy. Teilhard looks forward to a use of these powers which would be "general and normal" in contrast to their present "sporadic and haphazard" use.[30]

A hint of Teilhard's hopes for science is found in this passage: "The readjustment and internal liberation of our souls by direct action upon springs [powers] gradually brought to light by psycho-analysis. The arousing and harnessing of the unfathomable intellectual and affective powers still latent in the human mass."[31] In the section on love-energy, we have indicated the necessary role of affective Energy itself or Omega—"in order to love something like the world or even humanity, realities that are collective, impersonal, even monstrous in some respects." For man to vanquish his "dread of that frightful cosmic machinery in which he finds himself entangled," he needs to experience through the love-energy of Omega "a universe whose very evolution has been impregnated with love."[32] Hence, it would seem, the future science of energetics would also seek to correlate human and divine energy.

Such correlation is attempted in a very tentative and initial way by Teilhard's third instrument of evolution, "the union of science and religion." On the *Phenomenon's* second page he indicates that "like the meridians as they approach the poles, science, philosophy and religion are bound to converge as they draw nearer to the whole."(30) In the final pages, Teilhard tries to show that science pushed to its limits (and therefore to the *whole*) becomes more and more religious—"tinged with mysticism and charged with faith." (284)

In its synthesizing phase which has just begun, science is drawn towards a triple faith: in progress, in human unification, in Omega. If such beliefs become part and parcel of science's presuppositions and activities, it is not difficult to see how it would outdistance its present stage of analysis and emerge in adoration. Looking to science's future, Teilhard predicted:

What we much too simply call 'Research' will be charged, colored, warmed by certain forces (Faith, Adoration) which thus far have been considered as strangers to Science. The more attentively I look at Research the more I see it ultimately forced by internal necessity to concentrate its effort and its hopes upon some divine focus.[33]

Since evolution is a unifying process, it is inevitable that knowledge itself become more and more unified. As science progressively "turn[s] towards the summit, towards the *totality* and the *future,* [it] . . . cannot help engaging in religion. Religion and science are the two conjugated faces or phases of one and the same complete act of knowledge." (285)[34]

One final point must be noted: the emphasis upon the function of choice in the beliefs which science will adopt. When discussing Omega it could easily appear that reason alone was operative and that there was nothing of freedom and choice. That this does not represent Teilhard's thought is evident from this section on the union of science and religion. Though there are rational arguments for Omega's existence and activity, arguments alone are insufficient. Evidence for Omega, unlike most mathematical and scientific evidence, does not compel human assent. The affirmation or denial of Omega is in the realm of human freedom; more than that, affirmation or denial of Omega embodies the most fundamental and existential of all our choices. As Teilhard says, the three faiths towards which science naturally tends—progress, final unity, Omega—are "strictly undemonstrable to science." Hence "we decide, under the pressure of facts," but the pressure is noncoercive. Otherwise, it could not be said that science in embracing the three-fold faith "out-distances itself and emerges in terms of *option* and *adoration.*" (284)

The Penultimate and the Ultimate

Having seen the human instruments which favor and push forward the convergent evolution of man's spirit, we naturally wonder about the "last things." If the ultimate is situated in an existence and activity beyond this world, we would like to know not only what we can affirm about this ultimate state but also about the penultimate, the final shape of man's future on this earth.

Because history shows evolution as constantly mounting to ever new critical points, we rightly can expect that before the ultimate state of humanity is achieved, there should be at the end of time the supreme critical point. What will precede and precipitate this critical point? Teilhard proposes two possibilities, both based on structures found in previous evolution. The first hypothesis, "final convergence . . . *in peace*," is characterized by diminishing evil and increasing good. An initial reading of the *Phenomenon* could possibly yield the opinion that Teilhard favored this as the more probable hypothesis, since it "expresses the hopes towards which we ought in any case to turn our efforts as to an ideal."(288) This does not mean that he considers the first hypothesis more likely, but that in terms of an ideal to be striven for (and probably unachievable) it is more provocative of our best efforts than is the second hypothesis.

More realistic than the first, the second hypothesis presents the penultimate stage of man as one of growing conflict and division. The forces of good and evil increase concurrently. Perhaps the ultimate change of state would be precipitated by a direct confrontation and conflict of the two forces completely matured. Teilhard says this hypothesis is "more in conformity with traditional apocalyptic thinking,"(289) and he favors it as more realistically proportioned to the evolutionary facts.[35] The gospel parable of the master ordering the workers to allow the cockle to grow along with the wheat until the harvest, points to the simultaneous growth of evil and good forces, as do the last judgment scenes which separate definitively the good and the bad.

Though hell as the final outcome for a portion of humanity is never explicitly mentioned in the *Phenomenon,* it is clearly understood. The primeval option in the Garden of Eden is

echoed by the ultimate human option: "Refusal or acceptance
of Omega?"(288) "Refusal of Omega": this is not the hell
which is thrust upon a man for an inadvertence by a probably
unjust God. Rather, it is the hell which, in a real sense, is
created by the magnitude of man's liberty, something well appreciated and expressed by Jean-Paul Sartre in *No Exit* and
C. S. Lewis in *The Great Divorce*. Teilhard does not blink at
the anguishingly somber side of human freedom—the possibility
of choosing self as "the pole of adoration" while refusing
Omega, and this choice issuing in "an ecstasy [of] discord." (289)

Mooney states the point well: "Teilhard never loses sight of
the fact that 'the right outcome' of evolution is one thing, while
that of the individual is quite another. Ultimate victory for
humanity through union with Omega does not mean personal
victory for each human being."[36] Since the progress of evolution
is towards increased consciousness and increased freedom, the
penultimate stage of evolution will certainly see man "having
reached this apogee of his responsibility and freedom, holding
in his hands all his future and all his past, making the choice
between arrogant autonomy and loving excentration."[37] The
state of those who accept and of those who refuse Omega is
contrasted: "some of them spiritualised matter in the limitless
fulfilment of an eternal communion, and others materialised
spirit in the conscious agonies of an interminable decomposition."[38] The difference can be projected as "ultimate life (i.e.,
a fullness of consciousness embracing at once all reality) or
ultimate death (i.e., an infinite splintering of consciousness upon
itself)."[39]

That his conception fits with the Christian conception of a
particular and general judgment by Christ is obvious. The
seriousness of the diverse outcomes makes human liberty an
incalculably immense force for good or evil. As a consequence,
divine judgment may be looked upon as a ratification of individual options. There is no question but that in all of Teil-

hard's writings the most "dense and driven" passage is that on hell and judgment in *The Divine Milieu*. No one can be drawn naturally to the idea or reality of a hell, but the question raised by Teilhard is not one of likes and dislikes, but of reality. Is man capable of consequential or only of inconsequential choices? Can he really dispose of himself, or is he only play-acting? Teilhard in the *Phenomenon, The Divine Milieu* and many other places makes clear his thought that fully human consciousness and freedom must be presented with the ultimate option and their diverse concomitants.[40] Accordingly we find him piqued when accused of a soft-headed and/or soft-hearted optimism which is impotent to face up to the problem of evil. One can feel the edge of his resentment in the *Phenomenon's* appendix: "It would be a complete misunderstanding to inter-pret the view here suggested as a sort of human idyll rather than as the cosmic drama."(311) The progress of evolution and the certainty of a "suitable outcome," far from minimizing individual human freedom, invest it with such extensions and consequences as to fill men with a Kierkegaardian "fear and trembling":

> Essentially Progress is a *force,* and the most dangerous of forces. . . . When Plato acted it was probably in the belief that his freedom to act could only affect a small fragment of the world, narrowly circumscribed in space and time; but the man of today acts in the knowledge that the choice he makes will have its repercussions through countless centuries and upon countless human beings. He feels in himself the responsibilities and the power of an entire Universe. . . .
>
> This will be the final choice: revolt or adoration of a world. And then, by an act which will summarise the toil of centuries, by this act . . . justice will ensue and all things be renewed.[41]

One incidental point must be taken up before considering "The Ultimate." This is the possibility of life on other planets. Whether there is life on other planets, what this would mean for man's further evolution on this planet, what hopes man can place in possible planetary migration—these and related questions engaged Teilhard's attention to the end of his life. To take the last question first: What hopes can man place in planetary migration, perhaps to a planet in another galaxy? Teilhard discovered in a soirée that the affirmation of the possibility of planetary migration was being used to avoid answering the fundamental question about the convergence of this planet's evolution:

> From his own viewpoint, the Marxist will approach willingly and with an open mind the idea of an eschatology for a classless society in which the Omega point is conceived as the point of natural convergence for humanity. But suppose we remind him that our Earth, because of the implacable laws of entropy, is destined to die; suppose we ask him what will be the outcome allowed humanity in such a world. Then he replies—in terms that H. G. Wells has already used—by offering perspectives of interplanetary and intergalactic colonisation. This is one way to dodge the mystical notion of a Parousia, and gradual movement of humanity towards an ecstatic union in God.[42]

Teilhard disallows the evasion and keeps asking the fundamental question about a "suitable outcome" for noospheric evolution, whether it be terrestrial, sidereal or galactic. It is true that in the *Phenomenon* (1940) he considers "invading other inhabited planets or getting into psychical touch with self-reflective creatures on other planets as . . . hypotheses [whose] probability is too remote for them to be worth dwelling on."[43] But as time went on, the probabilities increased in Teilhard's mind, so that shortly before his death he conceives of "a universe that has suddenly become fantastically big, formidably organic, and more than probably poly-human (*n* thinking planets—perhaps millions . . .)."[44] Hence, "the *attempt* will be made to overstep the limits of the earth." But Teilhard is quick to ask whether man "does not feel that, if he is to reach his own centre, he must have made his way to the farthest limit of all things?" And this is Omega, the transcendent Center of centers. As a matter of fact, the ultimate effect of space migration, while it gives "man a wider base for action, to that same extent it could not but intensify the forces that throw us together."[45]

Hence, the law of complexity/consciousness is applicable to psychic convergence whether there be one or many noospheres. There must be for each and for all taken together a critical point of maximum convergence followed by the ultimate state of humanity. But a difficulty which the priest-scientist did not seem to have considered is this: if mankind spreads to many galaxies, would a unified noospheric convergence be possible in view of the time-lag in communications and the corresponding differences in psychic developments? The same difficulty with *one* noospheric maturation for the cosmos exists within the hypothesis of rational life having evolved independently in many galaxies—a possibility we have not really begun to confirm or disprove.

In describing "the Ultimate" state of man on this earth, however, Teilhard in the *Phenomenon* has diverse formulations:

Mankind . . . will be obliged . . . to abandon its organo-planetary foothold so as to shift its centre on to the transcendent centre . . . This will be the end and the fulfilment of the spirit of the earth. (287)

Ecstasy in concord; or discord. . . . (289)

A system whose unity coincides with a paroxysm of harmonised complexity. (262)

By a perennial act of communion and sublimation, he [Christ] aggregates to himself the total psychism of the earth. And when he has gathered everything together and transformed everything, he will close in upon himself and his conquests, thereby rejoining, in a final gesture, the divine focus he has never left. Then, as St. Paul tells us, *God shall be all in all* . . . . This is indeed a superior form of 'pantheism' . . . perfect unity, steeped in which each element will reach its consummation at the same time as the universe. (294)

Teilhard's never ceasing concern with the future of man, and specifically with the ultimate state of man, marks him as a Christian phenomenon who has "invested the belief in a Second Coming [the Parousia of Christ] with an importance and significance it has not possessed since the end of the first century."[46] The "pilgrim of the future" lights up the future of man so that it is not only attractive in itself but also capable of helping men to acquire a perduring zest—for life, for dedicated activity, for "more being."

PHENOMENON'S *Summary in Fifty-three Words*

The Phenomenon of Man concludes with a very brief and condensed summary:

> To make room for thought in the world, I have needed to 'interiorise' matter: to imagine an energetics of the mind; to conceive a noogenesis rising upstream against the flow of entropy; to provide evolution with a direction, a line of advance and critical points: and finally to make all things double back upon *someone*. (290)*

"To make room for thought": The unifying, synthesizing mind of Teilhard is immediately evident. Thought possesses its primacy among the things of the cosmos, but it must be coherently joined with all the parts and processes of the universe. This is done initially by "interiorizing matter," that is, by making consciousness a property of all matter, by giving a "within" as well as a "without" to every material unit, by giving some sort of psyche to all matter.

"To construct an energetics of the spirit": Teilhard saw the

---

*The meaning becomes clearer if the French were rendered as follows: "To make room for thought in the world, I had to 'interiorise' matter; to construct an energetics of the spirit; to conceive an increasing noogenesis contrary to the flow of entropy; to provide evolution with a meaning, a direction and some critical points; and finally to make all things double back on *someone*." This wording is used in the discussion that follows.

necessity of finding a law or laws that expressed the operations and dynamics of man's spirit. To make this energetics or science of energy meaningful, he must find a law that is applicable to all manifestations of energy whether physical, psychical or mystical. He accomplishes this by means of the law of complexity/consciousness. His law shows that whenever energy is expended in increasing complexity, there is a corresponding increase in consciousness, and that the direction of evolution has been, is and will be towards ever higher complexity and its correspondingly higher consciousness.

"To conceive an increasing noogenesis contrary to the flow of entropy": The picture of evolution is *not* painted black by the prospect of increasing entropy—the steady decline of energy available for evolution's activity, ending in the dismal "heat death" of the cosmos. What is far more significant is the *rise* of psychic powers and energies, "increasing noogenesis," in accord with the law of complexity/consciousness.

"To provide evolution with a meaning, a direction and some critical points": The meaning and direction of evolution are a function of the law of complexity/consciousness; evolution is rising towards higher and higher activities and forms of consciousness. This is what is *"going on."* In this ascent to higher consciousness, Teilhard thinks that phenomena dictate the necessity of certain critical points. These are points where, though there is continuity in the process, the new types and states of consciousness which arise are qualitatively different from prior types.

"To make all things finally double back upon *someone*": Once consciousness is human and therefore spiritual and personal, Teilhard develops the necessity of humanity's convergence upon a supremely personal and personalizing center of evolution, Omega, for the further evolution and final consummation of mankind.

Thus does Teilhard summarize the central insights and innovations of *The Phenomenon of Man*. But its final words are words of genuine humility: "In this arrangement of values I may have gone astray at many points. It is up to others to try to do better."(290) True to what he had discovered in evolution's past, he felt that his success as a thinker could only be "proved" by his thought being improved upon: "If I do have a mission to accomplish, the degree of my success in fulfilling that mission will only be able to be judged in terms of the extent to which I am surpassed."[47] At least seven years before Teilhard's death and therefore before he became widely known, Père de Lubac sought the reason for the popularity of Teilhard's thought; in de Lubac's paragraph which follows, the "N" refers, almost beyond doubt, to Teilhard.

> It is because a certain N. thought for himself, searched for himself, made an effort to express to himself, with all possible rigor and sincerity, what he was thinking, what he was believing, that he has obtained, without having aimed at it, so large an audience. He put himself into his work with all his Christian faith, all his mystic soul, all the culture of his learning, all his needs as an unsatisfied intellectual. He lived; he has reached the living. More than that, he created some life. . . . A Christian who searches is, in his innermost efforts, searching with everyone for everything.[48]

This has many echoes of what Teilhard humbly had to say about his own thought: "In all my work I am conscious of being no more than a sort of sound-box, amplifying what people around me are thinking. Take from me what suits you and build your own structure."[49]

READING SUGGESTIONS

1. *Read PM*, 273-290.

2. *See Glossary for*: 'artifice' [education(289) = reduction], *change of state [complicity(276) = accord], conjugated,

*emergence, emersion, *energetics, *evasion [eyes (of noo-
sphere) = science in fullest sense], *issue, *mind, mysticism,
outlet.

3. *Passages to be noted*:
   273, "However convergent it be, etc." The consummating union
   of Humanity cannot be attained in time and on earth but
   through a change of state (death) a new mode of united
   existence is established.
   277, "As though regulated etc." T. implies that there is a quantum or a specific quantity of energy available for cosmic evolution. Hence the energy used for the development in one area
   means the lessening of energy in other areas.
   282, "Eugenics," for many readers, seems to suggest only Hit-
   lerian overtones. Not so for T., who qualifies eugenics: "subordinated to other values," "medical and *moral* factors" and
   "on a standard worthy of our personalities." Accordingly,
   knowledge and persuasion, *not* force, would be all-important
   in the eugenics which T. sees as respecting man's freedom—"a
   nobly human form of eugenics."
   284, *"Firstly in its impetus."* T. in this and the next two paragraphs strives to show that both science and religion have a
   common belief in progress, in unification and unity, and in
   Omega.

4. *Parallel Readings*:
   issue: *AM,* 165-171, 244-270; *FM,* 61-81 (64-84), 113-123
   (117-28); *MPN,* 112-121; de Lubac, *Religion,* 47-55.
   hyper-personal *issue: DM,* 150-155; *FM,* 270-280 (283-294),
       306-308 (321-23); de Lubac, *Religion,* 132-142.
   human activity: *SC,* 81-85, 174-186.

5. *Critiques*: evolutionary progress: *Rideau, 174-178 and Chaix-
   Ruy, 226-274; certitude of *issue*: Smulders, 140-162.

10

CHRISTOGENESIS

Teilhard's hyperphysics has shown that evolution is basically an ascent of complexity/consciousness; evolution has progressed from cosmos to organisms and through vertebrates to man's spirit—cosmogenesis, biogenesis, anthropogenesis, noogenesis. Hyperphysics searched the conditions necessary for evolution's "successful outcome," and thus rounded out its analysis by a study of noogenesis. This investigation revealed Omega's existence and influence as necessary for the continuation and ultimate consummation of the noosphere's development.

"The Union of Science and Religion"

We find, however, that Teilhard adds to nearly every formulation of hyperphysics a brief account of Christogenesis as the form and completion of noogenesis. These additions are always classified as lying outside the realm of hyperphysics.[1] In the *Phenomenon* Teilhard calls "The Christian Phenomenon" an "Epilogue," that is, a section which belongs outside the book's intrinsic boundaries. He recognizes that hyperphysics narrows its view to what is observable by all men, independent of their philosophical and religious options. The *whole* phenomenon of Christianity, therefore, cannot be subject to a scientific investigation since the essential knowledge of Christianity is dependent on a free Christian commitment. This neither makes useless nor illegitimate what Teilhard does: inspects those phenomenal aspects of Christianity which *are* observable by all and which reveal themselves as remarkable parallels to and confirmations of hyperphysics' main theses.

If such significant features of Christianity were unobservable by all, Teilhard could rightly be reproached with introducing Christianity for the worst of reasons—purely partisan ones. If this were so, the Epilogue would be as *outre* and laughable as instances of "Catholic Arithmetic." But the facts are otherwise. The effort to construct a coherent theory of the whole of evolution naturally leads a thinker to consider the place and significance of the Christian phenomenon.

Not only is Christianity a phenomenon with an observable history of structures and functions, but it is also a phenomenon which proposes a world view just as hyperphysics does. It is at least interesting and at most imperative for a hyperphysicist, theistic or atheistic, to compare, for similarities and dissimilarities, his world view with that of Christianity. Studying the phenomenon of Christianity should lead the hyperphysicist to extensions, modifications, confirmations and/or disproofs of various aspects of his world view. Such is the task Teilhard undertakes in the Epilogue.

The panorama of cosmic evolution led him to see the necessity for an Omega with quite specific properties, and to discover in man's further evolution very definite needs. One of the principal features of Omega is that he is the *personal* center for the convergent noogenesis. If he is such, Teilhard can legitimately wonder if it is not "inevitable that its [his] existence should be manifest to us here and now through some traces."(291) If Omega exists, then "some excess of personal, extra-human energy should be perceptible to us if we look carefully."(292) Since Christianity is the world-religion which most clearly proposes just such a revelation, Teilhard sees cause for a special investigation of "The Christian Phenomenon."

If he were trying to introduce a Christian "apologia by artifice" instead of the skimpy suggestions he proposes, he would certainly have been better advised to produce much more data and to analyze it in far more detail. But his intentions are other and more modest; he merely wants to propose a sketch of the interrelatedness of the evolutions of the cosmos and of Christ, of hyperphysics' and Christianity's world views.

There are good reasons for saying with Teilhard that hyperphysics points beyond itself to Christianity as not only an integral part of evolution but even "at the heart of the social phenomenon" of convergent noogenesis.(299) He also sees Christianity as pointing to the validity of the construction posited by hyperphysics. There exists, he finds, a mutual "fit," a mutual confirmation and strengthening. In many ways this is what we should expect in a universe that is presumed to be coherent, making sense as a whole. "The Christian Phenomenon's" confirmation of hyperphysics is especially valuable because it is drawn from "an added [i.e., a different] source of knowledge."[2]

One can rightly look upon the Epilogue as an early attempt to affect some "conjunction of science and religion," that which Teilhard proposed as an essential instrument for increasing the value and growth of noogenesis.(283-5) Such a union works mutual benefits: not only is hyperphysics confirmed and enlarged by the Christian perspectives, but Christianity itself is in need of Pope John's "opened windows" which admit the world's fresh air which can inspire, form and invigorate the Church's thought and action.[3] Teilhard's images for what the world can do for Christianity's growth are quite vivid: "Evolution has come to infuse new blood, so to speak, into the perspectives and aspirations of Christianity."(297) "This coming together . . . of a great mass of naturally religious spirits . . . portend[s] . . . the laying of new foundations to which the old Church is gradually being moved."[4] Because this influence of the contemporary world on the Church *is* something incidental to the *Phenomenon's* aim, it is merely mentioned but not amplified.

Christianity—Confirmation of Hyperphysics

What constitutes a "proof" or confirmation of the sweeping theory proposed by the *Phenomenon*? Internal coherence and "fit" help to justify its validity, but this is certainly not the only nor the prime source of justification. Theories with splendid intrinsic coherence have been created—but frequently they possessed the truly fatal flaw of not fitting the facts. The early Greek theory of the four elements—earth, air, fire and water—is just one case in point. A valid theory must above all integrate and explain all the known facts. Aiming to explain the whole phenomenon of man, Teilhard must synthesize all the available evidence bearing on man and his evolution. Since Christianity is a large and partially observable fact, its evidence can help to confirm or disprove the theory which Teilhard proposes.

With reason, de Lubac and Smulders feel that Teilhard tends to be "too hasty in his search for 'coherence' . . . [or] at least, that being in a hurry to translate his unifying vision into intellectual terms, he made use of over-abrupt short cuts."[5] Their evaluation, perhaps, is less applicable to the fundamental coherence which Teilhard discovers existing between cosmogenesis and Christogenesis: "If the world is convergent and if Christ occupies its centre, then the Christogenesis of St. Paul and St. John is nothing else and nothing less than the extension, both awaited and unhoped for, of that noogenesis in which cosmogenesis—as regards our experience—culminates." (297) Christogenesis—the unifying growth of Christ's Mystical Body in and through time—confirms the *Phenomenon's* thesis that cosmogenesis is ultimately a process of unifying human spirits in and through Omega. As we have already noted, in the fullness of Teilhard's vision, there are not two evolutions but only one evolution with two facets, just as there are not two centers, Christ and Omega, but only Christ-Omega:

On the other hand, what happens when our minds awake first to a suspicion and then to clear evidence that the *Christ of*

Revelation is one and the same as the *Omega of evolution?*

Across the immensity of time and the disconcerting multiplicity of individuals, one single operation is taking place: the annexation to Christ of those whom he has chosen; one single thing is being formed: the mystical body of Christ.[6]

The Christian has certainty that Christogenesis is the fundamental motion or drift of historical process. Hyperphysics, however, can investigate the experimental data open to every human reason and find a directed movement in the evolutionary process. When it finds that this movement's direction possesses significant parallels to Christogenesis, hyperphysics has a right to feel that this constitutes a confirmation of its basic thesis.

Biological Value of Christianity

In Christianity Teilhard finds three "biological" elements which go to confirm his synthesis: 1) the general directions of Christianity's beliefs; 2) the extensiveness and qualitative newness of the Christian phylum; and 3) its vigorous powers of growth, assimilation and vivification.

The two points of dogma which Teilhard signalizes as embodying Christianity's essential belief are *personalism* and *universalism*—the same two points which necessarily characterize recent and future noogenesis.[7] Hyperphysics, though it leads to the projected unification of the *personal* and the *all*, cannot solve the deep psychological problem connected with man's existential condition in this cosmos: "Now how are we going to love something like the world or even humanity, realities that are collective, impersonal, even monstrous in certain respects? . . . [How is man going to conquer his] dread of that frightful cosmic machinery in which he finds himself entangled[?]"[8] There is no solution for this vexing and central problem of human evolution, Teilhard is convinced, at the level of human resources. The "experienced resolution" of the problem is found solely in God's historical incarnation, the "day Of his going in Galilee; Warm-laid grave of womb-like grey,"⁹ the becoming man of the infinite, the "All," the transcendent second person of the Blessed Trinity. By God's incarnation, the noogenetic requirement that the "All" somehow become humanly personalized is perfectly satisfied:

> Christ, principle of universal vitality because sprung up as man among men, put himself in a position (maintained ever since) to subdue under himself, to purify, to direct and to superanimate the general ascent of consciousness into which he inserted himself. By a perennial act of communion and sublimation, he aggregates to Himself the total psychism of the earth. And when he has gathered everything together and transformed everything . . . then, as St. Paul tells us, *God shall be all in all.* (294)

> There are men today . . . among whom the lived conjunction of the two ideas of Incarnation and evolution has led to the creation of a synthesis of the personal and the universal. For the first time in history men have become capable not only of understanding and serving, but of *loving evolution.*¹⁰

That is the illuminating synthesis which Christianity contributes to all those who wish to study the whole phenomenon of man but who discover that hyperphysics alone cannot lead them to an ultimate explanation. The Christian thinker is in a position "to look upon the discovery of Christogenesis as an ultimate explanation as well as a final crowning of the cosmogenesis discovered by science."¹¹

But, Teilhard asks, just what is Christianity? A vast association? A gentle philanthropism? "A big family? Yes, in a sense it is. But in another sense it is a prodigious biological operation," personalized by the presence and evolutive influence of Christ at its center. (293)¹² Since the "operation" tends towards the consummation when God "shall be all in all," and since a successful outcome of this "operation" is infallibly assured by the power and promise of Christ, the uncertainty of hyperphysics' conclusions and suggestions is overcome by the certainty of God's revelation. Teilhard has to admit that the deep human needs that he investigates again and again—the need for a fully coherent explanation of man's cosmic and temporal situation, the need for a well-grounded optimism about the value and permanence of human activities—cannot be adequately satisfied by hyperphysics alone. Another source of knowledge and hope, Christian revelation, serves to complete and confirm hyperphysics' unsure aspects and predictions.

> If we refuse to recognize the Christian fact, we are going to see the vault of the Universe, that for a moment opened above us, hermetically sealed.

> But if we take the step, if, following a reasonable probability, we are willing to see in the Church's living thought the reflection of divine thought adapted to our evolutionary state—then, our spirit can again move forward. And climbing . . . to the summit of things, we see not only some center that holds things together, not only some psychological First Mover, not only some being who speaks, but a Word who is incarnate.[13]

Ultimately, then, a "light other than that of pure science" is needed for an adequate vision of and hope for evolving man. (313)

Teilhard's Pantheism

The Christian vision of man culminates in Heaven—with the irreversible union of Christ and redeemed humanity. An intimation of this union is revealed in the Last Supper prayer of Christ: "Let them all be one. Just as you, Father, are in union with me and I am with you, let them be in union with us."[14] Teilhard expresses the final union thus:

> Then, as St. Paul tells us, *God shall be all in all.* This is indeed a superior form of 'pantheism' without trace of the poison of adulteration [losing identity] or annihilation: the expectation of perfect unity, steeped in which each element will reach its consummation at the same time as the universe.

> The universe fulfilling itself in a synthesis of centres in perfect conformity with the laws of union. God, the Centre of centres. (294)

The final union of Christ and redeemed mankind is more than prefigured by Christ's contemporary presence in and union with men and the cosmos. To express this Teilhard frequently spoke of a "Christian pantheism."

To justify a "Christian pantheism," Teilhard makes an initial distinction between a true and a false pantheism. The false pantheism, existing in two main forms, is characterized by an *identification* of God, men and cosmos (God becoming all), so that there is no longer any distinction between what initially might have been separate existents. This pantheism is poisoned by man's loss of identity or total annihilation. Spinoza is an excellent example of such pantheism. He scoffed at the belief in personal immortality, and he dreamt of "absorption in the immense calm in which is swallowed up all personality."[15]

True pantheism, on the other hand, is the *union* of Christ, man and cosmos, effected by a personalizing love; as the union becomes more intimate, the distinction between Christ and individual humans becomes more sharp, because the human elements become more personalized, more themselves.[16] Another way of contrasting true and false pantheism is to note that false pantheism achieves a unity by the *suppression* of multiplicity, whereas in a true pantheism unity is effected by the *concentration* of multiplicity.[17]

The two main forms of false pantheism which Teilhard considers are Oriental and Humanitarian Pantheisms. Though Teilhard admires the Oriental sense of the Whole ("the Orient fascinates me by its faith in the final unity of the Universe"), he finds fault with Oriental Pantheism's "*suppression* . . . of the Multiple," with the destruction of human identity and of "all individual riches," and with its devaluation of matter, research, personalization and earthly progress.[18] Humanitarian Pantheism, on the other hand, "represents around us a very new form of Religion." Outside of Marxism its manifestations are not "codified," but it is nonetheless a religion in the sense of "a contagious faith in an Ideal to which to give one's life." Principally, Humanitarian Pantheism proposes that "the supreme interest of existence consists in devoting oneself, body and soul, to the Universal progress—as expressed in the tangible developments of Humanity." The extent of this pantheism can be gauged by the evidence that "under various forms (communist or nationalist, scientific or political, individualistic or collectivist) we see being born and established around us, for a century, a Religion of Evolution."[19]

Teilhard's criticisms of this neopantheism begins with an appreciation of its element of truth: "By nature and by occupation I am too much a child of the World, not to feel myself at home in a temple constructed to the glory of the Earth. . . . I find erected [here] a sort of absolute, the birth of a grander consciousness and its essential cortège of creations and researches. I see myself provoked to unlimited efforts for the conquest of time and space." The false element in this pantheism is located in its refusal "to search if, in order to legitimize the gift they make of themselves, this Spirit presents itself to them endowed with immortality and personality. These two properties necessary, I believe, to justify human effort, they deny them, most often. . . . Hence, for me arises very quickly a sensation of insecurity, of achievement, of 'asphyxiation.' "[20]

Teilhard's own option of a "Christian pantheism" has a double root—theory and action. The necessity for "seeing things whole" demands an essential unity between Creator and creature. In explaining this unity, Teilhard remains true to orthodox Christian thought. However, he, like St. Thomas Aquinas, has been accused often of a false pantheism. The root of these accusations is "the inability to envisage any true personal monotheism except in the position of a God who is 'cut off from the world.' "[21]

If the only orthodox way to preserve the distinctness of God and creatures is by their absolute separation, then Christianity has a whole history of heterodoxy, beginning with St. Paul speaking to the council of the Areopagus: "it is in him [God] that we live, and move and have our being."[22] God's conservation of the cosmos can be looked upon quite correctly as the continuation of his act of creation; where his action is, he is. Since God can be discovered *in* any and every creature, he can be adored as found.

What most characterizes Teilhard's thought here is his "pantheism of action"—finding and experiencing God in all creatures and especially in our work and in the passivities we endure. That is the principal theme of *The Divine Milieu*, but with the significant clarification that God's presence is mediated now through Christ's incarnation and through the eucharist.[23] Teilhard was quite aware that there is always a danger of a false pantheism flowing from a true one (the same danger resides in any truth), but he insists that if a thinker retains a transcendent God as well as a historically incarnate God, the danger of a false pantheism is excluded. Analyzing natural mystical tendencies Teilhard observes:

> We must not let ourselves be disconcerted by the patent errors into which many mystics have fallen in their attempts to place or even to name the universal Smile. . . . It often happens that, like infants opening their eyes for the first time, men do not accurately locate the reality which they sense behind things. Their gropings often meet with nothing but a metaphysical phantom or a crude idol. . . . The false trails of pantheism bear witness to our immense need for some revealing word to come from the mouth of him who is.[24]

One other feature of Christianity, the triune personality of the one God, is a powerful preventive of false pantheism. If in God the Christian maintains "the distinction in persons, oneness in being, and equality in majesty," he should be able to continue living and growing in the mystery of Christ's intimate union with men and the cosmos, and of his perduring nonidentity with them.[25] The trinitarian mystery is also important in the early part of what might be called Teilhard's metaphysics. Because creation is a mirroring forth of the life of the three divine Persons, the metaphysical dynamism of being is a movement from created multiplicity towards its beatifying union with the three united yet distinct divine Persons.[26] Teilhard, however, is much more concerned with the present and with the proximate future, not nearly so much with the ultimate beginning or end of the universe. Hence, not the Trinity but the incarnate presence of Christ plays the dominant part in Teilhard's explanation of God's presence in an evolving world.

Christogenesis: Model for Noogenesis

Perceptive thinkers who possess knowledge from several quite distinct sources find their thought in one area fructified by that of another area. This phenomenon is quite marked in the evolution of Teilhard's thought. His science fertilized his theology and vice versa. Let us consider the instance which he remarks upon in this section of the *Phenomenon*:

> The universe fulfilling itself in a synthesis of centres in perfect conformity with the laws of union. God, the Centre of centres. In that final vision the Christian dogma culminates. And so exactly, so perfectly does this coincide with the Omega Point that doubtless I should never have ventured to envisage the latter [a convergent noogenesis in and through Omega] or formulate the hypothesis rationally if, in my consciousness as a believer, I had not found not only its speculative model but also its living reality [a Christogenesis]. (294)

Teilhard confesses that his knowledge of the unifying Body of Christ manifested in the Catholic church served as the inspiration and model for the basic features of *The Phenomenon of Man*: a cosmogenesis that became a noogenesis which, because it is convergent, must be centered in and by a transcendent personal Center:

As we know, the belief that the human individual cannot perfect himself or fully exist except through the organic unification of all men in God is essential and fundamental to Christian
doctrine. To this mystical super-organism, joined in Grace and
charity, we have now added a mysterious equivalent organism
born of biology: the "Noospheric" human unity gradually
achieved by the totalising and centrating effect of Reflection.[27]

That the revelation and experience of the Mystical Body of
Christ should serve as the inspiration for Teilhard's bold extension of science is not surprising. Early in Christian history,
the mystery of God's triune personality prodded an Augustine
to begin a philosophical exploration of human personality. In
the Middle Ages, the key philosophical insight of St. Thomas,
the primacy of the act of existence, was inspired by the biblical
revelation of God's proper name. And recently, Bernard
Lonergan's creative study of human knowledge was preceded
by a study of Trinitarian processions and of Christ's modes of
knowing. The conclusion to be drawn from this phenomenon of
theology's fructifying other ways of knowing is not that such
inspiration guarantees the validity of the new insight. A scientific or philosophical theory must be judged on its own merits,
not upon the source of its inspiration. A proper conclusion,
though, is that if the new theory coincides or fits with the
revealed data, this is confirming but not necessarily conclusive
evidence for the validity of the theory.[28]

We have seen that the convergent noogenesis of mankind's
evolution must be both universal and personal: "The outcome
of the world, the gates of the future, the entry into the super-
human . . . will open only to an advance of *all together*, in a
direction in which *all together* can join and find completion in
a spiritual renovation of the earth."(244-5) An elite may
spark in many ways the movement towards the universal union
of mankind, but the goal of human evolution is not the union
of an elite, whether of race, intelligence or any other particular-
ity. Human evolution must, in the process of unifying all men,

personalize them, make them more deeply themselves because they are united "center to center" by love.

This same universalism and personalism Teilhard finds in Christian teaching—and at the very center of it. Christianity is not a religion for Jews rather than Gentiles, for free men rather than slaves, for learned rather than unlearned.[29] The personalism of Christianity is manifest in its constant teaching of God as concerned providence and a self-revealer who invites a believer's personal response. Particularly impressive to Teilhard is the union of this personalism and universalism in the doctrine of the Mystical Body. Christ, the "Center of centers," "draws all things to himself" so that they might have "life and have it more abundantly."[30] "The universe fulfilling itself in a synthesis of centres in perfect conformity with the laws of union. God, the Centre of centres. In that final vision the Christian dogma culminates."(294) Because Teilhard finds that his generalized theory of evolution protects and enhances both universalism and personalism in a way parallel to what is revealed about Christ's Mystical Body, he feels that this "fit" is simultaneously a confirmation of his theory as well as an indication of the value and truth of Christianity.

Christianity—A "Biological" Phenomenon

Having shown how Christianity's teaching coincides with that of hyperphysics, Teilhard now wishes to inspect the "biological" characteristics of the Christian organism. Quantitatively we see Christianity spread through two thousand years and having made its influence felt in all aspects of human culture throughout the world. The sheer "quantity" of its uninterrupted existence and influence, as well as its having overcome innumerable external and internal vicissitudes, mark it as a phenomenon which must be integrated into any coherent theory of evolution.

Qualitatively Christianity is even more remarkable as a distinct phylum within human evolution. It has introduced a specifically new kind of consciousness into noogenesis—Christian love. Teilhard does not examine the love of Christianity's founder but looks rather to the massive manifestations of Christian love in its "thousands of mystics," in its "further thousands" who renounce all for the love of Christ and for the extension of his love through service to his "members," and finally in the countless faithful Christians. What is significant for the hyperphysicist looking at this phenomenon is the appearance and growth in the noosphere of a genuine universal love. The hyperphysicist is led to ask whether or not this is precisely the type of love necessary to bring noogenesis to fulfillment.

Christianity—"The Religion of the Future"

Christianity is designated by Teilhard as "the Religion of the Future" because of its vigorous powers of growth and its demonstrated power to satisfy the needs of a convergent noogenesis. The vigor of Christianity is seen by way of contrast to the senescence or death of ancient religions. In China Teilhard experienced the relics of the "dead religion" of Buddhism and its incapability to adjust to the "shock" of our twentieth century science and activity.[31] Christianity, Teilhard feels, is revealing itself under the impact of this "shock" as "inherently more vigorous in itself and as more necessary to the world than it has ever been before."(296) It reveals Christ investing "himself organically with the very majesty of his creation." In this "atmosphere of greatness and interconnectedness" the Christian religion has the vigor to continue living and to grow "with still greater speed and intensity." In part Christianity's vigor is situated in its bringing to natural hopes and desires an unexpected concreteness and certainty: "If the world is convergent and if Christ occupies its centre, then the Christogenesis of St. Paul and St. John is nothing else and nothing less than the extension, both awaited and unhoped for, of that noogenesis in which cosmogenesis—as regards our experience—culminates." (297)

Christianity validates and solidifies, then, the natural mysticism and adoration to which an extended science leads. Hyperphysics' uncertainties and vaguenesses are overcome by the historical and contemporary concreteness of Christ and by Christianity's certainties, shrouded though they be with shadows.[32] The world's evolutionary need for "the *personal* at the summit of *spirit*" can certainly be filled only by Christianity:

> At the present moment Christianity is the *unique* current of thought, on the entire surface of the noosphere, which is sufficiently audacious and sufficiently progressive to lay hold of the world, at the level of effectual practice, in an embrace, at once already complete, yet capable of indefinite perfection, where faith and hope reach their fulfilment in love. *Alone,* unconditionally alone, in the world today, Christianity shows itself able to reconcile, in a single living act, the All and the Person. (297-8)

It is for this reason that Teilhard designates Christianity as the "religion of the future." Because its "perspectives and aspirations" so coincide with hyperphysics' projections of the future, Teilhard feels that a man of science must ask himself whether or not Christianity is the fulfillment and completion of a cosmogenesis become noogenesis. "Is not the Christian phenomenon, which rises upwards at the heart of the social phenomenon, precisely that?(298-9)[33] Asked another way: Does not the Christian phenomenon reveal itself as the very heart of the evolving social phenomenon of a converging noogenesis?

The Catholic Phenomenon

For Christian readers it is worth noting further extensions of Teilhard's thought, extensions that do not fit within the narrow limits of *The Phenomenon of Man.* In "Turmoil or Genesis?" the fourth theorem reads: *"The Church is neither an Epi- nor a Para-Phenomenon in the growth of the Human Social Organism, but constitutes the very Axis (or Nucleus) about which it Forms.*"[34] For Teilhard, here, "Church" signifies the Church which is centered about Rome. But his apparent exclusivism is not as exclusive as it first seems in the following strong and direct statement:

> Were I to speak here as a Catholic, I would have to add that the Church, not from any "arrogance" but from structural necessity (under pain of denying her own identity), simply *cannot* avoid considering herself to be the *very axis* upon which the expected movement of gathering-together and convergence can and must take place.[35]

Mooney explains one of the exclusive aspects of Catholicism: infallibility. He notes that Teilhard's approach is in terms of "cephalization," the process of producing a more complex and centered "brain" for the higher and higher consciousness of mankind:

> To say that the Church is infallible is simply to recognize that it possesses what any living phylum possesses, namely the capacity to find its way through innumerable gropings toward maturity and fulfilment. Moreover, it is in perfect conformity with the great law of 'cephalization' which dominates the whole of biological evolution, to localize this phyletic infallibility either in the Councils or in the Pope, in so far as they formulate the thought of the Church. Outside Catholicism there are undoubtedly very many who know and love Christ and who are therefore just as united to him as Catholics, perhaps more so. But these 'are not grouped together in the "cephalized" unity of a *body* which reacts in a living way, as an organized whole, to the combined energies of Christ and humanity. They drink the sap of the tree as it flows from the trunk, but they neither penetrate beneath the bark to the tree's life source, nor do they participate in its inner growth. . . . To be a Christian in the fullest and deepest sense one has to be a Catholic."[36]

Interestingly enough, as Mooney notes, Teilhard's "belief in the central importance of the Catholic Church is asserted most strongly in those years when very severe strictures were being imposed upon him by his religious superiors as well as by other authorities in Rome."[37]

His Catholic belief is not a "blind faith," bereft of any empirical support. Just as there are "rational invitations to Faith" in Christ, so according to Teilhard there are rational invitations to faith in the Catholic Church. Through his extensive travel, he had experienced the Church's universality in space. And by calling the Catholic Church the central phylum of evolution, he clearly was aware of its vast and impressive extension in time. Similar phyla have disappeared, but Teilhard finds the Church more vigorous than ever. The eminent historian, Thomas Macaulay, not a Catholic nor fond of the Catholic Church, had to confess as a result of his survey of western civilization:

> The Catholic Church is still sending to the farthest ends of the earth missionaries as zealous as those who landed in Kent with Augustine, and still confronting hostile kings with the same spirit with which she confronted Attila. . . .
> Nor do we see any sign which indicates that the term of her long dominion is approaching. She saw the commencement of all the governments and of all the ecclesiastical establishments that now exist in the world; and we feel no assurance that she is not destined to see the end of them all. She was great and respected before the Saxon had set foot on Britain, before the Frank had passed the Rhine, when Grecian eloquence still flourished at Antioch, when idols were still worshipped in the temple of Mecca. And she may still exist in undiminished vigour when some traveller from New Zealand shall, in the midst of a vast solitude, take his stand on a broken arch of London Bridge to sketch the ruins of St. Paul's.[38]

Macaulay describes the "without" of the Church. Far more impressive for Teilhard as a "rational invitation to faith" is the Church's "within." Unfortunately his phenomenology scarcely explored this facet of the Church, but that he possessed the empirical basis is quite clear:

> I am absolutely convinced that there is infinitely more truth in

the empirical and complex attitude of the Church than in all our simplifying philosophies. The practice of the saints, even though difficult to rationalize, is the reality that must be accepted, that is "imposed," the concrete truth. It is that, accordingly, that must mould our attempts at systematizing, and it will never be possible for it to be fully contained in them.[39]

There are sufficient clues in Teilhard's writings to see something of the impact upon his soul of the Church's canonized saints. There are similar indices of the influence of the deep spirituality of his mother, of the heroic courage and patience of his favorite and invalid sister, Marguerite-Marie ("Guiguite"), and the single-minded generosity of another sister, Françoise, "intelligent and individualistic," declaring that "there are two things I shall never give up, my books and my freedom," and who came to do just that as a Little Sister of the Poor, nursing the aged in Shanghai.[40]

Teilhard also had the larger family of his confreres in the Society of Jesus (Jesuits) wherein he established many intimate and inspiring friendships. The geologist Dr. George Barbour, when asked what stood out most in Teilhard's personal life, replied after much thought, "I suppose his love of his religious community. Frequently he would push—or try to push—on ten more miles in order to stay overnight with fellow Jesuits in a mission station."[41]

Still larger was Teilhard's experience with Catholics and the Catholic church in the four corners of the earth. His words in "Le Christique," completed just a month before his death, summarize the prime evolutionary significance of Catholicism as he had experienced it throughout his life: "No religious faith, either now or at any moment in history, has ever released a greater warmth, a more intense dynamism for unification, than Christianity is doing at the present time, the more it is Catholic."[42]

The factual centrality of the Church of Rome did not blind Teilhard at all to its existential status as a "pilgrim Church," one with "spots and wrinkles," in constant need of reformation. "Christianity had deceived me, at first appearance, by its limited representation of the World, and by its incomprehension of the role of matter."[43] In 1936 he can speak of an "aging Christianity," but insisted that only those who love the Church are in a position to criticize her fairly. He was not scandalized "that the emancipating spirit of the Church is indissolubly bound up with its existence in an organized body, whatever may be the vulgar corruptions and inconveniences inherent in this incorporation, Vatican intrigues or repository trash."[44] Love of the Church involves pain from seeing her disorders and imperfections:

> Blessed are those who suffer at not seeing the Church so fair as they would wish and who are only the more submissive and prayerful for it. It is a profound grief, but of high spiritual value. . . . There are motives [for belief in the Church] that God is master of, and *in spite of* stumbling blocks. Why is it that so many minds see nothing but the stumbling blocks and wait until they have removed them before they look at the motives?[45]

Perhaps it is just as well to end this section about "The Catholic Phenomenon" on a negative note, since our study will terminate with a consideration of the *Phenomenon's* Appendix, "Some Remarks on the Place and Part of Evil in a World in Evolution." Teilhard saw fit to make it a part of his book: the *Path* ought to follow his lead.

"The Mystery of Iniquity"

Why did Teilhard add an appendix, composed about a decade after the completion of the *Phenomenon*? Père Charles, theologian and lifelong friend, urged Teilhard to add the "Remarks . . . on Evil," probably in the hope that this addition would aid in the gaining of permission to publish the *Phenomenon*. The Appendix was written in Rome while Teilhard was actively seeking this permission. He says that he added the piece

as "my answer (or, if you like, my excuse) to the frequent reproach of naive or exaggerated optimism" which is thought to
be manifested by the absence in the *Phenomenon* of any mention of "pain or wrong." That this criticism was able to nettle
Teilhard (as completely wrong-headed criticism was not) can
be sensed in the edge on his words: "What good would it have
done to have drawn attention to the shadows on the landscape,
or to stress the depths of the abysses between the peaks? Surely
they were obvious enough." (311)

The title of this section, "The Mystery of Iniquity," does not
imply that nothing can be known about evil and its coexistence
with a God affirmed to be good. On the contrary, we wish to
underline our *knowledge* of conspicuous evils *and* of God's
manifest goodness; what is mysterious or dark for our understanding is how to reconcile the two. It is not that we are
completely clueless in our efforts to reconcile evil with God's
goodness; rather, we are sure that we will always be seeking
for more comprehensive understanding, no matter how far our
knowledge and trust carry us.

Teilhard more than once acknowledges that evil is indeed a
mystery.[46] He does not deny the existence of evil: after all, it
was in the midst of the cataclysm of the First World War that
he conceived and set down the main lines of his synthesis. His
childhood was probably idyllic, but the reality of evil was soon
experienced shortly after he entered the Society of Jesus and
was forced into exile because of his religious profession. To this
could be added an almost endless account of interior and exterior evils which came his way.[47]

The trouble that Teilhard's friendliest critics find with his
synthesis is not that he denies evil, but that he does not "allow
more room to the drama of sin." Père de Lubac feels that
human sin can be explored far more deeply by hyperphysics
than Teilhard actually does.[48] Mooney also criticizes him:

There is Teilhard's strange tendency to depersonalize sin when
speaking of reparation. His attitude here is both illogical and

superficial, since he thereby divorces reparation from the function of love in his own system and tends to consider sin itself simply as a regrettable invasion of physical evil into the realm of freedom.[49]

Concerning original sin, there is no question that Teilhard, reacting overstrongly to certain emphases, thought that the traditional expression of original sin was a source of useless gloom and served to destroy needed hope in the future progress of evolution. Over and over he experienced the traditional or common understanding of original sin as a towering scandal to the "Gentile," his agnostic colleagues. Consequently, the usual explanation of original sin would have to be changed if Christianity were to become a meaningful world view for the "Gentiles":

> Original sin (under its present form) opposes at every point the expansion of our religion on the natural level. It cuts the wings of hope. Every time we are about to launch out into the open spaces of optimistic conquest, it inexorably pulls us back into the oppressive gloom of reparation and expiation.[50]

Teilhard also felt that for the Christian, Christ could not have truly cosmic dimensions if original sin is restricted to "an accident which took place towards the end of the Tertiary era in some small corner of the earth."[51] According to Mooney, what Teilhard's revision proposed was a "universalization" of original sin:

> [His was] an effort to universalize original sin by identifying it with the physical imperfection of the world at the moment of creation, and then with the inevitable presence of physical evil in the ensuing process of evolutionary change. In this sense it must be considered the 'cosmic fundament' of moral evil and not its 'historical actuation', which would occur only with the advent of fully responsible human action.[52]

Mooney is correct when he says that Teilhard's thought on original sin "represents an honest attempt at a much needed reform which, for lack of theological judgment, inevitably mis-carried." But his criticism is too sweeping when he judges that Teilhard's opinions on original sin "are of little theological value."[53]

But why does not personal human sin have a more pro-portionate place in Teilhard's writings? Why is it that we can find in him "hardly a trace of that 'super-natural—or trans-natural entropy' which, in the lives of each of us, and until the final consummation, continues to provide a disconcerting obstruction that Christ alone can remove?"[54] Though hyper-physics is constructed precisely to give entrance into the world of the "within," Teilhard "generally stops at the threshold of this interior universe."[55] Even inside the limits imposed by hyperphysics, Teilhard clearly could have pushed further his investigation of the data of evil, especially the phenomenon of personal malice. Michael Murray suggests that an apologetic aim is partially responsible for Teilhard's near silence on personal sin:

> Teilhard was engaged in *combatting* the general discouragement of his time, and concurrently he was trying to heal the split between Church and world. He was addressing himself simul-taneously to the churchman disgusted with the world and to a world disillusioned with itself and alienated from a Church which seemed to offer it not so much a hope as a backstairs by which to escape. Furthermore, he was appealing to the surviv-ing optimists—scientists, humanists, Marxists—who continued to found their hopes upon the quicksands of material progress and man's natural goodness, by proclaiming Christ to them as the only sure foundation and goal of their faith. Hope, not dread, was the key of his message.[56]

Mooney places the chief cause of Teilhard's "softness" on the personal element of sin in his overreacting to the theological and psychological problems caused by some traditional rep-resentations of original sin. In one view mankind is struggling to return to a primitive state of natural perfection—hardly progress in any usual sense of the word; another view would have humanity so damaged by the fatal flaw of original sin that any real progress is impossible. In addition to trying to counteract these misrepresentations, there is the sheer hazard of trying to rethink sin in the context of an evolving universe instead of the traditional stationary one. The magnitude of this task is full of risks, not the least of which is the tendency to reduce sin to some earlier form of evil. Finally we may note the intriguing possibility suggested by Mooney:

> We may well ask whether the ultimate reason for such an attitude was not Teilhard's own over-sensitivity to evil. Is it not possible that he himself felt the terror of man's rejection of love too deeply to consider it objectively? Could not his optimistic unconcern for sin have been a reaction against a natural disposition towards extreme pessimism?[57]

Whatever the causes of Teilhard's deficiency in sufficiently inserting the fact of human sin, both original and personal, into his synthesis, there are two anomalies which help to focus the problem. In the first place, one might say that the reason Teilhard is forced to ignore the personal element in both original and personal sin is that in the universal perspective adopted by hyperphysics there is no room for the individual aspects of sin. Sin cannot be presented as a rupture between Christ and individual men because of the huge sweep of Teilhard's perspective. The statistical aspect of sin tends to be the only aspect investigated. A process of evolutionary ordering necessarily involves disorder; it is statistically necessary that there be moral and physical evils in an evolving cosmos, just as it is statistically necessary that some letters fail to reach their destinations. But how are we to explain that with regard to other evils (for example, pain, failure, death, et cetera), Teilhard's phenomenology can be quite detailed in its exploration of particulars, but is largely silent on personal sin?

In the second place, there seems to be something more than the usual tension between the power of human freedom and

God's omnipotence and universal will to save man. We have seen strong stress on the power of human freedom which Teilhard highlights by the starkness of the fundamental option: refusal or acceptance of Omega. At least initially he is equally clear on the magnitude of the consequences of the human power of freedom: "ecstasy in concord; or discord," heaven or hell.(289) "Ultimate life (i.e., a fullness of consciousness embracing at once all reality) or ultimate death (i.e., an infinite splintering of consciousness upon itself)."[58] Ambiguity occurs when he considers hell, "which so affronts our human views." Visibly he struggled with this dogma. He would rather not believe in it. Knowing that it is revealed he sought to incorporate it into this synthesis: "We could perhaps understand falling back into in-existence . . . but what are we to make of eternal uselessness and eternal suffering?" Then by his emphasis on being "forbidden to hold with absolute certainty that any single man has been damned," by his prayer that "the flames of hell . . . may never touch anyone," and by his stressing God's power "to turn each and *every* particular evil into good," there seems to be some diminution of the fullness of human freedom and of the magnitude of chosen evil or good, and their diverse consequences.[59]

On the positive side, it must be said in Teilhard's favor that his *general* theory of evil aided him to make a significant contribution. Mooney affirms that "it is not too much to say that Teilhard's approach to the cosmic aspect of redemption constitutes a major step forward towards a fuller understanding of the relationship between the Person of Christ and the natural evolutionary process."[60] Considering the whole gamut of his thought, inasmuch as it has theological ramifications, Mooney's judgment is:

With the sole exception of his very tentative theory on original sin, all of his [Teilhard's] opinions fall within this area of free theological discussion. They concern change in the intelligence of the faith, not in the faith itself. The final judgment of this present work, therefore, is that Teilhard's theological effort to rethink the mystery of Christ in terms of *genèse* [evolution] constitutes a viable, though at times highly disputable, interpretation of Christian revelation.[61]

With this we can agree, though noting that the above is a limited evaluation—from the theological viewpoint, which necessarily leaves unmentioned other very important aspects of his thought.

We can here but remind the reader of one connected aspect of Teilhard's thought—his ascetical teaching. True, *The Divine Milieu*, the foremost example of his ascetics, practically excluded the consideration of personal sin: "the reader need not, therefore, be surprised at the apparently small space allotted to moral evil and sin: the soul with which we are dealing is assumed to have already turned away from the path of error."[62] Within these limitations, however, Teilhard is able to present a much admired "lived resolution" of the problem of evil in "The Passivities of Diminishment."[63] His thoughts on death, a "universal power of diminishment and extinction," have been for many readers the source of heightened understanding, decreased fear and strengthened hope. As he hints at the very end of *The Phenomenon of Man,* the various evils of a cosmos in evolution, because they share in the way of the Cross, are both capable of being and will be transformed into good by the "resurrecting power" of him who is "the first and the last, the living and the dead and the risen again."[64]

READING SUGGESTIONS

1. *Read PM*, 291-299.

2. *See Glossary for*: [becoming 'element' (294,= becoming incarnate], *biological, City of God, *consistence, sublimation, pantheism.

3. *Passages to be noted*:

294, "The universe fulfilling itself etc." T. affirms that his experience in the Church, the organic Body of Christ, was the inspiration and model for *PM*'s vision of a convergent cosmogenesis.

294-296, "Existence-Value." T. indicates that Christianity is an existing and evolving phylum within the cosmos; it is not a mere ideology, but an extensively active current in the noosphere, especially remarkable for the intensity and universality of the love which it generates.

297, "take the place of evolution"= to carry evolution on in a new mode.

4. *Parallel Readings*:

cosmic Christ: *FM,* 93-96 (96-100); *HU,* 19-37, *41-55, 133-155; *WTW,* 46-71, 290-302; de Lubac, *Man,* 29-38.

Christ as Omega: *FM,* 22-24 (23-5); *SC,* 34-36, *53-66; Mooney, 71-103 (78-111).

Christogenesis: *SC,* 14-20; *Mooney, 146-188 (156-199); de Lubac, *Man,* 39-48.

Christianity and cosmogenesis: *DM,* 68-73; *FM,* 223-226 (231-35); *SC,* 98-112, 118-127; de Lubac, *T. Explained,* 21-37; Mooney, 48-66 (55-73).

pantheism: *DM,* 116-121; *WTW,* 47-48; de Lubac, *Religion,* 152-160; Mooney, 179-181 (190-192).

evil: *DM,* 80-94; *PM,* 311-313; *Mooney, 122-145 (130-155); de Lubac, *Man,* 39-48; *Murray, 90-105.

ascetical teaching: *DM,* 112-155; *MM,* 180-181; *SC,* 66-78; *WTW,* 115-149, 203-224, 226-248, 250-269.

5. *Critiques*: general: Chaix-Ruy, 275-294; *de Lubac, *Religion,* 206-220; Nogar, *Lord,* 122-126; *Rideau, 245-255.

language: de Lubac, *Man,* 39-41 and *Religion,* 66-67.

evil: de Lubac, *Man,* 99-110; Rideau, 72-73; Tresmontant, 94-98.

extreme Incarnationism: Mooney, 202-206 (213-217).

natural and supernatural: Mooney, 206-209 (218-221).

FOOTNOTES

NOTE:

1) Full publishing data is given in the Bibliography.

2) Quotations from sacred scripture are from *The Complete Bible: An American Bible* (Chicago: Chicago University Press, 1939), unless otherwise indicated.

3) In the footnotes, "T." is the abbreviation used for "Teilhard."

ABBREVIATIONS

Works of Teilhard de Chardin

AM:	*The Appearance of Man* (1966).
DM:	*The Divine Milieu* (1965)—*not* 1960 edition.
Écrits:	*Écrits du temps de la guerre* (1965).
FM	*The Future of Man* (1964 and 1969; pages in 1969 edition are given in parentheses after those of the 1964 edition).
HIB:	*How I Believe* (1936)—*not* 1969 edition.
HU:	*Hymn of the Universe* (1965).
LT:	*Letters from a Traveller* (1962).
LTF:	*Letters to Two Friends* (1968).
MM:	*The Making of a Mind: Letters from a Soldier-Priest* (1965).
MPN:	*Man's Place in Nature* (1966).
Oeuvres:	*Oeuvres de Pierre Teilhard de Chardin* (1955-).

PM: *The Phenomenon of Man* (1965)—*not* 1959 edition.

SC: *Science and Christ* (1969).

VP: *The Vision of the Past* (1965).

WTW: *Writings in Time of War* (1968).

Other Works Frequently Cited

Abbott: Walter M. Abbott, S.J., editor, *The Documents of Vatican II* (1966).

Braybrooke: Neville Braybrooke, editor, *Teilhard de Chardin: Pilgrim of the Future* (1964).

Cuénot: Claude Cuénot, *Teilhard de Chardin, A Biographical Study* (1965).

Francoeur, World: Robert T. Francoeur, *The World of Teilhard de Chardin* (1961).

Francoeur, Perspectives: Robert T. Francoeur, *Perspectives in Evolution* (1965).

de Lubac, Man: Henri de Lubac, S.J., *Teilhard de Chardin: The Man and His Meaning* (1965).

de Lubac, Religion: Henri de Lubac, S.J., *The Religion of Teilhard de Chardin* (1967).

de Lubac, Teilhard Explained: Henri de Lubac, S.J., *Teilhard Explained* (1968).

Mooney: Christopher Mooney, S.J., *Teilhard de Chardin and the Mystery of Christ* (1966 and 1968; pages in 1968 edition are given in parentheses after those of 1966 edition).

Murray: Michael Murray, *The Thought of Teilhard de Chardin, An Introduction* (1966).

Nogar, Lord: Raymond J. Nogar, O.P., *The Lord of the Absurd* (1966).

Nogar, Wisdom: Raymond J. Nogar, O.P., *The Wisdom of Evolution* (1966).

Path: W. Henry Kenney, S.J., *A Path Through Teilhard's Phenomenon* 1970).

Rabut: Olivier Rabut, O.P., *Teilhard de Chardin: A Critical Study* (1961).

Rideau: Emile Rideau, S.J., *The Thought of Teilhard de Chardin* (1967).

Smulders: Piet Smulders, S.J., *The Design of Teilhard de Chardin* (1967).

Speaight: Robert Speaight, *The Life of Teilhard de Chardin* (1967).

Tax, Evolution: Sol Tax, editor, *Evolution After Darwin* (1960).

Tresmontant: Claude Tresmontant, *Pierre Teilhard de Chardin: His Thought* (1959).

Wildiers: N. M. Wildiers, *The Thought of Teilhard de Chardin* (1968).

Footnote for Preface

[1]*LT*, 261.

Footnote for Chapter One

[1]Cf. letter of August 22, 1925, in Mooney, 193 (204). The " 'hominization' written *ad usum gentilium"* refers to an early draft of *The Phenomenon of Man* "for the use of Gentiles," that is, for nonbelievers.

Footnotes for Chapter Two

[1]Cuénot, 400.
[2]Cuénot, 3.
[3]Cuénot, 4.
[4]Cuénot, 3.
[5]Pierre LeRoy, S.J., "Teilhard de Chardin: The Man," in *LT*, 46.
[6]*Poems of Gerard Manley Hopkins,* ed. by Robert Bridges (Oxford: Oxford University Press, 1930), 26.
[7]Tresmontant, 7.
[8]Hans J. Morgenthau, "Death in the Nuclear Age," *Commentary,* XXXII (Sept., 1961), 234.
[9]Mircea Eliade, *Cosmos and History* (New York: Harper Torchbook, 1959), 92.
[10]*Ibid.,* 3-4.
[11]"The Spiritual Power of Matter" (1919), in *HU,* 67.
[12]Sherwood Anderson, *A Story Teller's Tale* (New York: B. W. Huebsch, 1924), 270.
[13]*PM*, 36.
[14]The first of the three sketches which make up "Christ in the World of Matter" centers upon a picture "representing Christ offering his heart to men." *HU,* 42-50.
[15]John Kobler, "The Priest Who Haunts the Catholic World," *Saturday Evening Post* (Oct. 12, 1963), 48.
[16]I Corinthians 15:26-8.
[17]Philippians 1:21; Galatians 2:20; Philippians 3:12.
[18]"Cosmic Life" (1916), *WTW,* 51-2.
[19]Matthew 22:37, 10:34-8; John 18:36, 15:18-19, 17:9.
[20]Alfons Auer, "The Christian Understanding of the World" in *The Christian and the World* (New York, Kenedy, 1966), 30.
[21]See Abbott, 235, 237, 239.
[22]Cuénot, 7.
[23]*The Imitation of Christ,* Bk. I, chap. 1; Bk. III, chap. 16; Bk. III, chap. 31.
[24]"Terrena despicere, et amare caelestia" is found in the postcommunion prayer for the feast of the Sacred Heart, surely a thorny anomaly

for T's intense devotion to the Sacred Heart *and* the world. Some other expressions are in Masses for the feast of St. Paulinus and for the third Sunday after Pentecost. The recent *Sacramentary* blunts the sharp disjunction of the original prayers by translations of highly questionable fidelity to the original. However, more realistic praying seems preferable to scholarly precision.

[25]*MM*, 223-4.

[26]*DM*, 68.

[27]William A. Luijpen, O.S.A., *Phenomenology and Atheism* (Pittsburgh: Duquesne University Press, 1964), 319.

[28]Letter of August 18, 1950 in Cuénot, 272.

[29]René D'Ouince, S.J., "L'Épreuve de l'obéissance dans la vie du Père Teilhard de Chardin," *L'Homme devant Dieu* (Paris: Aubier, 1964), vol. III, 341.

[30]Matthew 6:24.

[31]"Cosmic Life" (1916), *WTW*, 17.

[32]Letter of March 15, 1916, in de Lubac, *Religion*, 243.

[33]*HIB*, 7-8.

[34]"Christologie et évolution" (1940), in Rideau, 325-6. See also "Some Reflections on Progress" (1941), *FM*, 76-7 (79-80), "The Heart of the Problem" (1949), *FM*, 260-1 (272-3).

[35]*MM*, 114. For a contemporary discussion of the problem of the double vocation, see George B. Murray, S.J., "The Hyphenated Priest," *Review for Religious*, vol. 25, no. 4 (July, 1966), 693-702.

[36]*HIB*, 7.

[37]Letter of Oct. 11, 1936, in Cuénot, 214.

[38]Rideau, 36. This, like most of his sections, is heavily documented with generous quotations from Teilhard.

[39]*Ibid.*, 325, 327.

[40]"Mastery of the World and the Kingdom of God" (1916), *WTW*, 90.

[41]"La parole attendue" (1940), in Rideau, 301.

[42]The Heart of the Problem" (1949), *FM*, 265 (277).

[43]Admittedly this is an oversimplification of the thesis of Harvey Cox's *The Secular City*, but it does seek to express the "drift" of this work which has been clearly superseded by his later writings.

[44]"A Note on Progress" (1920), *FM*, 23 (24). For other expressions of the "one evolution" see Mooney, 148 (158).

[45]For a scriptural view of the unity between Christ, mankind and the cosmos, especially as this is expressed by St. Paul, see Mooney, 87-103 (95-111).

[46]"Le Christique" (1955), quoted in WTW, 91.

[47]Pierre LeRoy, S.J., in *LT*, 45.

[48]"Le Coeur de la matière (1950), quoted in Mooney, 30 (35).

[49]*Evolution after Darwin*, ed. by Sol Tax (Chicago: University of Chicago Press, 1960), III, 107.

[50]See Raymond J. Nogar, O.P., *The Wisdom of Evolution* (New York: Doubleday, 1963). Chapter II presents the paleontological evidence; chapters III-V give the evidence from other sources.

[51]Newman quoted by A. Dwight Culler, *The Imperial Intellect: A Study of Newman's Educational Ideal* (New Haven: Yale University Press, 1955), 267. For Newman the second option *was* unthinkable.

[52]Pope Pius XII, *Humani Generis* (Washington: National Catholic

Welfare Conference, 1950), 16-17.

[53]See Jean de Fraine, S.J., *The Bible and the Origin of Man* (New York: Desclee, 1962), sec. III, "The Teaching of the Church."

[54]Several representative studies are listed in the Suggested Readings at the end of this chapter.

[55]Galileo quoted by James Brodrick, S.J., *Robert Bellarmine* (Westminster, Maryland: Newman, 1961), 354-5. Galileo assigns the aphorism to Cardinal Baronius.

[56]John L. McKenzie, S.J., *The Two-Edged Sword* (Milwaukee: Bruce, 1956), 108.

[57]Teilhard quoted by de Lubac, *Man*, 9.

[58]Teilhard quoted by Rideau, 295.

[59]*DM*, 110.

[60]Acts 9:1-6.

[61]See Chapter X, *Path*, for further developments of the relation between Christ, Christians, and cosmos.

[62]Ephesians 4:11-13, emphasis added. This translation is presently used for the liturgy of the vigil of the Ascension. See also Colossians 2: 18-19. In John 15:1-9 there is the reinforcement of Jesus' own designation of himself as the vine and the apostles as branches; the most obvious thing about vines is that they grow with "gay abandon."

[63]"The Priest" (1918), *WTW*, 220; Letter of Oct. 20, 1924 quoted in de Lubac, *Man*, 157.

[64]"Christianisme et évolution" (1945), in de Lubac, *Man*, 32.

[65]George Vass, S.J., "Teilhard de Chardin and Inward Vision" in *The Heythrop Journal*, II, no. 3 (July, 1961), 247.

[66]Abbott, 715.

[67]"Cosmic Life" (1916), *WTW*, 59.

[68]Mooney, 13 (13).

[69]*LT*, 257 and 261.

[70]*DM*, 46, ftn.

Footnotes for Chapter Three

[1]*LT*, 263.

[2]P. B. Medawar, review of *PM* in *Mind* 70 (1961), 99; in Huxley's introduction to *LT*, 14.

[3]*PM*, 30. Cf. Cuénot, 120, 213, and Rideau, 38-44, 332-42. T. had almost countless synonymns for hyperphysics: hyperbiology, ultra-physics, generalized physics, phenomenology, natural history, etc.

[4]Aage Petersen, *Quantum Physics and the Philosophical Tradition*, mimeographed edition (New York: Belfer Graduate School, 1966), 10.

[5]"The Phenomenon of Man" (1930), *VP*, 161.

[6]*Ibid.*, 162.

[7]*Ibid.*, 161.

[8]Reported in *Science News Letter*, Apr. 24, 1965.

[9]The last paragraph is a very adequate, but dense, synopsis of what T. thinks he achieves by *PM*'s hyperphysics; the paragraph will be explained in some detail in the *Path's* ninth chapter.

[10]September 23, 1940, letter in George Barbour, *In the Field with Teilhard de Chardin* (New York: Herder & Herder, 1965), 110.

[11]Jean Piveteau, in his introduction to Teilhard's *MPN*, 9.

[12]To forestall some of this criticism, T. added *PM*'s Appendix, "Some Remarks on the Place and Part of Evil in a World in Evolution," and his notes on freedom, spirit and pantheism (307-10).

[13]On the need for a "renewed" theology, see Rideau, 575-6, and Murray, 48.

[14]"The final chapter of philosophy consists in the search for the unexpressed presuppositions which underlie the beliefs of every finite human intelligence." Alfred North Whitehead, "John Dewey and His Influence," in *The Philosophy of John Dewey*, ed. by P. A. Schilpp (Evanston, Illinois: Northwestern University Press, 1939), 478.

[15]*PM*, 254-72.

[16]de Lubac, *Man*, 133.

[17]Cuénot, 101.

[18]N. M. Wildiers thinks that T.'s nonscientific writings do not proceed by an ordering coming from his apologetics, but are structured by "the desire to illuminate his own mind." Quoted in de Lubac, *Religion*, 231, but the identification of Wildiers and the *locus* will only be found in the original, *La Pensée religieuse du Père Teilhard de Chardin* (Paris: Aubier, 1962), 332.

[19]*HIB*, 10.

[20]One is strongly reminded of Augustine's *Confessions* and *The City of God*. The psychiatrist Karl Stern develops several of the similarities in an essay to be found in both *Teilhard de Chardin: Pilgrim of the Future*, edited by Neville Braybrooke, and in *The World of Teilhard*, edited by Robert T. Francoeur.

[21]"The Priest" (1918), *WTW*, 222.

[22]*LT*, 73. Note the "renewal theme," the enrichment of the Church by the world. For Vatican II's view, see Abbott, 239, 245-7.

[23]August 22, 1925, letter in Mooney, 193 (204). "Hominization" is the title of an essay written at the same time, 1925, and "divinization" refers to the first draft of *The Divine Milieu*.

[24]"Christianisme et évolution" (1945), quoted in de Lubac, *Man*, 121.

[25]*MM*, 186.

[26]de Lubac, *Man*, 120. In 1941, "as though he already felt the postwar 'existentialist' wave which he was to come up against when he returned to France from China," he resolved "to devote himself by all possible means to the defense of the idea of the reality of a progress (collective and personalizing) against every secular or religious pessimism." (de Lubac, *Man*, 107-8; *MM*, 276.) Perhaps this writer is wrong, but it seems inconceivable that a pope prior to John XXIII could have protested against the Church's "withdrawal into itself." Paul VI recently asserted that in the contemporary world the Christian faith must "become ever more a social, professional and civic commitment." (*America*, 114, No. 24 [Jn. 11, 1966], 820.)

[27]*LT*, 228; Cuénot, 40.

[28]*DM*, 54.

[29]de Lubac, *Man*, 118.

[30]de Lubac, *Religion*, 233.

[31]One of T.'s essays is entitled "Le Christ évoluteur," "Christ, the Evolver," 1942.

[32]Cf. "Note pour servir à l'évangélisation des temps nouveaux" (1919), quoted in Mooney, 193 (204).

[33]"The Wreck of the Deutschland," *Poems*, 11.
[34]*MM*, 159.
[35]For Teilhard's synopsis of his apologetics, see Mooney, 34-5 (39-40).
[36]"Le Christique" (1955) and "Comment je vois" (1948), quoted in Mooney, 25 (29).
[37]de Lubac, *Religion*, 183: Mooney, 24 (25).
[38]*Scientific American*, CCII, no. 4 (April, 1960), 206.
[39]See Huxley's introduction to *LT*, 14.
[40]"Esquisse d'un univers personnel" (1936), *Oeuvres* VI, 73; letter of May 27, 1923, quoted in Cuénot, 378.
[41]*HIB*, 9.
[42]The psychological need of a meaningful world-view is forcefully made in Viktor E. Frankl's *Man's Search for Meaning* (New York: Washington Square Press, 1963). The original title was *From Death-Camp to Existentialism*.
[43]Baruch 3:27.
[44]"Note pour servir à l'évangélisation des temps nouveaux" (1918), *Écrits*, 380-1.
[45]*HIB*, [3].
[46]*LT*, 205.
[47]de Lubac, *Man*, 15.
[48]"How May We Conceive and Hope that Human Unanimisation Will Be Realised on Earth?" (1950), *FM*, 287 (301).
[49]"Life and the Planets" (1946), *FM*, 97 (101).
[50]The titles of the *Phenomenon's* four "books" are: Before Life Came; Life; Thought; Survival. We must note the deficient translation of the first and last titles. *"Prévie"* is better translated "Pre-Life" in order to show the thrust of evolving matter towards life, and also to connect the beginning with the end as Teilhard does by titling Book IV *"Survie."* The English "Survival" is literal enough but completely misses the meaning and connotation of the original. Both "Super-Life" and "Future Life" are connoted by the original—hardly covered by the joyless "Survival."
[51]Letter of June 19, 1951, in Cuénot, 288.
[52]*HIB*, 9, with T.'s punctuation. For further aspects of "philosophic option," see Mooney, 49, 65 (54-5, 71-2).
[53]"Science et Christ" (1921), *SC*, 36.
[54]*LT*, 261. *FM*, 267-9 (279-82) points out the correlations between "faith in the world" and a faith in Christ.

Footnotes for Chapter Four

[1]*LT*, 261.
[2]Braybrooke, 119.
[3]de Lubac, *Religion*, 11-12. The *Path's* final chapter, "Christogenesis," seeks to express this religious dimension of T.'s thought. It is significant to note that the first three theorems of T.'s "Turmoil or Genesis?" parallel the three conclusions of *PM's* summary. The fourth and final theorem of "Turmoil or Genesis?" is: "The Christian phylum is not an accessory or divergent shoot in the human social organism, but constitutes the axis itself of socialisation." *FM*, 215 (223).
[4]On pp. 335-7, Rideau gives many leads to T's theory of truth. In *HIB*, using the concept of "faith," T. analyzes the tension between evidence and

freedom in world views. Both at *PM's* beginning and end, T. makes the role of freedom clear by calling his assumptions and conclusions "postulates" and "options." (30, 306)

[5]"Turmoil or Genesis?" (1948), *FM* 217, (225-6).

[6]Cf. *ibid.,* 215 (223-4).

[7]*Ibid.,* 216 (224).

[8]*Ibid.,* 215 (223-4).

[9]*Ibid.,* 216 (224).

[10]Sir James Jeans, quoted by T. in "Man's Place in Nature" (1947), *VP,* 221-2. A cosmic view equally as stark is expressed by Bertrand Russell, *Mysticism and Logic* (New York: Doubleday, 1957), 45 and 54.

[11]Vercors, *The Murder of the Missing Link* (New York: Pocket Books, 1955). The British title is *You Shall Know Them*; this translates the original French title.

[12]"Turmoil or Genesis?" (1948), *FM,* 219 (227).

[13]*Ibid.,* 218-20 (226, 228).

[14]Julian Huxley, *Evolution in Action* (New York: Harper & Brothers, 1953), 147-8.

[15]"The Singularities of the Human Species" (1954), *AM,* 210.

[16]Murray, 17.

[17]"Turmoil or Genesis?" (1948), *FM,* 221 (229-30).

[18]Rosemary Park, "Alma Mater, Emerita," in *The University in America,* Occasional Paper of The Center for the Study of Democratic Institutions, Santa Barbara, 1967.

[19]"The Grand Option" (1945), *FM,* 45 (47-8).

[20]Quoted in Ayn Rand, *For the New Intellectual* (New York: Signet, 1963), 168.

[21]"Turmoil or Genesis?" (1948), *FM,* 221 (229).

[22]"Basis and Foundation of the Idea of Evolution" (1926), *VP,* 140.

[23]For the concern of this Symposium with psychosocial evolution see vol. II, and the reports of Panels Four and Five in vol. III of *Evolution After Darwin,* edited by Sol Tax.

[24]Cuénot, 255.

[25]"The End of the Species" (1953), *FM,* 301 (315); "Life and the Planets" (1945), *FM,* 122 (126-7).

[26]"Turmoil or Genesis?" (1948), *FM,* 221-2 (230), but following the French. Note that for T., "juridical" is a "bad word." It means, in this context, a trivial or chance arrangement in the human sphere, having nothing really in common with essential evolution. Cf. *PM,* 305.

[27]Revelation 1:8.

Footnotes for Chapter Five

[1]See Blaise Pascal, *Pensées,* translated by W. F. Trotter (New York: Dutton, 1958), No. 72. For good reasons T. and Pascal are frequently compared. The similarities go beyond common geographical origins and a common apologetics. See Cuénot, 211 and 233-4.

[2]*Ibid.,* No. 72, p. 17.

[3]*HIB,* 12-14.

[4]Alfred North Whitehead, *Science and the Modern World* (New York: Mentor, 1948), 115.

[5]"The New Spirit" (1942), *FM*, 83 (87).

[6]Whitehead points out the truth of this statement in the context of relativity space-time. See his *Science and the Modern World,* 50-3 and 110-18.

[7]E. L. Mascall, *Christian Theology and Natural Science* (London: Longmans, Green, 1957), 155-61. For a metaphysical argument against entropy, see T. Alec Burkill, *God and Reality in Modern Thought* (Englewood, N. J.: Prentice-Hall, 1963), 179-85. Sacred scripture presents two divergent sets of texts: one in which this world will end in a cataclysm and another in which it is transformed into the "New Jerusalem." St. Thomas, for root metaphysical reasons, holds the latter position in *S.T.,* I, 104, 4.

[8]The first edition has "physical" instead of "psychic," and that can cause unbounded confusion in trying to grasp T.'s thought.

[9]"The Phenomenon of Man" (1930), *VP,* 162.

[10]Errol Harris, *The Foundations of Metaphysics in Science* (London: George Allen and Unwin, 1965), 150-4, 175, 485.

[11]A. N. Whitehead, *Science and the Modern World,* 65, 71.

[12]See *PM,* 66, for T.'s phrasing of the three questions.

[13]Simpson quoted in George B. Murray, S.J., "Teilhard and Orthogenetic Evolution," *Harvard Theological Review,* 60 (1967), 285.

[14]Theodosius Dobzhansky, *Heredity and the Nature of Man* (New York: New American Library, 1964), 151-2. For a biologist's missing T.'s specialized usage of "orthogenesis," see George B. Murray's article listed in the previous footnote.

[15]This passage would be clearer if it read: "a sense of quality or of novelty, already achieved, enabling us to distinguish in nature certain absolute levels of perfection or growth, without upsetting the physical unity of the earth."

[16]Science's lack of historical evidence for the formation of atoms and molecules is noted in *PM,* 49-50, 79, 83, 90.

[17]For the significant expressions of critical points and changes of state, see *PM,* 78-9, 86, 89.

[18]See Errol Harris, *The Foundations of Metaphysics in Science,* 163-84, for an in-depth analysis of the similarities and dissimilarities of living and nonliving things.

[19]The last phrase is a quotation from Jules Lachelier. See *Pierre Teilhard de Chardin, Maurice Blondel: Correspondence,* edited by Henri de Lubac, S.J. (New York: Herder and Herder, 1967), 18.

[20]*PM,* 171, 169.

Footnotes for Chapter Six

[1]Cf. Mooney, 62-3 (68-70).

[2]There is more of paradox here than T.'s hyperphysics can handle adequately. Though man's spirit *is* the product of evolution and time, his spirit truly transcends both evolution and time. This point is made forcefully in de Lubac, *Religion,* 212-3. "Time—of the psyche and of the world—exists only for a spirit *rooted in eternity* and *vivified by it.* The embodied psyche inaugurates time only because it is open to eternity and can 'imitate' the Creator's activity to some degree. Because its center *merges* with eternity, it *develops* in time without ever disappearing completely." Jean Mouroux, *The Mystery of Time* (New York: Desclee, 1964), 74.

[3]Following the literal sense of the French, this passage would read: "Man is not the centre of the universe as once we thought in our simplicity, but something much more wonderful—the rising arrow of a grand biological synthesis."

[4]"The Formation of the Noosphere" (1947), *FM*, 157 (163); "A Note on Progress" (1920), *FM*, 15 (16).

[5]*MM*, 119, 125. See also 28-9 and 66.

[6]*MM*, 29.

[7]*MM*, 258.

[8]*MM*, 265-6.

[9]Marshall McLuhan and Q. Fiore, *The Medium is the Massage* (New York, Bantam, 1967), 125, speaks of the "corporate participation" in President Kennedy's funeral.

[10]"The Formation of the Noosphere" (1947), *FM*, 165 (171-2).

[11]"The Spiritual Repercussions of the Atom Bomb" (1946), *FM* 143-4 (148-9), T. felt that "it is war, not mankind, that is destined to be eliminated" by the atom bomb. For one thing, the "very excess of destructive power placed in our hands must render all armed conflict impossible." Another reason "is that war will be eliminated at its source in our hearts because, compared with the vast field for conquest which science has disclosed to us, war's triumphs will soon appear trivial and outmoded." [*FM*, 146-7 (152)] Thus far T.'s optimism seems somewhat short of verification. But his optimism is shared by many another, for example, Marshall McLuhan, who states that "whenever hot wars are necessary these days, we conduct them in the backyards of the world with the old technologies. These wars are happenings, tragic games. It is no longer convenient, or suitable, to use the latest technologies for fighting our wars, because the latest technologies have rendered war meaningless. The hydrogen bomb is history's exclamation point. It ends an age-long sentence of manifest violence!" (*The Medium is the Massage*, 138) Jerome Perelinski has an excellent summary article, "Teilhard's Vision of Peace and War" in *The Catholic Worker*, March, 1968.

[12]Cuénot, 342-3, with a minor change.

[13]Tax, *Evolution*, II, 1-16, 169-86, 309-71.

[14]Marshall McLuhan, *Understanding Media: The Extensions of Man* (New York: McGraw-Hill, 1965), 3-4. McLuhan observes that "today, after more than a century of electric technology, we have extended our central nervous system itself in a global embrace, abolishing both space and time as far as our planet is concerned. Rapidly, we approach the final phase of the extensions of man—the technological simulation of consciousness, when the creative process of knowing will be collectively and corporately extended to the whole of human society, much as we have extended our senses and our nerves by the various media."

[15]"The Mass on the World" (1923), *HU*, 29; *ibid.*, 30.

[16]The French could be better rendered as follows: "of achieving, through something of itself, a supreme consummation—without which it would rightly feel itself to be stunted, frustrated and cheated. By the nature of the work, and correlatively by the psychological needs of the worker, a total death, an unscalable wall . . . are 'incompossible' with the mechanism of the activity of reflection."

[17]Letter of February 13, 1953, quoted in Cuénot, 349-50.

[18]Murray, 21.

[19]See E. E. Harris, *The Foundations of Metaphysics in Science,* (New York: Humanities Press, 1965), 166-9. He shows that in living things and even in crystals "physical and chemical properties are consequences of the structure of the whole, and are determined by its organizing principle of unity and not by a simple summation of the properties of its several constituents or parts." (166)

[20]Tresmontant, 50-51.

[21]Karl Marx, *The Communist Manifesto* (Chicago, Regnery, 1954), 37.

[22]For T.'s critique of Communism see "The Heart of the Problem" (1949), *FM,* 264 (264-7); "How May We Conceive and Hope That Human Unanimisation Will Be Realised On Earth" (1950), *FM,* 286-7 (300-1); Mooney, 183 (193-4); Tresmontant, 44.

[23]Jacques Maritain stresses the necessity of knowledge of the future in the political realm: "I have already drawn attention to the difference between a *utopia* and a *concrete historical ideal.* A utopia is a model to be realised as an end and a resting-place—and it cannot be realised. A concrete historical ideal is a dynamic image to be realised as a movement and a line of force, and it is exactly as this that it is realisable. Hence, we see, its realisation may be far off and yet serve in the present as an aim, and during what may be a long continued period of preparation govern action, at each moment proportionate at once to a future end and to present circumstances." *True Humanism* (New York: Scribner's, 1938), 254. The future of the noosphere, of course, includes the political as one of its many facets.

[24]An interesting exemplification of God's respect for secondary causes is found in the unexpected conclusion of a detailed analysis of medical miracles at Lourdes. Various medical specialists examined the reports pertinent to their specialty; see especially the report of the opthalmologist, Dr. Louis Merlin, who shows that the curative powers of the healed are operative in the miraculous healing. Hence, the miraculous is not to be explained as a superseding of nature and its powers, but rather in God's cooperation with nature to make it superactive. Though the cure is instantaneous or near-instantaneous, it is clearly effected by the natural curative powers of the healed. Faith leads the believer to see God's activity cooperative with that of the patient. Cf. "Affections of the Eyes," in *New Problems in Modern Ethics,* edited by Peter Flood (Westminster: Newman, 1953), 177-93.

[25]T. seems to have more than an adequate grasp of space's immensities. See "Life and the Planets" (1946), *FM,* 98-101 (103-6).

[26]Madeleine Barthélemy-Madaule, "Teilhard de Chardin, Marxism, Existentialism: A Confrontation," in *International Philosophical Quarterly,* I (1961), 659. The first part of this article expiores in depth the "world-anxiety" and the "cosmic dimensions of anxiety" as T. experienced them. "Like the existentialist, Teilhard goes all the way to the limits of inconsolability." (666) The quote in the text can be found in a slightly different version in "Hominisation" (1923), *VP,* 74.

[27]*MM,* 165.

Footnotes for Chapter Seven

[1]"Life and the Planets" (1945), *FM,* 115 (119-20). "Mankind" and

also "Humanity" are capitalized not only because T. habitually did so, but also to emphasize the special organic reality T. understood by these words.

[2]T. was still interested in "what concerns human origins (and, curious thing, the formation of continents—why? undoubtedly because it is 'planetary')." March 1, 1948, letter in Cuénot, 280.

[3]*LT*, 101.

[4]October 12, 1926, letter in Cuénot, 79-80.

[5]Cuénot, 212. It is significant, by way of contrast, to note that Errol Harris, who in his *The Foundations of Metaphysics in Science* is very sympathetic to the *Phenomenon's* key concepts, is completely silent on the whole question of the future of man.

[6]John Kobler, "The Priest Who Haunts the Catholic World," *Saturday Evening Post* (October 12, 1963), 47. "Certitude of universal survival" is a misleading formulation of the collective outcome which T. projects— as we shall see.

[7]"Life and the Planets" (1945), *FM*, 117-8 (122). T. develops his root meaning of "monist" as one who sees the unity in the plurality, in *FM*, 45-6 (47-8), and in *HIB*, 13-15.

[8]As the editors of *WTW* point out, T. was not very clear on the meaning of the phrases "the Soul of the World" or "the Spirit of the Earth" he used in his World War I writings. *"Finally, in later writings, 'the soul of the world' was to merge into and even be identified with, the noosphere."* (*WTW*, 178)

[9]*MM*, 181 and 160.

[10]"Turmoil or Genesis?" 1948, *FM*, 223-4 (232).

[11]For T.'s sensitivity to collectivism, see "The Directions and Conditions of the Future" (1948), *FM*, 234-6. T. notes that in 1948 he was less sanguine than before about believing "that the tightening of the human mass will *of itself* suffice to warm the human heart" for a personalizing totalization. [*FM*, 235-6 (245)]

[12]"Life and the Planets" (1945), *FM*, 118 (123), but following original.

[13]"The Planetisation of Mankind" (1946), *FM*, 136 (141-2).

[14]"A Note on Progress" (1920), *FM* 17 (18); "L'Etoffe de l'univers" (1953), *Oeuvres*, VII, 403.

[15]"The Directions and Conditions of the Future" (1948), *FM*, 235 (245), speaks of a "mysterious wall of growing repulsion."

[16]Jean-Paul Sartre, *No Exit and Three Other Plays* (New York: Vintage, 1955), 47. T. has poignant criticism of those who are totally pessimistic about the current convergence. "It is so easy to write and get oneself read if one sets up as a prophet of distaster. 'Frighten me. . . .' " [*FM*, ftn. 1, 250 (262)]

[17]"La grande monade" (1918), *Écrits*, 242-3, quoted in Rideau, 364.

[18]McLuhan, *The Medium is the Massage*, 63.

[19]Robert S. Morison, "Towards a Common Scale of Measurement," in *Science and Culture,* edited by Gerald Holton (Boston: Beacon, 1967), 280.

[20]Emile Durkheim, *Suicide: A Study in Sociology* (Glencoe, Illinois: Free Press, 1951), 386.

[21]Josiah Royce, *The Religious Aspect of Philosophy* (Boston: Houghton Mifflin, 1885), 175.

[22]Emile Mersch, S.J., *Theology of the Mystical Body,* translated by Cyril Vollert, S.J. (St. Louis: Herder, 1952), chapter 4 and especially

chapter 5, "The Teaching of Philosophy on Man and His Unity." The latter chapter develops the many natural instruments which make the family of man "one body." Fr. Mersch does not develop the specifically evolutionary unity of which T. makes so much.

[23]Lecomte du Noüy, *Human Destiny* (New York: Signet, 1949) stresses the necessity of a "collective conscience" and "an international plan of moral development."(187-8) He echoes T. clearly in his emphasis upon action and its motivation: "If only more people could grasp this, if they gloried in their work, if they rejoiced in it, the world would soon become a better world." (189)

[24]"The Directions and Conditions of the Future" (1948), *FM*, 237 (246-7).

[25]Blondel quoted in Mooney, 101 (110).

[26]Jacques Barzun, *Science, The Glorious Entertainment* (New York: Harper & Row, 1964), 17.

[27]See *FM*, 188-9 (195-6), where T. explores the Promethean and Christian mentalities.

[28]For the evolutionary role of some disciplines other than science, see Rideau, 124-5, 461-2. In *MPN*, 107, T. affirms that "artistic research . . . is not biologically separable from scientific research."

[29]"Life and the Planets" (1945), *FM*, 120 (124).

[30]Mooney, 90 (98). Neither Mooney, de Lubac, nor Rideau criticize T.'s exposition of the Mystical Body. Mooney, 233-4 (249-50), marshalls many Biblical authorities to reinforce T.'s realism. See especially Barnabas Mary Ahern, C.P., "The Christian Union with the Body of Christ in Cor., Gal., and Rom.," *Catholic Biblical Quarterly*, XXIII (1961), 199-209, which is also printed in *Contemporary New Testament Studies*, edited by Sr. M. Rosalie Ryan, C.S.J. (Collegeville: Liturgical Press, 1965), 397-406.

[31]Quoted in Ahern, *ibid.*, 398.

[32]Pius XII, *Mystici Corporis* (New York: America Press, 1943), par. 100, p. 41.

[33]See *Path*, chap. 2, 20-1, 25-8.

[34]Ahern, "The Christian's Union," 406.

[35]See de Lubac, *Religion*, 206-20; Rideau, 174-8 and 549-60; Mooney, 204-7 (214-9).

[36]T. makes the comparison in *FM*, 257-8 (269-70), 262 (274), 298-9 (312-3).

[37]*LT*, 321; "La Montée de l'autre" (1942), *Oeuvres*, VII, 79.

[38]"Does Mankind Move Biologically Upon Itself" (1949), *FM*, 259 (271).

[39]"Some Reflections on Progress" (1941), *FM*, 75 (78).

[40]"Life and the Planets" (1945), *FM*, 120 (124-5).

Footnotes for Chapter Eight

[1]Anthropologist Howell observes that the essential structure of the human brain has remained unchanged for 65,000 to 70,000 years. (Tax, *Evolution*, III, 168) Biologist Waddinton says that "the biological process seems at present to face man more with evolutionary dangers than with evolutionary possibilities." (Tax, *Evolution*, III, 172) Zoologist Ernst Mayr states that "there is no evidence of any biological improvement [in

man] in at least the last 30,000 years." (*Animal Species and Evolution* [Cambridge: Harvard University Press, 1963], 658) Teilhard makes the same point in *PM*, 277; *FM*, 14-5 (15), 69 (72); *MM*, 166.

[2]*PM*, 250 and 282-3 indicate some biological possibilities of future evolution.

[3]"A Note on Progress" (1920), *FM*, 15 (15).

[4]Neurophysiologist Gerard speaks of evolution in "the collective mind of collective man." (Tax, *Evolution*, III, 205) For a fairly elaborate comparison of biological and cultural evolution see "The Points for Discussion," Tax, *Evolution*, III, 208-11.

[5]*MM*, 166.

[6]The "leap" is intimately connected with a "refusal or acceptance of Omega," as T. will show, *PM*, 288.

[7]*LT*, 269.

[8]"Life and the Planets" (1945), *FM*, 120 (124-5).

[9]For the distinction between T.'s two uses of "Omega," see Mooney, 54 (59-60).

[10]*MPN*, 121.

[11]"Le Christique" (1955), quoted in Mooney, 57 (63).

[12]"Social Heredity and Progress" 1945, *FM*, 34 (36).

[13]"The Directions and Conditions of the Future" (1948), *FM*, 237 (246-7).

[14]"It was for this purpose [the final consummation of men in the Mystical Body] that God gave atoms the tendency to aggregate into molecules, molecules to form living cells, living cells to move along the line of evolution which culminates in man, man to unite with his fellows in a society whose ultimate goal and purpose should be a union patterned upon the hyperpersonal unity of the Blessed Trinity and culminating in the Beatific Vision." John L. Russell, "Teilhard de Chardin, *The Phenomenon of Man*, II," *The Heythrop Journal*, vol. II, no. 1 (Jan., 1961), 10. See *Path*, Chapter 10, 191-2, for other indicies of trinitarian inspiration in T.'s thought.

[15]I have added the original capitalization for "Union." This may be an instance of Trinitarian inspiration in Teilhard. Since the preceding paragraph ends by speaking about the attraction of Omega, "Union" is almost certainly a synonym for Omega—and a most meaningful one from a Trinitarian viewpoint.

[16]The necessity for the universality of love can also be seen in Martin Buber, *I and Thou* (New York: Scribner's, 1958), 108, 78-9.

[17]Following the force of the French, this passage would read: "to accept the possibility, indeed the reality, of Someone, Loving and Loveable, at the world's peak above our heads."

[18]"Le Christique" (1955), quoted in Cuénot, 373.

[19]August 15, 1936, letter, in Cuénot, 209-10.

[20]Julian Huxley had an excellent and sympathetic grasp of noogenesis and personalization. Why he should experience special difficulty with the theological aspects of noogenesis is rooted in his blanket denial of God's existence: "And he [man] must face it [the responsibility for future evolution] unaided by outside help. In the evolutionary pattern of thought there is no longer need or room for the supernatural. The earth was not created; it evolved. . . . In their [religions'] evolution some (by no means all) have given birth to the concept of gods as supernatural beings en-

dowed with mental and spiritual properties and capable of intervening in the affairs of nature, including man." (Quoted in Tax, *Evolution,* III, 252-3)

[21]Mooney, 230 (245), ftn. 74.

[22]*PM,* ftn. 2, 263; "The Grand Option" (1945), *FM,* 52 (54).

[23]C. S. Lewis, *The Screwtape Letters* (New York: Macmillan, 1943), 74, 45-6.

[24]June 27, 1937, letter in Cuénot, 211.

[25]"The End of the Species" (1953), *FM,* 302 (316).

Footnotes for Chapter Nine

[1]Mooney, 181-6 (191-8), explains the various relationships between the Parousia and the completed convergence of the noosphere. His references can lead the reader to still other Teilhardian formulations.

[2]II Peter 3:7-12; Colossians 1:16-20. See Mooney, 185 (197), for an elaboration of the scriptural account of the Parousia.

[3]A more complete rendering of the French would read: "This essentially convergent movement will attain such intensity and such quality that, in order to unify still further, mankind, *taken as a whole,* will be obliged . . . to abandon its organo-planetary foothold so as to centre itself outside itself on the transcendent Centre of its increasing concentration." "Cosmic Life," (1916), *WTW,* 64.

[5]*DM,* 61 and 110.

[6]*HIB,* 12.

[7]*MM,* 167.

[8]T. also expresses this "hominisation of death" very technically in terms of energy: "By death, in the animal, the radial is reabsorbed into the tangential, while in man it escapes and is liberated from it. It escapes from entropy by turning back to Omega." (272)

[9]Letter of May, 1920, in Mooney, 112 (120). We can also note with Mooney the similar thought on death by Karl Rahner, *On the Theology of Death* (New York: Herder and Herder, 1961), 26-34. According to Rahner the separated soul has a totally new relationship to the whole of the universe, a *pancosmic* rather than an *acosmic* relationship. Mooney, when taking up the larger question of the physical unity of the cosmos—the physical interdependence of every element in the universe—shows how T.'s "profound sense of the whole" is elaborated by the philosopher Maurice Blondel and the theologian Karl Rahner. [Mooney, 101-3 (109-11)] On death itself, both individual and noospheric, see Mooney, 109-12 (117-21) and 182-5 (194-6).

[10]"Esquisse d'un univers personnel" (1936), *Oeuvres,* VI, 109.

[11]"A Note on Progress" (1920), *FM,* 21 (21).

[12]George Gamow, *Biography of the Earth* (New York: Viking, 1953), 237.

[13]C. P. Snow, *The Two Cultures and the Scientific Revolution* (Cambridge: Cambridge University Press, 1960), 5-6.

[14]*Ibid.*

[15]On contemporary cosmologies see Harlow Shapley's article in Tax, I, 23-38; E. L. Mascall, *Christian Theology and Natural Science* (London: Logmans, Green, 1957), 138-61, but especially 156-7; Francoeur, *Perspectives,* 83-5.

[16]Thomas J. Altizer, *Mircea Eliade and the Dialectic of the Sacred* (Philadelphia: Westminster Press, 1963), 149.

[17]Charles Frankel, *The Case for Modern Man* (New York: Harper & Brothers, 1955), 47.

[18]See Huxley's footnote 2 in his Introduction to *PM*, 18.

[19]It would seem that only a preevolution thinker could affirm with reason an infinite duration for man and the cosmos. Aristotle's thought is a fine example of such a view; though the Greeks eschewed the idea of the actually infinite, Aristotle's universe had neither beginning nor ending, and it lacked significant development in and through history. Given the discovery of entropy and evolution, such a view is now highly questionable.

[20]T. has a direct analysis of "indefinite human progress" in "The End of the Species" (1953), *FM*, 298-303 (312-9).

[21]The original, *durée finie*, is better translated as "finite duration." *Finie* probably also suggested to T. the notion of "completed."

[22]"The End of the Species" (1953), *FM*, 303 (317).

[23]Mooney, 182 (194).

[24]"From the Pre-human to the Ultra-human" (1951), *FM*, 297 (311).

[25]See *MPN*, 107, footnote, where T. says that "artistic research . . . is not biologically separable from scientific research . . . and constitutes an integral part of the same exuberant source of human energy." Rideau, 124-5, has a synthesis of T.'s views on art.

[26]Jan. 15, 1954, memorandum quoted in Cuénot, 357.

[27]The passionate next to last paragraph of "The Organisation of Research" is excellent evidence of the largeness of T.'s hopes for science. (279-80)

[28]*PM*, 282; see also "The Direction and Conditions of the Future" (1948), *FM*, 234 (243).

[29]Cuénot, 350.

[30]"The Formation of the Noosphere" (1947), *FM*, 177 (184), and cf. 167 (173-4). Vincent Cronin has an excellently balanced essay, "The Noosphere and Extrasensory Perception" in Braybrooke, 88-91.

[31]"The Spiritual Repercussions of the Atom Bomb" (1946), *FM*, 144 (149).

[32]"Réflexions sur le bonheur" (1943), quoted in Mooney, 161 (172).

[33]"En Regardant un cyclotron" (1953), *Oeuvres*, VII, 376-7.

[34]"Conjugated" here means conjoined.

[35]Teilhard "attributes more importance to the converse [second] hypothesis, and he constantly retains the tragic possibility of an evil choice and its consequences." (de Lubac, *Man*, 101, ftn.) During the first World War, he was oppressed by "the powerlessness of the world to develop successfully, I won't say the best, but at any rate a good part of itself." (*MM*, 176)

[36]Mooney, 124 (132).

[37]"A Note on Progress" (1920), *FM*, 19 (19).

[38]"Mon Univers" (1924), *FM*, 307, (322-3).

[39]"Introduction à la vie chrétienne" (1944), quoted in Mooney, 131 (140).

[40]See "The Outer Darkness and the Lost Souls," *DM*, 146-9; *HU*, 49; Mooney, 123-4 (131-3), 129-31 (138-40); de Lubac, *Man*, 60-61, *Religion* 116-20; Rideau, 187-8.

[41]"A Note on Progress" (1920), *FM*, 18-9 (18-9), with rearrangements.

[42]T.'s notes on a 1951 meeting which included three Marxist professors; recorded in Cuénot, 255.

[43]*PM*, 286; cf. 307.

[44]January 14, 1955, letter quoted in de Lubac, *Man*, 42.

[45]*MPN*, 113.

[46]J. Edgar Bruns, "Cosmogenesis and Theology," in Francoeur, *World*, 183.

[47]*Cahiers Pierre Teilhard de Chardin*, II, 35, quoted in Smulders, 23.

[48]Henri de Lubac, *Paradoxes*, transl. by P. Simon and S. Kreilkamp (South Bend, Indiana: Fides, 1948), 47-8.

[49]Letter of January 1, 1954, in Cuénot, 400.

Footnotes for Chapter Ten

[1]For Christological additions to hyperphysics see, for example, *FM*, 22-3 (22-4), 93-6 (96-9), 223-6 (231-3), 237 (246-7), 260-9 (272-82), 286 (301-2); *HIB*, 41-8; *AM*, 270-3.

[2]"Turmoil or Genesis?" (1948), *FM*, 223 (231).

[3]Vatican II's "Pastoral Constitution on the Church in the Modern World," paragraph 58, develops the mutual influences and benefits to be received by Church and World from greater openness to one another. (Abbott, 264-265)

[4]"A Note on Progress" (1920), *FM* 23 (23).

[5]de Lubac, *Man*, 40; cf. Smulders, 21.

[6]"Le Christique" (1955), quoted in Cuénot, 372; *DM*, 143. Cf. Vatican II's "The Church in the Modern World" which says that "earthly progress must be carefully distinguished from the growth of Christ's kingdom." (Abbott, 237) However, "The Decree on the Apostolate of the Laity" notes that "both the spiritual and the temporal realms . . . although distinct, are so connected in the one plan of God that He Himself intends in Christ to appropriate the whole universe into a new creation, initially here on earth, fully on the last day." (Abbott, 495) The Council indicates that the unification of the two realms is accomplished in Christ, the Alpha and the Omega: "The Lord is the goal of human history, the focal point of the longings of history and of civilization, the center of the human race, the joy of every heart, and the answer to all its yearnings. . . . We journey toward the consummation of human history, one which fully accords with the counsel of God's love: 'To re-establish all things in Christ, both those in the heavens and those on the earth' (Eph. 1:10)." (Abbott, 247)

[7]For personalism and universalism see *PM*, 244, 258-9, 265-6, 284-5, 293-4.

[8]"Réflections sur le bonheur" (1943), quoted in Mooney, 161 (172).

[9]G. M. Hopkins, S.J., *Poems*, "The Wreck of the Deutschland," stanza 7.

[10]"Super-humanité, super-Christ, super-charité" (1943), quoted in Mooney, 162 (173).

[11]"Catholicisme et science" (1946), quoted in Mooney, 163 (173).

[12]Père de Lubac in *Religion*, 192-4, discusses T.'s use of scientific terms in a theological setting. Though there are disadvantages, he feels that the vision communicated is eminently worthwhile.

[13]"Esquisse d'une dialectique de l'Esprit" (1946), *Oeuvres*, VII, 154-5.

[14]John 17:21.

[15]Marcel Méry quoted in de Lubac, *Religion*, 158. Cf. John Herman Randall, Jr., *The Career of Philosophy* (New York: Columbia University Press, 1962), 453.

[16]For an expansion of this theme see Mooney, 71-87 (78-95), 179-81 (191-2).

[17]Cf. *HIB*, 37.

[18]*Ibid.*, 36-7.

[19]*Ibid.*, 36-8.

[20]*Ibid.*, 38-9.

[21]de Lubac, *Man*, 25. Competent theologians such as de Lubac and Smulders defend T. against accusations of his proposing an unorthodox pantheism. See de Lubac, *Man*, 13, 19-20, 27; de Lubac, *Religion*, 152-60; Smulders, 121-3.

[22]Acts 17:28.

[23]Mooney explores in considerable depth this aspect of T.'s thought and does not find fault with T.'s essential affirmations. He attributes to T. "an authentic understanding of the Incarnation" but criticizes some of the concomitants of "an extreme Incarnationalism," especially an overemphasis on Christ's "passive physical omnipresence" to the detriment of what is primary, "the exercise of his freedom and love." [Mooney, 202-3 (214-5)] We feel that this criticism is less than well grounded, certainly not as well as Mooney's next criticism, that T. "ignores completely the fact that reparation for sin deals principally with the relationship of love between persons." [*Ibid.*, 203 (215)] There is no question that T.'s system is largely blind to personal sin and the need of Christ's reparative redemption.

With considerable forthrightness de Lubac defends the orthodoxy of T.'s "Christian pantheism"; "And if it is true that he [T.] attributes to the risen Humanity of our Lord (as others do) 'a presence in the world as vast as the very immensity of God,' can we be certain that in holding this against Teilhard our censure may not at the same time embrace St. Paul? If we hold that 'from the standpoint of human reason the "cosmic Christ" is necessarily an expression tainted with pantheism and contradictory of a personal God' [a quotation from Bernard Charbenneau] we are even more certain to be attacking the great Apostle while under the impression that we are criticizing only his interpreter." (de Lubac, *Man*, 35-6) See also de Lubac, *Religion*, 160, 201-2; and Rideau, 164-6.

[24]*DM*, 129-30. T. develops at considerable length how the historical Incarnation and the Catholic Church, *"a traditional and solidly defined axis,"* ground the true pantheism of Christ's omnipresence in the cosmos, and also prevent the Christian from falling prey to a false pantheism. See *DM*, 116-28.

[25]Preface of the Mass for the feast of the Blessed Trinity.

[26]For Trinitarian aspects of T.'s thought see Mooney, 171-7 (182-8); Rideau, 154-7, 505; Smulders, 78-81; Faricy, 109; John L. Russell, "Teilhard de Chardin, *The Phenomenon of Man*, II," in *The Heythrop Journal*, vol. II, no. 1 (Jan., 1961), 10.

[27]"Turmoil or Genesis?" (1948), *FM*, 223 (232).

[28]Josef Pieper, *Scholasticism* (New York: Pantheon, 1960), 161, makes reference to T. in connection with the "conjunction of *fides* [faith] and

ratio [reason] inspired by theology [which] . . . can realise the powers of natural reason to the full, allowing it the widest scope to achieve knowledge of our world."

[29]Just one indication of Christian universalism is Romans 1:13-16.

[30]John 12:32 and 10:10.

[31]On Eastern religions see *LT*, 127; *PM*, 296. *HIB*, 35-9 has a more extended analysis. For further references see Mooney, 256 (278).

[32]T. discusses the obscurity and certainty of faith at the end of *How I Believe*: "The obscurity of the Faith, I think, is only a particular case of the problem of Evil. And, in order to surmount its *mortal* scandal, I see only one possible way: to recognize, that if God lets us suffer, search, doubt, it is that He *cannot*, now and in one stroke, heal us and show Himself to us. And if *He cannot*, it is uniquely, because we are still *incapable*, on account of the state in which the Universe finds itself, to receive more light. In the course of a creation which is developing in time, Evil seems to be inevitable, even to God. Here again the liberating solution is given to us by Evolution. . . .

"Our doubts, as well as our sins, are the price and even the condition of a universal achievement. I accept, under those conditions, to walk, just to the end, and on a route of which I am more and more certain, toward horizons more and more drowned in the mist." (*HIB*, 48)

[33]The literary effect of this whole paragraph has been considerably diminished in translation. The original is a series of rhetorical questions.

[34]"Turmoil or Genesis?" (1948), *FM*, 223 (231).

[35]"Le Goût de vivre" (1950), *Oeuvres*, VII, 249, note 1.

[36]Mooney, 158-9 (169). The quotation is from T.'s "Introduction à la vie chrétienne" (1944). See paragraphs 13-17 of Vatican II's "The Dogmatic Constitution on the Church" (Abbott, 30-7). The Council sets forth a quite nuanced account of the relationships between the Catholic Church and other Christian and non-Christian individuals and communities.

[37]Mooney, 159-60 (170).

[38]T. B. Macaulay, *Critical and Historical Essays*, edited by A. J. Grieve (London: Dent, 1921), II, 39.

[39]A 1919 memorandum to Maurice Blondel, quoted in de Lubac, *Religion*, 237.

[40]de Lubac, *Man*, 6. See also Cuénot, 5 and 402.

[41]Reported by a participant at the 1965 Chicago University Symposium. Speaight gives considerable detail of T.'s "trials and tribulations" in the Society of Jesus and his continual fidelity. See Speaight, 113-7, 136-41, 146-7, 171-5, 205-7, 277-9, 282-7, 298-301, 307.

[42]"Le Christique" (1955), in Mooney, 160 (170).

[43]*HIB*, 43.

[44]*MM*, 143. Other remarks on criticism of the Church can be found in *LT*, 228, and Cuénot, 214.

[45]*MM*, 59.

[46]See *MM*, 176; "The Directions and Conditions of the Future" (1948), *FM*, 235 (245).

[47]See Cuénot, 215, 401-2; Murray, 94-5.

[48]de Lubac, *Man*, 104.

[49]Mooney, 143-4 (153).

[50]That this is the understanding of original sin by many contemporary atheists is pointed out by Jean Lacroix, *The Meaning of Modern Atheism*

(New York; Macmillan, 1965), 46-7; see also Garrett Barden's introduction, 8.

[51]"Réflexions sur le péché originel" (1947), in Mooney, 137 (146).

[52]Mooney, 140-1 (150).

[53]*Ibid.*, 141 (151). The very effort to relate the doctrine of original sin to an evolving universe is a great service to theology. Many thinkers consider the identification of a problem as the greatest service rendered by original minds. T. was one of the earliest thinkers to see the need of rethinking theology within the context of an evolutionary framework. Recently, his theory on original sin has been taken up and developed, especially by two Dutch theologians. Schoonenberg and Hulsbosch, whose works are listed in the Bibliography.

[54]de Lubac, *Man,* 104.

[55]*Ibid.,* 100.

[56]Murray, 91-2.

[57]Mooney, 144 (153-4). A poignant and partial confirmation of this suggestion is T.'s wartime report, not on the combatants in the war, but on some civilians: "During our last days on the road, through a very bad country from the religious point of view, I had the opportunity, in talking with the people and parish priests, to gain a certain amount of human experience. You can't imagine the revolting state of selfishness, ill-nature, meanness and human pettiness to which these peasants are reduced, deprived of religion and educated on the state's republican principles! . . . I've never yet come into contact, so palpably, with the real decomposition of humanity that comes with the disappearance of religious feeling. One feels that one's in the presence of a veritable organic taint, as real as a disorder that attacks the tissues of the body." (*MM,* 174-5)

[58]"Introduction à la vie chrétienne" (1944), in Mooney, 131 (140).

[59]*DM,* 147-9; "Operative Faith" (1918), *WTW,* 247.

[60]Mooney, 143 (153).

[61]*Ibid.,* 209 (221).

[62]*DM,* 44.

[63]*DM,* 80-94.

[64]*PM,* 313, 308; *HU,* 34. "Resurrecting power" is a more adequate translation of the original "vertu ressuscitante" than *PM's* "redeeming virtue." (308, ftn. 2)

GLOSSARY

N.B. 1) Following the selectivity of the *Path*, this Glossary concentrates upon essential sections of *The Phenomenon of Man*: pages 29-36 and 213-308. If additional help is needed, consult the indices of *PM, Path,* Mooney and Rideau.

   2) Starred words, e.g., **affinity,* indicate particularly significant words which T. uses in a special way. One might profitably peruse the starred words in this Glossary before (and after!) reading *PM*.

   3) All page references, unless otherwise indicated, are to *The Phenomenon of Man,* Revised English Edition, 1965.

*accidental: 1) An accidental change or modification is one which does not affect the nature or essence of a being, e.g., growing larger fins, getting a suntan, etc. It is contrasted to an *essential* change, for example, the change from nonliving to living. 2) Also used in the sense of nonorganic or not contributing to the unification and activity of a whole being or of an organic group.

additivity: An evolutionary process by which elements arrange themselves not by simple addition or aggregation but by uniting in such a way as to make new characteristics appear; controlled complexification in a predetermined direction. See 108; **complexification, orthogenesis**.

adulteration: Translation of *mélange*, which T. uses to indicate a unit's loss of identity by being mixed or joined with other units.

affinity: Mutual attraction of any sort, for example, gravitational, magnetic, or instinctual between animals, and love between persons. See 264-6.

albuminoids: Compounds which resemble albumen, e.g., proteins.

analogy: Corresponding to or like another, at least in *some* respects, such as in attributes, structures, activities.

anastomosis: 1) The union of hollow organs with each other, such as to form intercommunication and interaction. 2) The union of and intercommunication within any system or network.

anatomic: Physical, bodily or biological, in contrast to psychic or interior.

anthropocentrism: The doctrine which assumes that man is the center or ultimate end of the cosmos. T. rejects a static anthropocentrism of position, that is, a theory which holds that man is the geometric or juridical center of a world made up of a series of concentric spheres, but he admits an anthropocentrism of movement—a theory which represents man as infinitely complex and therefore the leading shoot or "center" of the psychic movement of cosmic evolution toward convergence and irreversible union with Omega-God. See 224.

anthropogenesis: 1) A general term used to describe an essential feature of the whole of evolution—the genesis or bringing to be of man (42, 50). 2) The historic and evolutionary appearance of man. See **hominisation**. 3) The process by which man now becomes more human, i.e., the psychosocial evolution of mankind toward the consummate unity in and with Omega. See 210, 241.

anthropomorphism: Attributing human shape or activities to nonhuman beings (gods, animals, objects) in order to explain them.

apocalyptic: A prophetic revelation of the future in highly figurative language.

apologia: A presentation of the grounds for a belief, e.g., the Christian belief. It frequently, but not necessarily, implies a defensive posture. See *Path* 40-9.

"artifice": Used in the literal sense of making tools which extend man's power.

*****autonomous**: In the biological sense which T. adopts, **autonomous** indicates the property of existing and/or acting independently of the whole with which it is connected. See 262-3.

auto-organisation: Self-organization; humanity's powers of liberty and creative reflection applied to guiding its own evolutionary development.

axes of belief(292): The general directions or orientations of the Christian belief.

biogenesis: The preparation for, birth of, and the directed development of life in the process of cosmic evolution. See **genesis**.

*****biological**: 1) A term used by T. in its ordinary sense of something pertaining to living organisms and their processes. 2) Frequently used by T. in an extended sense: any unity or process which operates as a dynamic whole, as an "organism." Thus, when he speaks of the "biological value" of human socialization (30), he is stressing the organic and vital unity of mankind in its social and spiritual evolution. 3) When T. speaks of Christianity as "a prodigious biological operation" (293), he is referring to Christianity as the growing or evolving body of Christ.

biosphere: The sphere or layer of living things which forms a unified "covering" over the earth; the sphere of living organisms penetrating the lithosphere, hydrosphere, and atmosphere.

biota: The French *biote* signifies a biological grouping not only from common birth, but even more, a grouping brought about by the mutual support and completion given and received in the effort to live and propagate. See 124.

block (243): Bloc; combination of groups into a political or social unity.

"bundles": Indiivdual packets or quanta of energy. See **quantum**.

centrality (287): Translation of French *centration*. See **centration**.

*centration: The general cosmic process whereby being, individually and collectively, infolds or becomes more centered, more conscious, more unified. See **interiorization**, **involution**, **convergence**.

*centre: 1) In a most general way, **centre** expresses the "within" or the source of unity and unification in a complex material unit. 2) Most often, **centre** is T.'s equivalent for *person*, both human and divine; it connotes what is most characteristic of personhood—reflective knowledge and unifying love (271). 3) Man, through the power of reflection, is "a *centre* in the form of a point" (165), who not only unifies all aspects of himself but also centres the rest of the world (172). 4) God, "Centre of centres" (294), draws forward by loving attraction the process of evolution which can best be understood as a progressive synthesis of centres. See 258-9, 271-2.

centre of perspective and **of construction**: Man is not only forced to *see* himself (perspective) as the centre of the evolving cosmos, but he *is* the very scene of evolution's constructive activity. See 32-3.

centro-complexity = Complexity/consciousness.

*****change of state**: 1) The apparently instantaneous change from a solid to a liquid, or from a liquid to a gas. 2) T. uses **change of state** in an analogous sense for the process whereby a growing complexity at one level of evolution "leaps" to another and higher level, for example, nonliving to living, nonhuman to human. See, **critical point**, **threshold**, **transformation**.

Christogenesis: The growth toward maturity of the mystical body of Christ; the "awaited and unhoped for" extension of noogenesis by means of Christ's continuing "incarnation." It is the fourth in a series of stages in cosmic evolution: cosmogenesis, the birth of the universe; biogenesis, the birth of life; anthropogenesis, the birth of individual human beings; and Christogenesis, the birth of ultrasynthesized mankind, the mystical body of Christ—the birth of the "whole Christ."

coalescence: Growing together into one body or organism. See **concresence**, **convergence**, **planetisation**.

*****coherence**, **coherent**: 1) in perspective: a world view is more coherent the more it explains the various parts and processes of reality. See 35; Rideau, 335-6. 2) *in being*: the whole of being or partial systems are said to be coherent inasmuch as their elements are united and harmonious, making up a unified whole, one because of common origin, movement, and destiny.

*****coiling**: The compressive unification of individuals, and specifically of men, that results in the release of increased psychic energy for further union. See **centration**, **convergence**, **involution**, **planetisation**, **totalisation**.

collectivisation, **collective**: The process by which the full, individual consciousness tends to be joined more and more to that of all other men, and thus to be progressively enriched. The goal is the formation of one common consciousness and existence, founded upon the indestructible individuality and the enrichment of each individual. See **hominisation**; 250-3; *FM*,

113-20 (117-26); Rideau, 366-7.

complex: Man as "infinitely complex" (303) implies that the complexity of man, especially of his brain, utterly transcends the levels of complexity found in subhuman forms. See **complexity**.

complexes (308): Organized and complex units.

complexification: This is not any sort of complication but only that which is made up of a fixed number of elements, and forms a closed and centered system. **Complexification** expresses the tendency of the evolving cosmos to form ever higher and more unified groupings. See **complexity**; 48, 70, 301.

*complexity: The result of the cosmic drift or bent of matter toward more unified arrangements of different elements; arranged or organized diversity, not by mere aggregation, as in a heap of sand, nor by mere repetition, as in a crystal. Examples of ascending complexities are the organizations of constituents in the atom, molecule, cell, protozoon, plant, animal, human, and Humanity.

*complexity/consciousness: One of the two supremely general laws of cosmic evolution, the other being the law of entropy. This law states that evolutionary change proceeds or curves toward ever higher complexity ("organized heterogeneity"), and that as a consequence higher forms of interiority or centeredness or consciousness result. In evolution's past there was a lower level of complexity and centeredness ("consciousness") in the subatomic stage than at the level of man and of mankind's growing psychosocial unification.

complexity-interiorisation = Complexity/consciousness.

complicity: T. uses *complicité* in the positive sense of an agreement, a fitting together of or a bond between two processes, structures, etc.

concatenations: The interconnections or bonds between things.

*concentration: A gathering together, especially of individual men, in a centered or personal way. See **centration**, **coiling**, **convergence**, **involution**.

concresence: An embryological term which T. uses to indicate the gradual "growing together" of separate things as evolution progresses.

confluence: The coming together of different individuals and groups.

conjugated: Used by T. in the literal sense of closely joined together.

*consciousness: 1) In the cosmic law of complexity/consciousness, **consciousness** means centeredness or unity or immanence or spontaneity in matter whereby it is capable of perfecting itself by means of what is done or happens to it. In this sense, it is a universal property of matter and is the antichance and antientropy factor in cosmic evolution. Further, heightened consciousness is the "specific effect" of greater complexity. See 56-7. 2) As ordinarily understood, it is the awareness of environmental stimuli, accompanied by the usual ability to make useful responses. 3) In sections dealing with man and human society, **consciousness** refers to the qualitatively different awareness of man—*self*-consciousness or man's knowing his knowing. T. also looks forward to a future hyperconsciousness in mankind, to be brought about by a continuing noospheric evolution.

*consistence, consistency: A solidity and permanence whereby a being holds together and is strongly integrated in itself *and* with all other existents. This is a Pauline word which T. frequently uses to express the necessity for a supreme center of unity, harmony, and cohesion—Omega. In a scientific or neutral context, **consistence** is used as a contrast to fragility or fictitiousness.

construction: This word tends to suggest for the general reader the construction of a building, but for T. it most often refers to *intellectual* constructions or creations, especially scientific theories and explanations. See 269.

continuity: In science, the unbrokenness or lack of interruption in a process or an extension. For example, within steel's elastic limits we get a continuous variation of stretching or bending which corresponds to the quantity of weight or force applied. There would be discontinuity in the process, if at a certain point a spring no longer stretched but suddenly began contracting with added weight. See *Path*, 65-7, 89-93.

*****convergence, convergent**: 1) A drawing closer together by an internal and autonomous movement. 2) The second phase of the Teilhardian dialectic of nature (after divergence): at each peak of evolution, and especially at that of *Homo sapiens*, the new multiplicity caused by ramification tends to be reduced to an ever closer psychic union and synthesis. 3) The *law of convergence* is the law of complexity/consciousness as it applies to mankind in his noospheric evolution whereby further evolution is necessarily convergent, that is, with a bent or drift toward greater interpersonal union among men and especially with Omega-God. 4) The coming together of different disciplines (e.g., science, philosophy, religion) or of different religions, and especially of the vision of an evolving universe and Christian faith in the incarnate Son of God. 5) Saying that evolution is convergent, as T. does, indicates: a. The cosmos is not static but moving, and in an assignable direction. b. The direction is towards higher complexity and consciousness, towards higher unity and vitality. c. With the advent of human consciousness, convergence now demands a pole or center for the continuation of convergent evolution. See *Path*, 108-13; Mooney, 45-6 (50-2).

corpuscle: Usually used metaphorically for: any unified whole. Hence, T. in speaking of "human corpuscles" emphasizes the purposive freedom and independence of individual men as well as their integral part in Humanity.

corpuscular (258): When T. speaks of personality as **corpuscular,** he means personality conceived of as an isolated, separated, and completely independent existence—a false conception in T's mind. This is rare usage for T.; ordinarily it has the "good" connotations of **corpuscle** and **corpusculation**.

corpusculation: The process whereby cosmic matter, while preserving its organic unity, collects into separate units which tend to constitute closed systems as well as groupings which are more or less autonomous.

cosmic drift: The direction and flow that matter in the evolutionary stream follows with the passage of time, toward higher complexity and unity.

*cosmogenesis: 1) Literally, the genesis or coming to be of a cosmos or ordered universe. Hence, **cosmogenesis** can indicate the total evolutionary process. See 303. 2) As a *particular* stage in the evolutionary process, it refers either to the process which precedes noogenesis (220) or more usually, the process prior to biogenesis (276).

cosmogony: An account or theory of the origin of the cosmos.

cosmos: 1) The universe as an embodiment of order and harmony, as distinguished from chaos. A complete and harmonious system. 2) For T., the cosmos is not primarily a materially organized universe but rather a "universe with a *personal* mesh," a universe constituted by the ordering of all things and processes to persons, and of persons to interpersonal relationship with Omega-God as the center or ground for all human relationships.

crescit eundo: [Latin] It increases as it proceeds.

*critical point: Though evolution is one continuous process, there are points at which the definitively new emerges from that which preceded. The critical point is the point at which the emergence of the new takes place. The image is taken from physics and chemistry, e.g., the critical point for boiling to take place is 100° C. See **threshold**.

curvature, curves: T. uses these metaphors, taken from non-Euclidean geometry and Einstein's relativity, to express one of the fundamental drifts of the universe. Usually they signify a curve of *arrangement*. At earlier evolutionary stages, it is similar to the inertia of a moving body, and the cosmos is seen as *necessarily* moving toward arrangements of higher complexity and consciousness, but in the human phases, freedom and human creativity qualify this cosmic drift, so that future evolutionary unification is subject to human choice. See 61, 287.

decentration: 1) Separation from or nonunion with others. 2) A primary phase in the dialectic of happiness, which consists in joining our being with that of others.

*****determinism**: T., following ordinary French usage, uses **determinism** for the individual, external or internal conditions, or for the sum of such conditions which determine or necessitate a particular biological phenomenon. **Determinism** refers, then, to the normal stability of structures and movements in the material world. However, since evolution involves the genesis of the genuinely new and most especially the genesis of human freedom and autonomy, determinisms in the "without" cannot be the sole explanatory principle. Hence, in an evolving universe, T. includes as a principle of at least elementary freedom and autonomy the "within" of matter. See 53, 256; "**within**."

disarticulating: Literally, to separate joint from joint.

doubling-back: See **involution**.

*****duration**: 1) Biological space-time, which is the concrete, natural movement of the whole evolving cosmos. See **space-time**. 2) A limited section of the space-time continuum.

dynamisation of money: Money, in the late middle ages, began to be intrinsically fruitful through ready possibilities of capital investments.

elemental, elementary: 1) Treating of elements or first principles. 2) T. sometimes (e.g., 306) uses "**elementary** hominisation" in the sense of the development of an element, where "element" means an individual man. See **elements**.

*elements: 1) Usually used as an abbreviation for "human elements," that is, individual human persons seen as integral and organic parts of a great whole, Humanity. 2) In a more general sense, **element** expresses any integral part of an organic whole. 3) Sometimes used in the usual chemical sense, for example, barium, carbon, uranium, etc.

*emergence, emerge: The appearance, through evolutionary synthesis, of the strictly new and unpredictable, and therefore irreducible to the isolated elements which go to make up the new whole. Principle examples of emergence: life, thought, superconsciousness. See 268-71. 2) *Principle of emergence*: in an evolutionary framework the old always produces the new, even though the new is sometimes (e.g., life, thought, etc.) irreducible to the earlier forms. After the appearance of a new species, there is an initial *divergence* due to the different possibilities discovered by groping, then a *convergence* or consolidation and concentration of creative gains which prepare for the **emergence** of a new and higher level of existence.

*emersion: 1) The appearance of an already existent reality or activity which thus far has not been perceived as existing or functioning. The prime example in *PM* is Omega (God), always existent but only now perceived as the conscious pole or center of human convergence. See 270-1. 2) In astronomy, emersion is the reappearance of a star which previously had been unobservable in the shadows of an eclipse. It is this usage which probably grounds T.'s meaning in 1) above. 3) The process of emerging, as from water; T. uses it (288) in the sense of leaving the temporo-spatial matrix of this universe.

end (**of a process**): 1) There is a fundamental ambiguity in "end" or "term." They tend to express the limit of a process, the conclusion of an event or a series of events, with death as almost the paradigm for the "end." 2) For T., holding a cosmic evolutionary process which is directed toward a consummate fulfillment, "end" signifies the successful, perduring, and irreversible outcome. A good analogy of his usage might be the "end" of a courtship—ideally and usually, it is the union of marriage.

endomorphism: A change produced in an intrusive rock (one which in a plastic state was forced between the layers of other rocks) by a reaction with the receiving rock.

energetics: The science, conceived by T., of energy—in its physical, psychical, and mystical forms, and how they influence the advance of evolution.

*entropy: The measure of energy's gradual degeneration to a useless, or unavailable condition. Nature's energy can never be destroyed; it is only converted from one form to another. But every time a conversion takes place, some of the energy is lost as heat that diffuses throughout the universe, persisting forever, but forever irretrievable. The concept of entropy, embodied in the Second Law of Thermodynamics, carries implications of the universe moving slowly towards an inexorable "heat death" (called "maximum entropy"). Entropy is the cosmic force which constantly runs counter to the rise of complexity/consciousness. The curve formed by these two opposing forces is the "curve of corpusculisation."

ephemeral: Short-lived; transitory.

epiphenomenon: A secondary phenomenon accompanying another phenomenon and, though apparently necessarily joined with it, it exercises no influence whatsoever. Leibniz's preestablished harmony of mental and bodily activities precluded any interaction or mutual causality between the two.

"Eppur, si muove.": [Italian] "But, it does move" are words attributed to Galileo when asked, in 1632, to retract his statement that the earth moved, but it is generally agreed that the response is apocryphal.

equilibrate: To harmonize, balance, direct, or order.

essence: A metaphysical term indicating in a being that which underlies all outward manifestations (phenomena), and is not therefore observable, but is inferred from phenomena. For example, one can infer that this is a *living being* from the various and observable vital functions which it performs.

eugenics: Literally, well-born. It now signifies the science which deals with influences that improve the qualities of a race or breed, especially of the human race. After Hitler's inhuman eugenical experiments, his seems to be the only kind of eugenics imaginable. However, T. suggests a eugenics that would respect human dignity and freedom; it would function through advancing scientific knowledge and through human persuasion, rather than through dictatorial fiats. See 282-3.

evasion (288): Translation for *évasion,* which here signifies an escape from the material limits of the cosmos.

***evolution**: For T., the process by which the universe is progressing along a permanent axis (increasing complexity/consciousness) toward a final point of convergence and consummate unification. T. usually identifies in evolution four stages or processes: cosmogenesis, biogenesis, noogenesis, Christogenesis. See **transformation**.

***excentrate**: 1) To center oneself outside oneself, as happens in the involvment of loving another. 2) In T.'s dialectic of happiness, it is specifically the final step, consisting of mankind's free sacrifice of their apparent autonomy, and their acceptance of a refashioning of their whole being accomplished by becoming sur-centered on Omega (Jesus Christ). See 287-8; *DM,* 93-4; *FM,* 55-6 (57-8).

exiguity: Meagerness; on 242, it means the very restricted dimensions of the earth.

existence-value: When T. speaks of the existence-value of Christianity, he refers to actual or real values associated with lived Christianity, in contrast to the ideal or speculative values in a philosophical or religious system.

extrapolate: To project some effect(s) by inference into an unexamined area from data in an examined one. What the world's population will be in 2000 A.D. is an extrapolation from present and recent population and its growth-rate.

face: T. frequently speaks of the universe assuming or achieving a **face** (e.g., 267), meaning that the universe becomes personalized because more and more influenced by the personal energies and attractions of Omega-God and by man's growing scientific knowledge.

faith: 1) "**Faith in the world**" is an intellectual conviction about the successful outcome of human evolution and a corresponding commitment to furthering it. See 232-4, 283-5; Mooney, 48-57 (54-64); *Path,* 54-5, 171-2. 2) "**Faith in Christ**" is for T. the conviction, gained through grace, that Jesus Christ is the center of cosmic evolution and guarantees its successful outcome by his death and resurrection. See Mooney, 58-9 (64-6), 164-5 (175-6).

finalism: A philosophical system which teaches that all events are determined by final causes or purposes. In this view there would be no place for chance or for genuine creativity and freedom.

finalist: A finalist interpretation of evolution affirms a discoverable pattern and direction in evolution. As a finalist, T. affirmed that evolution is moving toward ever greater complexity and consciousness, and in the human phase, by means of man's freedom and creativity.

florescence: State or period of being in bloom, or, figuratively, of flourishing. Accordingly, T. often uses **florescence** to indicate the final stage of terrestrial evolution.

focus: The center for some evolutionary process, especially for human evolution. See **centre, Omega**.

function: 1) Any quality or activity so related to another that it is dependent upon and varies with another. Thus, for T., consciousness is a function of complexity, so that an increase in complexity is always accompanied by an increase in consciousness. 2) A characteristic activity, as nutrition in living things.

functional difference: A qualitative difference.

*genesis: The usual translation for the French *genèse*, which is more specific than the English *genesis*. *Genèse* is not only a coming to be, a change, but one which is *directed* towards a consummation. Thus, cosmic evolution is not merely the history of the appearances of countless new forms, but rather the ordered movement toward anthropogenesis, with an ultimate consummation in the superunity of Humanity and Omega. See Mooney, 51(57).

geogenesis: The birth and/or directed growth of the planet Earth.

"grain of thought": One of T.'s expressions for individual reflective beings; an individual man viewed as an integral part of Humanity.

granular: When T. speaks of a "granular whole" (263), he is referring to a whole made up of countless human persons, each of whom is a "grain" or a personal centre. See **element**.

granulation: 1) The process by which a group becomes more and more dispersed into isolated and exaggerated individuals. 2) Matter's initial state in which there was an absolute minimum of organization and unity.

*groping: 1) T. defines it as "directed chance" (110), that is, the chance interplay of forces and objects which moves the cosmos toward the goal of higher complexity and consciousness. 2) The evolutionary "technique" used by expanding multitudes to discover a new form of life. In the prehuman phase of evolution, groping is a "blind" probing for the more viable forms of life, while in the human phase it is the conscious and planned probing, invention, "trying all and discovering all."

heterogeneous: 1) Having its source or origin outside the organism; having a foreign origin. 2) Different in kind; unlike. 3) Composed of parts of differing kinds. Contrasted to **homogeneous**.

hic et nunc: [Latin] Here and now.

hominid: One of the Hominidae.

Hominidae: The biological family which includes Australopithecus, Pithecanthropus, Neanderthal and all other prehistoric and living races of man, *Homo sapiens*. Complete tables of classification are found in Nogar, 156-7.

*hominisation: 1) The progressive movement of nonreflective animal life towards reflective human life. 2) The evolutionary but instantaneous passing from nonreflective animal life to reflective human life. See 168-74. 3) In the human phase of evolution, **hominisation** refers to the evolutionary ascent of mankind through the self-unification of socialisation to the extremely complex and centered unity of superhumanity. See 243, 305-7.

hominised: The human phase or mode of earlier structures, drives, activities, etc. See 36, 222.

homogeneous: 1) Continuous or unbroken in the one, same process. 2) Parts or elements which are the same in quality, structure, etc., so that in the whole there is a uniform similarity in parts and/or processes and their laws. 3) When applied to the whole of material reailty, **homogeneous** expresses the basic oneness of the cosmos.

Homo sapiens: The biological species of modern man, the single surviving species of the primate family Hominidae, to which it belongs.

humanism (humanist, humanitarian): 1) In general, the doctrine which believes in the development and value of mankind. 2) *Atheistic* humanism positively excludes the instrumentality of God from human progress. 3) *Christian* humanism, as proposed by T., synthesizes the genesis or directed development of mankind in the world with the genesis of Christ in mankind through the Church.

Humanity: A better translation of *Humanité* than the usual one, **mankind**. See **mankind**; *Path*, 124-9.

hyper: A prefix indicating a great degree of advancement beyond an earlier form. It is frequently equivalent to the prefixes **super** and **ultra**.

hyperphysics: A term coined by T. to indicate the new sort of science attempted in *The Phenomenon of Man*. Specifically, it is a study which seeks to encompass the whole of experience, both physical and psychical phenomena, in one, coherent and homogeneous explanation of the evolving world—a natural history of the cosmos' evolution, with man at the center. See 29-30; **metaphysics**; *Path,* 33-8.

ideology: A system of ideas characteristic of an individual or of a particular group.

immiscibility: Incapable of being mixed or united in such a way as to cease being itself. T. affirms immiscibility, or personal immortality, as a property of human consciousness and personhood. See 262.

individualisation: For T., it usually means a false and destructive effort at realizing oneself by isolating oneself from groupings of others. Constructive self-fulfillment is called **personalisation** by T. For an extended discussion, see 237-8.

infinitesimal: The immeasurably small or minute.

infolding: See **involution**.

*****instinct**: 1) A tendency towards actions which lead to achieving some good proper for the species or the individual, as the web-building of spiders. 2) T. frequently describes the process of evolution as the rise of instinct, that is, the movement towards less mechanized and freer tendencies to action. 3) Sometimes instinct is used as a synonym for consciousness (e.g., 302), but usually it retains the connotation of a conscious tendency to some action. 4) Frequently, **instinct** designates a specific characteristic of animals; in man its correlate is conscious foresight and invention. See *FM*, 218-9 (277-8).

Intercentric: Energies and activities are **intercentric** which are interpersonal, center to center, founded upon a radical love. See 263-8.

*****interiorisation**: 1) The process of an individual or of mankind becoming more integral or centered, of reaching a richer "within" or psyche, and so a higher consciousness. In the whole cosmic process, interiorisation expresses the movement from the physical or exterior to the psychic and spiritual. 2) The process of incoiling by which mankind becomes increasingly more self-conscious and autonomous, and by which the material universe and mankind become spiritual, and personal, and united. See **centration, coiling, involution, planetisation**.

introversion: Literally, directing one's attention within one-self. On 287, it is the translation for *retournement* which T. uses to indicate the metamorphosis or radical transformation whereby an entirely new mode of existence is brought about by earlier stages. Thus, reflection, brought about by biological evolution, gradually supplants biology to become the scene of contemporary evolution. And death is, in T.'s thought, the means whereby one enters into direct union with Omega and thereby escapes destruction and reversibility. See **transformation**; Mooney, 184-5 (195-6).

*****invention**: 1) Everything in human activity which contributes to the growth of the noosphere. See *FM,* 202-3(210-11).   2) Extended to the whole of evolution, **invention** is the activity (chemical, biological, or psychic) or the internal power of synthesis which pervades cosmic evolution. Hence, the gropings of the first cell are linked with the scientific research which yields new "inventions." See 223-6; *VP,* 96-7.

*****involution**: Literally, an unfolding or a coiling upon itself. 1) Most frequently, **involution**, applied to humanity in its present and future stages, means a centered compression or a doubling back upon itself and thus becoming more organically and psychically united. Some of T.'s many synonyms for **involuting** are: coiling, reflecting upon itself, doubling-back, concentrating, centrating, complexifying, confluence, converging, etc. (**Involution** is a somewhat unfortunate translation of *enroulement,* because in the strict biological sense of "retrograde development" it conveys exactly the opposite of what T. intends.)   2) **Cosmic involution** implies a universe evolving from matter in an extremely simple state towards an extremely complex and most unified noospheric state.

ipso facto: [Latin] By that very fact.

*****irreversibility, irreversible**: 1) A biological term indicating a one-way process such as strict death, in contrast to a reversible process such as the expenditure of energy which can be replaced by nutrition. 2) T. almost always uses the term to express the quality of a human being or of the products of human creativity whereby they are unable to regress qualitatively, neither by way of disintegration nor by way of perishing in the milieu of things about them. **Irreversible** is T.'s favorite synonym for immortality, probably because of its dynamic overtones. 3) Cosmic time is irreversible, that is, it is not cyclical nor destined for an entropic ending but is convergent and creative, demanding an irreversible union for mankind and his creations with a preexistent and transcendent center, Omega-God.

isotropic: Having the same properties in all directions.

*****issue**: The usual and misleading translation of T.'s *issue*, which in its most general sense means a way out, a solution, and end. Most often T. means a *suitable* outcome (e.g., 229), which in the care of human evolution means an ultimate and consummating superlife.

*****juridicism**, **jurist**, **juridical**: The antiorganic, antievolutionary perspective which T. frequently opposed: 1) In the natural-supernatural framework, juridicism affirms the unique value of spirit, soul, supernatural, and the individual to the detriment of the value of matter, body, the natural, and the social (which, for T., is the *organic* union of men). 2) Specifically, the theory that human unification or socialisation is merely the result of legal expedients or of chance events which pressure nonpermanent and insignificant groupings of men. 3) The theory that the Incarnation set up only individual, legalistic, and extrinsic bonds between Christ and an individual human being. See 35, 293, 304.

laminae: Horizontal sections of a cone.

*****layer**: 1) In biology, the irreducible unit of an evolving group, e.g., amphibians, reptiles, mammals. See 126-30 for a general description; on 247, T. lines up phyla, layers, branches. 2) The human layer is, then, the whole developing human species, seen as an organic reality.

leaps forward (305): See **rebound**.

*****mankind**: A frequent translation for *Humanité* which, for T., is *not* an abstract noun useful for classifying all the members of the human race, but rather the reality of all men constituting an existing, organic, evolving unit—Humanity. See 245-8; **Spirit of the Earth.**

*****matter**: Nearly always T. thinks and speaks of **matter** within an evolutionary context: 1) At the evolutionary beginning **matter** indicates the "immense plurality" of complete diversity combined with total disunity, but this **matter** possesses a cosmic drift toward ever greater organization, unity, and consciousness, and ultimately toward perfect spiritual unity. 2) As **matter**, the source of and convertible into energy, evolves in time, it manifests a double tendency: i) toward *maximum disunity* and dispersion (entropy); ii) toward *maximum unity* and convergence (complexity-consciousness and spirit). Viewed from the latter perspective, T. speaks of *"materia matrix,"* of **matter** as the matrix or generator of spirit with its freedom. 3) In the social context, T. speaks of the "materialisation" which appears when man is a newly-formed multitude cloaked by a second or neomatter of psychological and social determinisms. However, this matter is also to yield to the free unification and spiritualization of the noosphere. See 39-66, 256, 263.

mega-molecule: This is the British expression for *macromolecule,* a giant molecule such as protein, composed of hundreds or thousands of atoms. See 81-6.

mega-synthesis: A huge or supersynthesis. See 251.

metamorphosis, metamorphism: A striking change in form or structure of an organism, for example, the change of a tadpole into a frog, or the change of a caterpillar into a butterfly. **Metamorphism** is a geological term indicating a pronounced change in the constitution of rocks, caused by water, extreme pressure and heat, but T. uses it frequently in an applied sense. See **change of state**, **transformation**.

metaphysics: That branch of philosophy which treats of first principles; it includes the sciences of being (ontology) and of the origin and structure of the universe (cosmology). It is always intimately connected with a theory of knowledge (epistemology). In contrast to T.'s hyperphysics which searches for "an experimental law or recurrence," metaphysics searches for "ontological and causal relations." Concretely, hyperphysics is satisfied with discovering an observable relation between antecedents and consequents, e.g., when complexity increases, so too does consciousness. Philosophy, on the other hand, would seek to know whether increased complexity actually *caused* the increased consciousness or whether it merely accompanied it.

metazoa: A large zoological division comprising all the animals above the protozoans (one-celled animals). The protozoa with their single cell reproduce by fission, whereas most of the metazoa reproduce sexually and so each individual begins as a single cell.

milieu: [French] Surroundings; environment, both center and surrounding influences. See 222. In other writings, especially in *The Divine Milieu,* it means all the above, but specifically it refers to Christ as the center and ultimate source of all influences in the evolving universe.

millenarian: One who believes that there will come an age of a thousand years of blessedness upon this earth.

*****mind**: A frequent but somewhat misleading translation for *l'Esprit,* spirit, as on pages 33, 214, 248, 278, etc. Because T.

uses *spirit* in so many different but connected ways, it is difficult to convey his meaning by merely giving several concise definitions.

T.'s concept of *spirit* seeks to transcend the usual dichotomies of spirit and matter, mind and body, psychical and physical energies. He uses the evident *unity* of spirit and matter in man as a paradigm for overcoming these dichotomies, but without denying or distorting the distinctions. He sees spirit and matter not as two separate compartments or things, but as two directions: in an evolutionary framework the primordial stuff (matter) has a "within," a consciousness which has a bent toward ever greater consciousness (spirit) to be achieved by ever greater organized complexity. Evolution is, then, matter (multiplicity) becoming spirit (unity).

The properties associated with man's spirit are: reflective consciousness or thought which transcends sensation, space and time (169), freedom, purpose and love. Put another way, spirit, the goal of evolution, must be both personal and universal (257-64), and therefore evolution is to be consummated by a superunion of human spirits among themselves and with Omega through their knowledge, freedom and love. (277-8, 287)

There is, then, no dichotomy between spiritual (radial) and material (tangential) energies since they are facets of the *one* energy which is psychical. (62-6) This unity is shown in man's concrete actions wherein the two energies are united, and in the whole sweep of evolution which has brought about higher and higher forms of consciousness or spirit.

Men are united in their "internal or radial zone of spiritual attractions" by love. (265) In order for love to be effective in the unification of men's spirits, these as well as their creations (science, art, etc.) must be irreversible or immortal. (261-2, 269-70) See **consciousness**, (for contrast: **matter**), **noogenesis**, **psyche**, **radial energy**, **soul**, **Spirit of the Earth**, **within**.

modus vivendi: [Latin] Adaptive ways of living.

*monad: 1) A unit; something simple and indivisible. 2) In biology, any simple, single-celled organism. 3) T. uses the term "human monad" to mean the individual human being, paralleling the relation of a single cell to its supporting organism with that of the single human to the superorganisms of Humanity and the body of Christ.

myriad, human: All of humanity.

mysticism (296): Translation of *mystique,* which means a belief formed around an idea or feeling.

Necessarium est ut scandala eveniant: [Latin] "It is necessary that scandals come about." Luke 17:1.

Neolithic: Pertaining to the period of a Stone Age culture, following the Mesolithic Age. It was characterized by the use of polished stone implements; other activities were the making of pottery, agriculture, domestication of animals. The Neolithic Age marks the birth of civilization, roughly 12,000 years ago. See 203-12.

*noogenesis: 1) The birth and development of reflective (human) thought. 2) The evolutionary movement of the universe which progresses toward ever greater organized complexity with an accompanying greater spontaneity and psychism, reaching a critical point in the appearance of reflective thought and progressing toward superconsciousness. See genesis, socialisation, totalisation.

*noosphere: 1) Literally, the sphere of *nous* or mind. 2) The realm or sphere which "encloses" human thought and love. T. likens it to the biosphere in which all living things are in contact and interaction with one another. In the noosphere, superposed on the biosphere, there is collected all psychosocial and cultural changes, all artistic and scientific achievements, etc. It is, in a sense, a collective memory and intelligence, the milieu in which, increasingly, individual men and all men think, love, create, and feel together as integral members of one organism, Humanity. See 225-6, 238-9, 251-2; *FM*, 155-84 (161-91).

object, objective: **Object** is that which the mind knows; knowledge is considered to be **objective** when the object is known as it is in itself. The knower is the **subject**, and his knowledge is considered **subjective** when it is greatly conditioned by personal characteristics of the knower (subject) instead of being determined principally by the qualities of the object. See 32.

*Omega, Omega Point: These terms carry overtones, both scientific (omega, the last letter of the Greek alphabet, is frequently used as a mathematical symbol) and religious (Jesus Christ is called "the Alpha and Omega" in the *Apocalypse* or *Book of Revelation*, 1:8, 21:6, 22:13). T. uses both terms in two quite different but related senses: 1) The end point or term of the natural evolution of mankind (and therefore of the cosmos). The apex of the convergent, social and spiritual development of the earth. 2) God, preexistent and transcendent superperson, loving and lovable, omnipresent, as the activating center, source and goal of noogenesis, a description fulfilled by the risen Christ portrayed by John and Paul. See 262-3, 268-72, 293-4.

*ontogenesis, ontogeny: The life history or development of an individual organism; contrasted to phylogenesis, which is the race history of a group of organisms.

ontological: Ontological progress is one in which qualitatively higher forms of activity and existence succeed lower ones. It is contrasted to phenomenal, accidental, quantitative progress. See 305.

ontology: The science of being or reality; the branch of philosophy which investigates the nature, essential properties, and relations of being. See **metaphysics**.

*organic: Usually, of or pertaining to an organism, a single living whole. T., however, frequently extends its meaning to preliving and to social phenomena in order to stress the dynamic wholeness or unity of evolutionary processes and populations. Thus, when speaking of the "organic nature of mankind"(30), he stresses the dynamic unity of mankind in its noospheric evolution. An organic being possesses "physical links and structural unity," not merely a "superficial juxtaposition of successions and collectivities." (34)

organo-planetary foothold (287): The biological and earthly supports of human life and evolution.

*orthogenesis: 1) Literally, genesis or development in a pre-ordained path. 2) In biology, it indicates an evolution which in successive generations of a species follows some particular line, bringing about new types, irrespective of natural selection or other external factors. Such orthogenesis is usually associated with Lamarck's name. 3) T. almost never uses **orthogenesis** in the above sense, which is always applied to a *limited* section of the whole of evolution. Rather, he uses it to suggest that evolution, looked at *as a whole*, is progressive or moving in the direction of greater complexity and hence greater consciousness. As a consequence, man can be affirmed as the highest development of evolution, and the convergence of the Noosphere in Omega can be predicted. See 108-9, 140 ftn., 284; *Path*, 84-7.

outlet: Translation for *évasion,* escape. See **issue**.

Palaeozoic: (American spelling: Paleozoic.) The prefix "palaeo" means old or ancient. Hence, **Palaeozoic** means, literally, the earliest or most ancient forms of life. In geology, it has the technical meaning of a large period of earlier times, approximately 600-230 million years ago.

pan-human (249): A **pan-human** effort is one in which all men cooperate.

*pantheism: 1) Literally, "all God," which does not necessarily connote that *only* God exists. 2) Usually it means the doctrine that the universe, regarded as a whole *is* God; all laws, forces, manifestations, etc. of the self-existing universe are God; hence, God is everything, and everything is God. 3) T. uses **pantheism** in a Christian sense to describe noogenesis' final state wherein men are one with God, not by losing their identity, but one because of God's uniting love which will make God all in everyone. See 294, 309-11; *DM,* 116, 130; *FM,* 307-9 (323-4); *Path* 188-92.

pari passu: [Latin] At the same time; with equal pace or speed; correlatively.

paroxysm: Usually, in the sense of an extreme state of evolutionary development which signals a forthcoming change of state or metamorphosis.

particles, human: Individual persons conceived as integral parts of the whole, Humanity.

Pegasus: The magnificent winged horse sprung from Medusa at her death. With the blow of his foot he caused Hippocrene, the fountain of the Muses, to spring forth from Mount Helicon.

*personalisation: For T., the true process of self-realization whereby increasing union with others, especially with Omega, effects increasing centeredness, differentiation, and fulfillment as a person. See 262-8.

*phenomenon: 1) Literally, appearance. 2) Usually, aspects of beings which are observable by the senses, and therefore can be scientifically described and measured. 3) T. broadens the concept by including psychic phenomena (our own knowing, feelings, etc.) which are also experienced as "appearances." Excluded would be that which cannot be experienced but is inferred from phenomena, or is learned by faith in another's testimony. See **hyperphysics, science**.

philosopher's stone: A material postulated as capable of turning base metals into gold.

phyletic: Pertaining to a genetically related grouping of animals (or vegetables). See **phylum**.

***phylogenesis, phylogeny**: 1) The collective evolution within and by a group of animals or plants. See 222-4. 2) The race history of an animal (or plant) type.

***phylum**: 1) In biology, one of the twelve primary divisions of the animal (or vegetable) kingdom, and so named because the members of a phylum are assumed to have a common descent, to be a genetically related group. Examples of phyla in the animal kingdom are porifera (sponges), arthropoda (e.g., insects), chordata (e.g., vertebrates). 2) T., perhaps because of the French usage, tends to use **phylum** in an analogous sense for *any* recognizable group-system in the evolutionary process. Accordingly, T. can speak of the phylum of man, and of the Church as a "phylum of love." See 115-8; *MPN*, 8.

***physical**: 1) T. frequently uses **physical** as synonymous with ontological—whatever has reality in the present order of existents. He consistently opposed physical to juridical, abstract, extrinsic. 2) T. sometimes used "physical" to mean organic, i.e., either a single, living whole or what is like it—something with a dynamic unity and wholeness.

physics: T. often uses **physics** (e.g., 36) in the sense of hyperphysics, the study which embraces matter *and* spirit in one coherent, homogeneous explanation of the cosmos with a central focus on the human phase of the law of complexity/consciousness. See **hyperphysics**.

physiognomy: 1) The art of determining character or personal characteristics from the features of the face or the form of the body. 2) Face or countenance. Often T. uses this meaning, with the implication of a real personalization. Thus time and space are said to achieve a physiognomy (228), that is, achieve a "face" or become personal (instead of impersonal and forbidding) by being intimately associated with man's past and future evolution. 3) Appearance and structure. See 215.

pivot itself: Literally, "excentrate itself," to center itself outside itself on Omega. See 287; **excentrate**.

*__planetisation__: The process by which the human phylum progresses by coiling upon itself and develops as an organic unity instead of ramifying. The diverse races and civilizations tend to synthesize and converge in a single planetary civilization, sharing a rich and unified coreflective vision of reality. See 251-2; **hominisation**, **noogenesis**, **totalisation**.

*__play__: 1) Usually means the *interplay* or the action and reaction of all the factors in a situation (usually evolutionary). 2) The activity of some faculty or potentiality. Thus, 3) **Play of thought** is mental exercise and creativity. 4) Sometimes **play** means indeterminism, as in "double play" (a translation which an American would forego). See 307.

point of dissociation: The final point of cosmogenesis, when the spirit of mankind has reached an extreme and detaches itself from the Earth in order to be consummately united with Omega. See 273.

*__pole__, **conscious**: When T. speaks of a **conscious pole** of the world (291), he is referring to the attracting and unifying activity of Omega-God, an action somewhat similar to a magnetic pole's drawing particles about itself and also aiding the relationships between individual particles.

polymerisation: The union of two or more molecules to form a new and more complex molecule with a higher molecular weight.

positivism, **positivist**: The philosophy which admits only the validity of observable, measurable (=*positive*) facts, and excludes therefore strictly human phenomena such as reflection, love, creativity, etc.

pre-hominids: Races of mammals prior to but leading up to **Homo sapiens**. See **Hominidae**.

pre-reflective: Usually refers to the prehuman, animal phases of evolution.

primacy: "Pre-eminent significance."(30) Having first place, importance, or value in some serial or hierarchical arrangement of various factors.

primordial: Constituting a beginning; giving origin to something derived or developed; original.

prognostics: Forecast or prognostication of future events.

protozoa: (Literally, first animals.) The phylum of protozoans; any of a number of one-celled animals, usually microscopic, belonging to the lowest division of the animal kingdom.

proximity: 1) Nearness or limitedness. 2) T. usually understands **proximity** as a characteristic of a static, nonevolving cosmos in which space is seen as very limited, and time as of very short duration, in contrast to the cosmos seen by contemporary, evolutionary perspectives which reveal the immensities of space (including the infinitesimally small) and of time.

*psyche: Literally, the human soul, but frequently applied to the principle of life in animals. T. often extends the meaning even further: psyche is the principle of *any* unity whether living or nonliving, whether atomic or mammalian, because in cosmic evolution all lower unities lead to and foreshadow man, the evident possessor of a soul or psyche. See **consciousness, mind, radial energy, soul, Spirit of the Earth**.

*psychic: Usually, manifestations of the psyche (soul or mind), such as awareness, feeling, thought, etc. However, T. often extends the concept to include any manifestation of the "within" or consciousness, for example the blind drive of matter towards higher forms of unity. See **consciousness**.

punctiform: Literally, having the form of a geometrical point. T. uses **punctiform** as a characteristic of human reflection in order to indicate its essential and indivisible unity of spiritual centeredness, the source of human personality.

qualitative difference: A difference in kind or quality or species, in contrast to a quantitative difference wherein the difference is merely in degree. Thus the difference between a porpoise and a human child is qualitative or essential, but between a four and a six-month-old baby the difference is quantitative or accidental. See **accidental**.

quantum: 1) An elemental unit or quantity of energy. According to the quantum theory, the emission or absorption of energy by atoms or molecules is not continuous but by steps, each step being caused by the emission or absorption of a **quantum** of energy. 2) Any fixed amount of energy.

*radial energy: The cosmic and evolutionary energy present in all matter, but now most specifically present in man; it is the energy which builds up new wholes or systems that become more and more complex and so more and more centered and interiorized. See 64-6; **"within"**; cf. **tangential energy**.

radius: T. frequently uses this in the sense of "field" or area of influence, as in the case of a piece of iron entering into the radius of a magnet's influence. T. frequently uses **radius** in relation to the attractive influence of persons, divine and human.

*ramification: 1) The process whereby, as evolving life expands, "it splits spontaneously into large natural, hierarchical units" (113), which are capable of further splitting or branching. 2) Literally, branching; from the Latin, *ramus*, branch. See **verticil**.

*rebound: Usually refers to the *human* rebound; consciousness, now in the human phase, finds it necesary to react upon man himself in order to create by design a new complexity in matter, and prepare the way for the supreme, ultimate stage of noospheric superconsciousness. Human rebound involves a doubling or increase of radial energy available for further unification (252-3). See 248-50; *FM,* 176-7 (183-4), and especially *FM* 196-213 (204-21).

recoils: Translation for *reployements* (e.g., 251), which refers to the coilings or compressive unifications of a convergent evolution. See **coiling, centration, convergence**.

*reflection: 1) The power or activity of conscious thought which distinguishes man from all other living creatures. T. uses reflection either as *self*-reflection—knowing that one knows, or as the most characteristic activity of the human spirit, thought, which constitutes man as the shaper of future cosmogenesis. See 164-72, especially 165. 2) As the translator of *FM* observes, reflection also expresses the special convergence or coiling (reflecting back) upon itself of the human species, a process which "generates new (spiritual) energies and a new form of growth." For expressions of *communal* reflection, see 251 and *FM* 9 (9).

reflecting upon itself: See **involution**.

*replacing: Extending an earlier and lower process by a new and higher process which is really continuous with the earlier one. (The basic image is taken from relay racing where the baton is passed from one runner to another.)

*reversal: Translation of *renversement* and *retournement*, which, in T.'s evolutionary framework, signifies the process whereby the superstructure of thought and personality escapes from the limitations of the material substructure which brought it into being. For example, thought was at first a simple phenomenon of life, but in time it became capable of modifying the whole biological process. Likewise, death is a reversal or transformation whereby man's radial energy is no longer dependent upon tangential energy; hence, man is freed from entropy for a direct union with Omega-God. The Cross is "the great act of reversal" because it transforms the defeating death of Christ into his risen superlife. See **metamorphosis**, **transformation**; 242, 272; de Lubac, *Religion,* 132, ff.; Mooney, 111 (119-20).

*****science, scientific**: 1) T. sometimes uses these terms as they are ordinarily used for individual sciences, e.g., physics, biology, geology. 2) T. frequently uses these terms in a very enlarged sense to indicate hyperphysics (what *PM* is), that is, science pushed to considering the *whole* cosmic phenomenon and to considering man and his thought as the central phenomena in an evolving universe.

Some readers do not like to see **science** used in such an extended sense, but there is some reason for allowing T. the freedom to define his own vocabulary. The French *"mémoire scientifique"* is already much broader than our "scientific treatise," but becomes broader still when *PM* is identified as hyperphysics. See 29-36, 248-50, 278-85; **hyperphysics.**

*****sense of the earth and human sense**: These are equivalents of "spirit of the earth" and "spirit of Humanity"—the special, Teilhardian love of the earth and the human. See **mankind**, **Spirit of the Earth**.

sidereal: Literally, of or relating to the stars; starry. 1) T. uses **sidereal** most frequently as a synonym for cosmic—the whole expanse of the material universe. 2) From the viewpoint of astronomy, in contrast to a physico-chemical or a microscopic viewpoint. 3) "Sidereal dust" (217) signifies the Earth.

*****socialisation**: The psychosocial process by which mankind becomes more organically one, through its communication and transportation systems, through its educational, political, and scientific enterprises, through its artistic, personal, and spiritual creations. Socialisation is the evolutionary continuation of the earlier formation of species by biological enrichment through additivity. See **collectivisation, hominisation, totalisation**.

*solidity: A favorite Teilhardian word which expresses the "holding-togetherness" of the universe and of its parts in their process of evolution. Solidity is opposed to fragility and unconnectedness. See 268-9; **consistence**.

somatic: Of or pertaining to the body; corporeal; physical.

*soul: 1) Principle of life in an individual organism (plant, animal, man). 2) T. uses **soul** metaphorically for **any** principle of unity. See, for example, 258. 3) The principle which unites all men into "Humanity," a superorganism; he sometimes refers to this principle as a "super-soul." See 248, 268; **psyche, within**.

*space-time: 1) The four-dimensional continuum within which every material existent may be located by specifying its three spatial coordinates (height, width, depth) and its temporal coordinate (time, the fourth dimension). 2) T. usually speaks of biological space-time, which indicates the one, evolving whole of the cosmos. Parts of the cosmos can only be understood in their relation to and position in the whole evolutionary process. See 216-20; **duration**.

spirit: See **mind**.

*Spirit of the Earth: 1) Since evolution is a process of spiritualization or the rise of matter to ever higher psychical perfection, evolution can now be said to be forming a "Spirit of the Earth," a unified spiritual being intrinsically related to the earth (278). 2) Since spirit is a principle of unification, the noosphere needs a spirit to inform and unify its various elements as they "find completion in a spiritual renovation of the earth" (245). 3) State of one-souledness, to be brought about by the highest development and unification of human consciousness, whereby there will exist for and of the earth a total and common consciousness or spirit. (251) Needless to say, the "Spirit of the Earth" has great reality and concreteness in T.'s mind. See 278, 287; **mankind**, **mind**, **unanimity**.

spiritualise: The process of: a) an individual's bringing about a richer "**within**" or psyche for himself; b) mankind's "appropriating" the world's intellectual and aesthetic treasures by means of science, art, religion, etc.; c) the closer unification of human persons (spirits) with one another and with Omega, Spirit of spirits. See 259; **convergence**, **mind**, **noogenesis**, **personalisation**.

star: The French *astre* means a heavenly body, and hence can be used to mean the Earth, as on 239.

stems: Ramifications or divergent variations created in an evolving species. Perhaps better translated as "branches" in most contexts, e.g., 302.

structural: 1) Of or pertaining to the ordered interrelationship of parts in and to a complex whole. 2) Pertaining to intrinsic or necessary relationships discovered by observing the pattern of phenomena. See Rideau, 52.

subject, **subjective**: One who knows, feels, etc. Knowledge is considered to be **subjective** when what is known is greatly conditioned by personal characteristics of the knower (subject), as for example, the jaundiced person seeing everything with a yellow hue. See **object**.

sublimation: 1) Action of transformation into a higher mode of being or activity. 2) In science, sublimation is the process of a solid directly transforming into a gas, without passing through the liquid state. See **metamorphosis**, **reversal**, **transformation**.

super: A prefix, not as strong as **ultra**, indicating a great difference in degree between this state and an earlier one. Père de Lubac says super-humanity, depending on T.'s point of view, can mean either the ultra-human or the trans-human, but that T. usually uses it in the first sense. See de Lubac, *Religion*, 65-6, 188, 216.

*survival: The unfortunate translation for *survie*, which misses T.'s projection of not merely a future life for man and mankind, but of superlife for them. (When speaking of the evolutionary survival of the fittest, he uses the bland *survivance*.) See **ultra-humanity**; *Path*, 116-7, 214, ftn. 50.

symbiosis: The living together in more or less intimate association or even close union of two dissimilar organisms, which often permits each to live with the advantages of the other, e.g., lichen with alga.

*sympathy: For T., the power and the activity by which men respond to the internal attractions toward greater psychic unity —seeing, feeling, desiring and suffering in themselves what all other men do, and experiencing this all together, at the same time. Sympathy is opposed to external compulsions toward unity, whether this comes from geographic or demographic pressures. Sympathy is thus "the beginning of love" [*FM*, 147 (152)] and the dynamism by which men experience themselves in the field of attraction toward all men, to the whole cosmos. See 264-9.

synergy: The combined action or operation, as of muscles, nerves, etc. In physiology, synergism refers to a combined action such that the total effect is greater than the sum of the causes taken individually, as in the action of a mixture of drugs. T. frequently uses **synergy** to indicate the reinforcement of human energies which comes from increasing unification. See **rebound**.

*tangential energy: The exterior or physical expression of the fundamental energy common to all evolving matter; it is the energy by which one body affects a like body exteriorly, for example, two hydrogen atoms.[1] See 54-6; **"without"**; cf. **radial energy**, **"within."**

---

[1] Radial energy, the other fundamental aspect of energy, unites the parts of a real whole into a dynamic and organic unity. Tangential energy may be considered as the energy of interaction between individuals and groups, and radial energy as the energy of preserving and increasing unity and forming still higher unities.

thought: See **reflection**.

*threshold: 1) Literally, the stone or timber which lies under a door; therefore, entrance or beginning. 2) T. almost always uses **threshold** to mean the passage from one form of existence to a radically new form, e.g., the passage from nonlife to life, or from nonhuman to human existence. **Threshold** can also mean the point in the passage where the actual change is effected. Synonyms used by T. are change of state, critical point, metamorphosis. 3) **Threshold of reflection**: the chasm separating man from other animals. T. views the culmination in man of the process of increasing psychism, going on in the cellular world for more than five hundred million years, as a change of state, analogous to the **threshold of life** which led to the birth of life in a sudden leap from the inorganic world. See **change of state**, **critical point**, **metamorphosis**, **transformation**.

*totalisation, **totalise**: The progressive formation of a unique whole ("totum") of humanity by means of socialisation and unanimisation. Love-energy is the fundamental factor in human totalisation. The individual participates in a planetary consciousness and love, while heightening his own personality according to the law that "union differentiates." See 265-8; **centration**, **hominisation #3**, **socialisation**, **convergence**.

trans: A prefix reserved for a union and activity which transcends the temporo-spatial limits of the cosmos, e.g., the transhuman which is brought about by the grace of Christ. See de Lubac, *Religion,* 216-7.

*transcendent, **transcendence**: 1) In general, having a mode of existence and activities which surpass those of some other beings. For example, man with his reflective consciousness transcends animals and their nonreflective consciousness. 2) Living organisms are *relatively* transcendent to inorganic matter even though they emerged from and are dependent upon it. 3) God is *absolutely* transcendent to all of time, space and evolution. In a lesser sense, human freedom transcends the world of matter and animal life, and the final and consummating unification of Humanity transcends the historical process of hominisation.

transformation: A Teilhardian concept which stresses the simultaneous continuity and discontinuity of a marked or dramatic change, such that the earlier stage is integral to the emergence of a new form, as for example in a change from nonliving to living or from reflective consciousness to transterrestrial hyperconsciousness. See **change of state**, **emergence**, **metamorphosis**.

transformism: 1) A biological theory which maintains that during past ages living beings transformed themselves into higher forms, the distinguishable difference being due to modifications or mutations in successive generations. 2) T. restricts **transformism** to biological changes in the organic world, but uses **evolution** to signify, in addition, social and psychological mutations which lead to evolution's goal of increasing complexity and consciousness. See **evolution**.

ultra: This is T.'s strongest superlative, stronger than **hyper** and **super**, but it does not indicate real transcendence as does the prefix **trans**. However, the ultra-human of this world leads to the trans-human of humanity's consummate union with Omega-God. See *FM,* 297 (311).

ultra-humanity: The final state of mankind at the completion of cosmic evolution, when man, individually and collectively, will have attained a superpersonalisation and superunion. This will be followed by the transhuman transformation and consummation of Humanity in and by Omega. See 287-9.

*unanimity, **unanimous**: Literally, one-souled. Since T. sees men progressing toward a megasynthesis of one being, Humanity, "the sum of all human beings," they will be increasingly informed by one soul. See 251-3.

union, law of: "Union differentiates." T. tries to show that our individual personalities are heightened in their richness and particular perfections by their intimate union with other persons, human and divine. See 264-7; *Path*, 148-50.

upsurge: Translation of *rebondissement,* which T. uses to indicate, in the human phase of evolution, a "rebounding" of human consciousness upon itself, which causes an increase in consciousness and psychic energy. See **rebound**.

verticil: 1) In botany, it is a circle of similar parts, such as leaves or flowers; a whorl. 2) For T., **verticil** usually expresses not merely growth and ramification, but growth with a pattern and a gathering of some sort.

vitalised: Literally, possessing and manifesting life. T. uses "more vitalised" (e.g., 301) in the transferred sense of more organically unified or conscious or centered, without implying life or the usual functions of life.

vitally: 1) Essential or necessary. 2) Used in the root sense, "vitally equivalent" (303) means the living forms are equal insofar as they are living and viable individuals or species.

Weltanschaung: Literally, a world view; frequently it signifies a personal outlook on the history and purpose of the world as a whole.

***"within"**: The psychical aspect or face of all matter; the **within** can be infinitely diminished (as in atomic particles) or extremely concentrated (as in man's reflective consciousness). The **within** is intimately associated with radial energy, consciousness, love and freedom. The other side of matter is the "without." See 68-74; **consciousness, psyche, radial energy**.

***"without"**: The material or physical aspect or face of the stuff of the universe. It is intimately bound up with tangential energy, complexity, chance and determinism. The other side or face of matter is the "**within**." See 68-74; **complexity, matter, tangential energy**.

world: Sometimes usage is restricted to indicating the planet Earth, but at other times **world** indicates the whole cosmos.

BIBLIOGRAPHY

NOTE: 1) A complete bibliography of T.'s writings, with over 500 entries, can be found in the biography by Claude Cuénot listed below in section II. An alphabetical arrangement of T.'s writings can be found in Robert North's *Teilhard and the Creation of the Soul.* The American Teilhard de Chardin Association, Inc., 157 East 72nd Street, New York, New York, 10021, has published "A Basic Teilhard Bibliography," 1970, and their *Newsletter* reports on new publications as well as on lectures, seminars, study groups, etc.

2) The original writings of T. are published in the series, *Oeuvres de Teilhard de Chardin,* by Editions du Seuil, Paris; from *Le Phénomène humain,* 1955 to the present, eleven volumes have been published.

I *Works of Pierre Teilhard de Chardin*

A. Translations of *Oeuvres*

The Appearance of Man. New York: Harper & Row, 1966. A series of quite technical essays, except for the last, "The Singularities of the Human Species," a 62 pp. essay like *PM,* written shortly before T.'s death.

The Divine Milieu. New York: Harper & Row, Torchbook, 1965. (This differs in pagination and translation from the 1960 edition.) This and *The Phenomenon of Man* are the two principal works T. most desired to publish. Both contain the most extended expressions of his thought and necessarily complement one another. *The Divine Milieu* is essential for its expression of Christ's role in cosmic evolution and in the milieu and ascetical life of the individual believer.

The Future of Man. New York: Harper & Row, 1964, and with different pagination and modified translation in Torchbook, 1969. A collection of essays written mainly in the latter part of his life. Most of the essays are fairly straightforward expressions of T.'s evolutionary thought, with great emphasis on the future shape of mankind's progress. This is one of the best entries into T.'s thought.

How I Believe. Peiping: privately printed, 1936. Newly translated by René Hague; New York: Harper & Row, 1969. A short and moving personal testimony to T.'s own growth in faith and his understanding of Christianity in relation to other religions.

Human Energy. New York: Harper & Row, 1970. Six essays from the 1930's centering about T.'s personalistic view of the evolving Earth and of human energy.

Man's Place in Nature. New York: Harper & Row, 1966. A simpler and better presentation of the first three-fifths of *The Phenomenon of Man,* describing the pattern and direction of evolution.

The Phenomenon of Man. New York: Harper & Row, 2nd edition and also Torchbook, 1965. (This differs in translation and pagination from the 1st edition, 1959.) This and *The Divine Milieu* are T.'s two principal works. Many find *PM* difficult to understand, and hence rises the need of a *Path. PM* explores the past, present, and future of cosmic evolution, with man at the very center. Those who want to learn more of T.'s ideas and vision will, sooner or later, want to read this book.

Science and Christ. New York: Harper & Row, 1969. A collection of essays from the whole span of T.'s life, centered about science and faith, evolution and Christ. "My Universe" is especially important and comprehensive, but rather difficult because of terminology and compactness.

The Vision of the Past. New York: Harper & Row, 1966. This series of essays centers about evolution and especially on *human* evolution. Most of the essays are written for the general reader who will gather from them a better understanding of the human implications of cosmic and organic evolution.

B. Miscellaneous Writings

Teilhard de Chardin Album. Edited by Jeanne Mortier and Marie-Louise Auboux. New York: Harper & Row, 1967. A handsome book giving a photographic account of T.'s life, accompanied by generous quotations of T.'s thoughts.

Building the Earth. New York: Avon-Discus, 1969. (Earlier editions by Dimension Books, Denville, N.J., 1965.) Six rather short essays with an emphasis upon man's hope for the future and what he should contribute now. Easily read and very popular, probably because T.'s solid optimism and deep faith in the future and in the God of evolution shine forth so clearly.

Hymn of the Universe. New York: Harper & Row, 1965, and Harper Colophon, 1969. A "must" book since it contains three principal examples of T.'s religious, even mystical, vision. Though some of T.'s imagery may be a bit jarring, these pieces exhibit an essential aspect of T.'s vision.

Writings in Time of War. New York: Harper & Row, 1968. This important collection of essays, written during his army service in World War I, is the early expression in variant forms of T.'s fundamental outlook. A few are fairly technical, but most are written for the general reader who should be prepared for frequently moving and poetical passages. This collection translates thirteen of the twenty essays in *Écrits du temps de la guerre, 1916-1919* (Paris: Grasset, 1965).

C. Letters

Letters from Egypt, 1905-1908. New York: Herder and Herder, 1965. Not very illuminating on the person or thought of T.

Letters from Hastings, 1908-1912. New York: Herder and Herder, 1968. A poor translation, with thirty letters of the French text omitted, and not very revealing of T.'s thought.

Letters from Paris, 1912-1914. New York: Herder and Herder, 1967. A poor translation of letters which are not too illuminating on

T.'s thought.

The Making of a Mind: Letters from a Soldier-Priest, 1914-1919. New York: Harper & Row, 1965. A very revealing collection of letters to his favorite cousin, Marguerite Teillard, showing the development of his ideas. Very profitably read together with *Writings in Time of War.*

Pierre Teilhard de Chardin and Maurice Blondel: Correspondence. New York: Herder and Herder, 1967. There are only thirty pages of letters exchanged by Teilhard and the famous philosopher. These together with the extensive notes shed light on several aspects of T.'s thought.

Letters from a Traveller. New York: Harper and Brothers, 1962 and also in Torchbook edition. A very popular collection of letters, running from 1923 to 1955, which gives an easy entry to T.'s personality and thought.

Letters to Two Friends, 1926-1952. New York: New American Library, 1968. These letters to very close friends frequently give an intimate knowledge of T. himself and serve also to enlarge the understanding of T.'s vision.

Letters to Léontine Zanta. New York: Harper & Row, 1969. Very personal letters to this close friend and important feminist; they give considerable insight into the development of T.'s spirituality and the quality of his spiritual direction.

II *Works on the Life and Thought of Teilhard*

A. Biographies

Barbour, George. *In the Field with Teilhard de Chardin.* New York: Herder and Herder, 1965. An intimate account of T. by a close friend and geological coworker.

Corte, Nicholas (= Léon Christiani). *Pierre Teilhard de Chardin: His Life and Spirit.* New York: Macmillan, 1960.

Cuénot, Claude. *Teilhard de Chardin: A Biographical Study.* Baltimore: Helicon, 1965. This was the standard biography until Speaight's appeared, and it is still quite valuable, especially for its extensive detail, quotations, and bibliography of T.'s writings.

Grenet, Paul. *Teilhard de Chardin: The Man and His Theories.* New

York: Largely biographical but with considerable attention to the polarities in T.'s thought, together with many selections from T.'s writings.

Leroy, Pierre, S.J. "Teilhard de Chardin: the Man" printed in both *The Divine Milieu* (Harper Torchbook, 1965) and *Letters From a Traveller* (Harper and Brothers, 1962). A very intimate and insightful, though brief, account of T. by a fellow Jesuit and paleontologist.

Mortier, Jeanne, and Auboux, Marie-Louise, eds. *Teilhard de Chardin Album.* New York: Harper & Row, 1967. T.'s life presented by selected writings and pictures in a handsome book.

Speaight, Robert. *Teilhard de Chardin: A Biography.* New York: Harper & Row, 1967. An excellent biography which gives an account not only of T.'s life but also of the development of his thought.

de Terra, Helmut. *Memories of Teilhard de Chardin.* New York: Harper & Row, 1964. This study by a fellow geologist and paleontologist, though frequently quite technical, throws light on T.'s personality and thought.

Towers, Bernard. *Teilhard de Chardin.* Richmond, Va.: John Knox Press, 1966. A short paperback, mainly on T.'s life, but containing a brief introduction to his thought.

B. Teilhardian Studies

Alexander, Thomas. *The Vision of Teilhard de Chardin Programmed for V.I.P.'S.* New York: Vantage Press, 1969. "A book that is not a book, but a computer program," which gives T.'s basic concepts and computer programs to test them.

Aller, Catherine. *The Challenge of Pierre Teilhard de Chardin.* New York: Exposition Press, 1964.

Braybrooke, Neville, ed. *Teilhard de Chardin: Pilgrim of the Future.* New York: Seabury Press, 1964. Contains two essays by T. himself and a delightful collection of essays by a variety of authors.

Bravo, Francisco. *Christ in the Thought of Teilhard de Chardin.* Notre Dame: University of Notre Dame Press, 1967. A fairly helpful study of T.'s Christology.

Cargas, Harry J. *The Continuous Flame: Teilhard in the Great Traditions.* St. Louis: B. Herder, 1970. A rather weak study comparing T. with thinkers through the ages, written for the general reader.

Chauchard, Paul. *Man and Cosmos: Scientific Phenomenology in*

Teilhard de Chardin. New York: Herder and Herder, 1965. An excellent study of T.'s hyperphysics and its ramifications by a neurophysiologist.

Chauchard, Paul. *Teilhard de Chardin on Love and Suffering.* Glen Rock, N.J.: Paulist Deus Books, 1966. A sensitive study of deeply related subjects in T.'s thought.

Crespy, Georges. *From Science to Theology: The Evolutionary Design of Teilhard de Chardin.* New York: Abingdon Press, 1968. An excellent study of important areas of T.'s thought by a Protestant theologian.

Cuénot, Claude. *Science and Faith in Teilhard de Chardin.* London: Garnstone Press, 1967. Three scholarly essays by a Teilhardian expert, together with a comment by Roger Garaudy, a Communist philosopher.

Delfgaauw, Bernard. *Evolution: The Theory of Teilhard de Chardin.* New York: Harper & Row, 1969. An extremely clear and well-written introduction to T.'s *The Phenomenon of Man.*

Devaux, André. *Teilhard and Womanhood.* Glen Rock, N.J.: Paulist Deus Books, 1968. A rather "thin" study which creates hope for an adequate investigation of this very important aspect of T.'s thought.

Faricy, Robert L., S.J. *Teilhard de Chardin's Theology of the Christian in the World.* New York: Sheed & Ward, 1967. A good but somewhat difficult study of T.'s ascetical theology.

Francoeur, Robert T., ed. *The World of Teilhard de Chardin.* Baltimore: Helicon, 1961. An early collection of essays which depend heavily on *The Phenomenon of Man* and are written by specialists in many different fields.

Gray, Donald P. *The One and the Many: Teilhard de Chardin's Vision of Unity.* New York: Herder and Herder, 1970. An excellent study of T.'s early writings on the eschatological communion of the many.

Kessler, Marvin, S. J., and Brown, Bernard, S.J. *Dimensions of the Future: The Spirituality of Teilhard de Chardin.* Washington: Corpus, 1968. Scholarly studies on, for example, tradition, love, the Church, sacraments, etc.

Kraft, R. Wayne. *The Relevance of Teilhard.* Notre Dame: Fides, 1968. A very well written introduction to T.'s thought by a metallurgist.

Ligneul, André. *Teilhard and Personalism.* Glen Rock, N.J.: Paulist Deus Books, 1968. Somewhat "thin" study of T.'s personalism and that of Emmanuel Mounier.

Lewis, John, and Towers, Bernard. *Naked Ape or Homo Sapiens?*

London: Garnstone Press, 1969. Extends T.'s view of human nature and future evolution by confronting Desmond Morris' *The Naked Ape,* Robert Ardrey's *Territorial Imperative,* etc.

de Lubac, Henri, S.J. *The Religion of Teilhard de Chardin.* New York: Desclée, 1967, and Garden City, N.Y.: Doubleday Image Books, 1968. An excellent and comprehensive study of T.'s religious thought by a prominent theologian and long-time friend of T.

de Lubac, Henri, S.J. *Teilhard de Chardin: The Man and His Meaning.* New York: Hawthorn, 1965, and New York: New American Library, 1968. Enlightening on several points but marred by polemics against critics of T.

de Lubac, Henri, S.J. *Teilhard Explained.* Glen Rock, N.J.: Paulist Deus Books, 1968. An excellent study of T. as missionary and apologete of Christianity.

Maloney, George, S.J. *The Cosmic Christ.* New York: Sheed & Ward, 1968. Studies sources from the Bible to the present for the antecedents of T.'s cosmic Christ.

Martin, Sr. Maria Gratia. *The Spirituality of Teilhard de Chardin.* Westminster, Md.: Paulist/Newman, 1968. Not easy reading but a fairly good study.

McElwain, Hugh, O.S.M. *Introduction to Teilhard de Chardin.* Chicago: Argus Communications, 1967. A good introductory study.

Meilach, Michael D., O.F.M., ed. *There Shall Be One Christ.* St. Bonaventure, N.Y.: The Franciscan Institute, 1968. Five scholarly essays on T.'s thought.

Mooney, Christopher, S.J. *Teilhard de Chardin and the Mystery of Christ.* New York: Harper & Row, 1966, and Garden City, N.Y.: Doubleday Image Books, 1968. A magisterial study based on a complete knowledge of the full range of T.'s writings. For this reason the critique in the final chapter is especially significant.

Murray, Michael. *The Thought of Teilhard de Chardin: An Introduction.* New York: Seabury Press, 1966. The best introduction to the whole range of T.'s thought.

North, Robert, S.J. *Teilhard and the Creation of the Soul.* Milwaukee: Bruce, 1967. A very difficult and not so rewarding study, but among other merits it has summaries of each chapter and an alphabetical listing of all of T.'s writings.

O'Manique, John. *Energy in Evolution.* London: Garnstone Press, 1969. A fairly technical investigation of energy and especially the energy of evolution.

POM Project. *Survival: A Study Guide for Teilhard de Chardin's The Phenomenon of Man.* Canoga Park, Calif.: The Phenomenon of Man Project, 1967. An effort to explain the *Phenomenon* by means of diagrams and brief text; helpful to some readers.

Rabut, Olivier, O.P. *Teilhard de Chardin: A Critical Study.* New York: Sheed & Ward, 1961. A fair-minded but not always fair evaluation of T.'s cosmology, philosophy, and theology.

Raven, Charles E. *Teilhard de Chardin: Scientist and Seer.* New York: Harper and Brothers, 1963. A moderately helpful study, but especially so on the intellectual influences upon T.'s thought.

Rideau, Emile, S.J. *The Thought of Teilhard de Chardin.* New York: Harper & Row, 1967. Something of an encyclopedia of T.'s thought in all of its facets, together with copious quotations from his writings.

Smulders, Piet, S.J. *The Design of Teilhard de Chardin.* Westminster, Md.: Newman Press, 1967. A solid study of T.'s thought but somewhat difficult to read and sometimes unnecessarily negative.

Tresmontant, Claude. *Pierre Teilhard de Chardin: His Thought.* Baltimore: Helicon, 1959. A very good introduction to most of the important aspects of T.'s thought, but Tresmontant's critique is based on an insufficient knowledge of T.'s full thought.

Wildiers, N. M. *An Introduction to Teilhard de Chardin.* New York: Harper & Row, 1968. An excellent, but not the easiest reading, introduction to T.'s synthesis by an eminent Teilhardian scholar.

C. Studies Partially on or Related to Teilhard's Thought

Baltazar, Eulalio R. *Teilhard and the Supernatural.* Baltimore: Helicon, 1966. Not a study of T. but an extension, sometimes over-defensive, of his thought in the development of an explicit philosophy of process.

Benz, Ernst. *Evolution and Christian Hope: Man's Concept of the Future from the Early Fathers to Teilhard de Chardin.* New York: Doubleday, 1966 and Doubleday Anchor Books, 1968. A useful critique of T.'s futurism.

Chaix-Ruy, Jules. *Superman: From Nietzsche to Teilhard de Chardin.* Notre Dame, Ind.: University of Notre Dame Press, 1968. A useful and critical comparison of T. with several modern thinkers.

Ferkiss, Victor C. *Technological Man: The Myth and the Reality.* New York: Braziller, 1969. An excellent study of the future evolution of man, based on a broad knowledge of history and the social sciences, with a critique of T.'s optimism.

Francoeur, Robert T. *Perspectives in Evolution.* Baltimore: Helicon, 1965. A well-wrought study of the history of evolutionary thought and of selected theological implications, e.g., creation of man and original sin.

Hulsbosch, Ansfried, O.S.A. *God in Creation and Evolution.* New York: Sheed & Ward, 1966. Inspired by T.'s thought, this study seeks to understand many important facets of the Bible within an evolutionary framework.

Leary, Daniel J. *Voices of Convergence.* Milwaukee: Bruce, 1969. A well-written comparison of T.'s thought with that of many contemporary thinkers, e.g., McLuhan, Shaw, etc.

Lepp, Ignace. *The Faith of Men: Meditations Inspired by Teilhard de Chardin.* New York: Macmillan, 1967. Sensitive reflections by a former Communist.

Rabut, Olivier A., O.P. *God in an Evolving Cosmos.* New York: Herder and Herder, 1966. Though poorly translated, a penetrating theological study, inspired in good part by T.'s perspectives.

Nichols, William. *Conflicting Images of Man.* New York: Seabury Press, 1966. A collection of essays on contemporary thinkers, with those on T. and Bonhoeffer to be noted especially.

Overman, Richard H. *Evolution and the Christian Doctrine of Creation.* Philadelphia: Westminster, 1966. A serious study, running the gamut from Origen to Whitehead and T.

Rahner, Karl, S.J. *Hominization: The Evolutionary Origin of Man as a Theological Problem.* New York: Herder and Herder, 1965. A difficult but masterful study of the genesis of man.

Schoonenberg, Peter, S.J. *God's World in the Making.* Pittsburgh: Duquesne University Press, 1964. A theological study, inspired by T.'s thought, of evolution, the origin of man, salvation, marriage, labor, and eschatology.

Zaehner, R. C. *Matter and Spirit: Their Convergence in Eastern Religions, Marx and Teilhard de Chardin.* New York: Harper and Brothers, 1963. A provocative study of this central Teilhardian theme.

D. Articles (This listing includes only articles quoted in the *Path.*)

Barthélemy-Madaule, Madeleine. "Teilhard de Chardin, Marxism, Existentialism: A Confrontation." *International Philosophical Quarterly,* I (1961), 648-67.

Cronin, Vincent. "The Noosphere and Extrasensory Perception."

Teilhard de Chardin: Pilgrim of the Future, ed. by Neville Braybrooke. New York: Seabury Press, 1964, 88-91.

D'Ouince, René, S.J. "L'Épreuve de l'obéissance dans la vie du Père Teilhard de Chardin." *L'Homme devant Dieu.* Paris: Aubier, 1964, vol. iii, 331-46.

Kobler, John, "The Priest Who Haunts the Catholic World." *Saturday Evening Post.* Oct. 12, 1963, 42-51.

Murray, George B., S.J. "Teilhard and Orthogenetic Evolution." *Harvard Theological Review,* 60 (1967), 281-95.

Perelinski, Jerome. "Teilhard's Vision of Peace and War." *The Catholic Worker,* March, 1968; also in *The Teilhard Review,* 3 (Winter, 1968), 52-61.

Russel, John L., S.J. "Teilhard de Chardin, *The Phenomenon of Man,* II." *The Heythrop Journal,* II (Jan., 1961), 3-13.

Vass, George, S.J. "Teilhard de Chardin and Inward Vision." *The Heythrop Journal,* II (July, 1961), 237-49.

III *Works Cited on Related Topics*

A. Books

Altizer, Thomas J. *Mircea Eliade and the Dialectic of the Sacred.* Philadelphia: Westminster Press, 1963.

Anderson, Sherwood. *A Story Teller's Tale.* New York: B. W. Huebsch, 1924.

Barzun, Jacques. *Science, The Glorious Entertainment.* New York: Harper & Row, 1964.

Brodrick, James, S.J. *Robert Bellarmine.* Westminster, Md.: Newman, 1961.

Buber, Martin. *I and Thou.* New York: Scribner's, 1958.

Burkill, T. Alec. *God and Reality in Modern Thought.* Englewood, N.J.: Prentice-Hall, 1963.

Cox, Harvey. *The Secular City.* New York: Macmillan, 1965.

Culler, A. Dwight. *The Imperial Intellect: A Study of Newman's Educational Ideal.* New Haven, Conn.: Yale University Press, 1955.

Dobzhansky, Theodosius. *Heredity and the Nature of Man.* New York: New American Library, 1964.

Durkheim, Emile. *Suicide: A Study in Sociology.* Glencoe: Free Press, 1951.

Eliade, Mircea. *Cosmos and History.* New York: Harper Torchbook, 1959.

Flood, Peter (ed.). *New Problems in Modern Ethics*. Westminster, Md.: Newman, 1953.

de Fraine, Jean, S.J. *The Bible and the Origin of Man*. New York: Desclee, 1962.

Frankel, Charles. *The Case for Modern Man*. New York: Harper and Brothers, 1955.

Frankl, Viktor E. *Man's Search for Meaning*. New York: Washington Square Press, 1963.

Gamow, George. *Biography of the Earth*. New York: Viking, 1963.

Harris, Errol. *The Foundations of Metaphysics in Science*. London: Allen and Unwin, 1965.

Hopkins, Gerard Manley. *Poems of Gerard Manley Hopkins*. Edited by Robert Bridges. Oxford: Oxford University Press, 1930.

Huxley, Julian. *Evolution in Action*. New York: Harper and Brothers, 1953.

Lewis, C. S. *The Screwtape Letters*. New York: Macmillan, 1943.

de Lubac, Henri, S.J. *Paradoxes*. South Bend, Ind.: Fides, 1948.

Luijpen, William A., O.S.A. *Phenomenology and Atheism*. Pittsburgh: Duquesne University Press, 1964.

Maritain, Jacques. *True Humanism*. New York: Scribners, 1938.

Mascall, E. L. *Christian Theology and Natural Science*. London: Longmans, Green, 1957.

Marx, Karl. *The Communist Manifesto*. Chicago: Regnery, 1954.

Mayr, Ernst. *Animal Species and Evolution*. Cambridge, Mass.: Harvard University Press, 1963.

McKenzie, John L., S.J. *The Two-Edged Sword*. Milwaukee: Bruce, 1956.

McLuhan, Marshall. *The Medium Is the Massage*. New York: Bantam, 1967.

_____. *Understanding Media: The Extensions of Man*. New York: McGraw-Hill, 1965.

Mersch, Emile, S.J. *Theology of the Mystical Body*. St. Louis: B. Herder, 1952.

Mouroux, Jean. *The Mystery of Time*. New York: Desclee, 1964.

Nogar, Raymond J., O.P. *The Lord of the Absurd*. New York: Herder and Herder, 1966.

_____. *The Wisdom of Evolution*. New York: Doubleday, 1963.

du Noüy, Lecomte. *Human Destiny*. New York: Signet, 1949.

Pascal, Blaise. *Pensées*. New York: Dutton, 1958.

Petersen, Aage. *Quantum Physics and the Philosophical Tradition*. New York: Belfer Graduate School, 1966.

Pope Pius XII. *Humani Generis*. Washington: National Catholic

Welfare Conference, 1950.

————. *Mystici Corporis*. New York: America Press, 1943.

Rahner, Karl. *On the Theology of Death*. New York: Herder and Herder, 1961.

Rand, Ayn. *For the New Intellectual*. New York: Signet, 1963.

Randall, John Herman, Jr. *The Career of Philosophy*. New York: Columbia University Press, 1962.

Royce, Josiah. *The Religious Aspect of Philosophy*. Boston: Houghton Mifflin, 1885.

Russell, Bertrand. *Mysticism and Logic*. New York: Doubleday, 1957.

Ryan, Sr. Mary Rosalie, C.S.J., ed. *Contemporary New Testament Studies*. Collegeville, Minn.: Liturgical Press, 1965.

Sartre, Jean-Paul. *No Exit and Three Other Plays*. New York: Vintage, 1955.

Snow, C. P. *The Two Cultures and the Scientific Revolution*. Cambridge: Cambridge University Press, 1960.

Tax, Sol, ed. *Evolution After Darwin*. III vols. Chicago: University of Chicago Press, 1960.

Vercors. *The Murder of the Missing Link*. Translated by Rita Barisse. New York: Pocket Books, 1955.

Whitehead, Alfred North. *Science and the Modern World*. New York: Mentor, 1948.

B. Articles

Ahern, Barnabas Mary, C.P. "The Christian's Union with the Body of Christ in Cor., Gal., and Rom." *Catholic Biblical Quarterly*, XXIII (1961), 199-209.

Auer, Alfons. "The Christian Understanding of the World." *The Christian and the World*, ed. at Canisianum, Innsbruck. New York: Kenedy, 1965, 3-44.

Morgenthau, Hans J. "Death in the Nuclear Age." *Commentary*, XXXII (September, 1961), 231-34.

Morison, Robert S. "Towards a Common Scale of Measurement." *Science and Culture*, ed. by Gerald Holton. Boston: Beacon, 1967.

Murray, George B., S.J., "The Hyphenated Priest." *Review for Religious*, XXV (July, 1966), 693-702.

Park, Rosemary. "Alma Mater, Emerita." *The University in America*. Occasional Paper of The Center for the Study of Democratic Institutions, Santa Barbara, 1967.

Whitehead, Alfred North. "John Dewey and His Influence." *The*

Philosophy of John Dewey, ed. by P. A. Schilpp. Evanston, Ill.: Northwestern University Press, 1939, 477-8.

INDEX